# PROTECTING THE LIBRARY AND ITS RESOURCES

# PROTECTING THE LIBRARY AND ITS RESOURCES

*A Guide to Physical Protection and Insurance*

*Report on a study
conducted by*

GAGE-BABCOCK & ASSOCIATES, INC.

LIBRARY TECHNOLOGY PROJECT

AMERICAN LIBRARY ASSOCIATION

CHICAGO

*Library of Congress catalog number 63-19683*

Edward M. Johnson, *Editor*

# FOREWORD

When the Association of Research Libraries met in Montreal in June, 1960, one of the items on the Association's agenda was a report on a series of fire tests conducted at Norwood, Massachusetts, in December, 1959. It was obvious that these tests, which had already induced some insurance companies to recommend the use of sprinklers in bookstacks and catalog areas, were of major significance to libraries, and considerable discussion of the report ensued.

Consideration by ARL of this report on fire tests led to discussions of the problem with officers of the Council on Library Resources and the Library Technology Project of the American Library Association. Following these discussions, the Advisory Committee of ARL authorized its executive secretary to request the Library Technology Project to undertake a series of objective tests designed to identify the best methods, materials, types of construction, equipment, and devices for fire prevention and detection in libraries.

In the course of further examination of the problem, it was decided that the LTP should carry out a full-scale study of the experience of libraries with fires and other types of losses and with the procedures, equipment, and building designs needed to prevent such losses. Much of this kind of information was available through previous research and the experience of the fire protection engineering profession, and did not call for special tests. In addition, because insurance for libraries had not been given adequate treatment for almost two decades, the study was broadened to include this subject. Although actual fire tests would have been useful in determining the effectiveness of certain types of library construction, internal arrangement, and equipment, it was decided to defer such tests for later consideration.

Exploration of the problem culminated some months later in a proposal from the American Library Association to the Council on Library Resources for the support of a study based on the objectives outlined above. The Council on Library Resources, which had evinced interest in this problem from the outset, approved the proposal and made a grant of $50,000 to finance the investigation. Gage-Babcock & Associates, Inc., of Kansas City, a firm of independent fire protection engineers, was chosen to carry out the study. The grant was administered by the Library Technology Project with the aid of a committee of librarians.

The Council on Library Resources and particularly its principal officers, Verner W. Clapp, President, and Melville J. Ruggles, Vice-President, have again made librarians their debtors by their interest in and support of this undertaking. Likewise, the library profession is indebted to the staff of the Library Technology Project for administering the project and for the publication of this manual.

It is hoped that this book, which represents a condensation of a vast amount of technical data assembled during the course of the study, will prove useful to librarians in solving the problems related to providing effective protection for libraries and their resources.


Stephen A. McCarthy
Director of Libraries
Cornell University
May, 1963

# ACKNOWLEDGMENTS

This manual on the protection of the library and its resources is the result of the efforts of many people. The Library Technology Project extends its appreciation to all of those who participated in the investigation and in the preparation of the manual.

Members of the advisory committee for the project were:

Walter W. Curley, Director, The Suffolk Cooperative Library System, Patchogue, New York, and Chairman of the Insurance for Libraries Committee, American Library Association.

Stephen A. McCarthy, Director of Libraries, Cornell University.

Keyes Metcalf, Librarian Emeritus, Harvard University.

Charles W. Mixer, Assistant Director of Libraries, Columbia University.

Melville J. Ruggles, Vice President, Council on Library Resources, Inc.

Frazer G. Poole, director of the Library Technology Project, American Library Association, and chairman of the committee for the present project.

E. C. Leonhart, John T. W. Babcock, and Lester A. Eggleston were the principal members of Gage-Babcock & Associates, Inc., independent fire protection engineers of Kansas City, Chicago, San Francisco, and Detroit, who conducted the study and prepared the final report.

Special thanks are due to Gordon A. Danforth, the Library Technology Project's insurance consultant, for his part in the preparation of the text devoted to library insurance.

In addition to the illustrative materials provided by many institutions and equipment manufacturers, important contributions were made by the following:

The Hartford Fire Insurance Group, Hartford, Connecticut, for material included in the Glossary.

The National Archives and Records Service, Washington, D. C., for information included in Appendix F, "The Salvage and Restoration of Damaged Materials."

The Minneapolis Public Library for the fire drill regulations and evacuation plan presented in Chapter 3.

# CONTENTS

# PART TWO:  INSURING THE LIBRARY

# ILLUSTRATIONS

# INTRODUCTION

Experimental fire tests held in 1959 in a simulated library stack area aroused considerable interest among librarians throughout the United States and Canada. The experiment, conducted at Norwood, Massachusetts, by the Associated Factory Mutual Insurance Companies under the sponsorship of the New York Public Library, was made in response to a decision by the library's insurance company to the effect that New York Public's multi-tier stacks constituted a fire hazard; in fact, a hazard so serious as to call for the installation of automatic sprinkler protection in the stack areas.

Notwithstanding the apparent relevance of the tests to the New York Public Library situation, it soon became apparent that the results were being applied on a broad scale as insurance companies began to make more frequent recommendations that libraries install sprinkler systems for the protection of their collections. A case in point was the new John M. Olin Library at Cornell University. The design of the building called for modern sheet-steel freestanding stacks with the levels completely separated by concrete floors. The plan for protection against fire included an alarm system based on heat detection units and hand-operated hose lines to extinguish a fire.

The conditions at Cornell appeared to be so different from those simulated in the Norwood tests that a second experiment was arranged by the authorities of the university which would more closely approximate the situation in the Olin Library. This test was conducted on June 29, 1960, in a concrete-block training building offered by the Ithaca, New York, Fire Department.

The main conclusion reached in the test was that the solid sheet-steel shelving and the absence of drafts from floor to floor had so reduced the possibility of a fire spreading in the stack area of the Olin Library that the automatic fire detection system would enable even a slow-responding fire department to extinguish the fire with minimum damage.

On the basis of this test, library officials decided not to install sprinklers. Cornell's insurance company then classed the building as "sub-standard" with corresponding premium penalties. Only after extended negotiations did the insurance company agree that, because of the excellent construction and the high quality of housekeeping and supervision, the probability of fire was indeed remote. The building was reclassified as "standard" and the penalty was dropped.

The key question posed by the conflicting results of these two tests — i. e., are sprinkler systems actually necessary in libraries or are alternatives to sprinklers possible which will provide equally satisfactory protection? — generated further, more complex questions. These made it clear that much more information was needed about the whole problem of protecting library property from fire. A more precise formulation of this problem in terms of the larger concept of protection of library resources in general and, hence, a recognition that its scope should logically include the subject of library insurance were the genesis of this project.

The study was designed to accomplish four general objectives: (1) the development of methods for arranging the storage of library materials and systematizing operations to achieve a condition of minimum hazard from fires, explosions, water damage, windstorms, vandalism, and other causes of damage and loss; (2) the development of design criteria incorporating known principles of safety to be applied to new construction and the rehabilitation of existing buildings; (3) the design and preparation of a model insurance policy written especially for libraries, along with the encouragement of more favorable insurance ratings and loss adjustment procedures, and the development of markets (i.e., companies willing to underwrite such insurance) for the new policy; and (4) the preparation of a manual that would serve as a general guide to librarians in the purchase of insurance and the physical protection of their property.

The first phase of the study was a search of the literature for as much information as could be obtained on library fires of the past. A comprehensive questionnaire on library losses was prepared and sent to 2,032 representative libraries in 48 states, the District of Columbia, and Canada. (A facsimile of the questionnaire is shown as Appendix D.) One thousand-seventy of the questionnaires were completed and returned. A summary in chart form of the information derived from analysis of the questionnaires is presented as Appendix E. The research staff supplemented the information derived from the questionnaires by visits to selected libraries and discussions with many individual librarians.

Perhaps the most significant single conclusion to be drawn from this study — derived from a statistical analysis of the more than one thousand questionnaire-responses and an exhaustive search of all available records — is that, on the average, fifteen fires can be expected to occur in North American libraries every year with a total loss of one million dollars. When one considers the current rapid expansion of library facilities and services it may fairly be assumed that this annual loss will probably increase.

# INTRODUCTION

Librarians need not be reminded of the incalculable value of their collections as records of our civilization. From another viewpoint, library assets in the United States — the buildings, the books, and other property — represent values in excess of five billion dollars. How the library profession can best safeguard this tremendous national resource from fire and other disasters is the essence of the present study. A full understanding of what libraries are, how they operate, and their vulnerability to damage was necessary to the development of an intelligent program of protection. Correspondingly, a systematic presentation of the ways in which libraries can and do suffer losses and the most effective techniques for preventing them and for reducing their impact through insurance is the basic purpose of this report.

# PART ONE

# Providing
# Physical Protection

# CHAPTER 1

# Types of Physical Losses

For the purposes of this discussion, a *loss* may be defined in general as "an unintentional parting with something of value." Moreover, losses are fortuitous, i.e., unexpected; they occur outside of the ordinary predictable course of events.

Losses in libraries can be divided into two general categories: losses resulting from damage to (or the destruction or disappearance of) physical property, or those resulting from injury to persons or death. The emphasis in this report is given to the former category. The discussion of personal injury or loss of life, as these affect the operations and financial or legal status of the library, is focused primarily on insurance protection against such losses.

The physical property of the library — grounds, buildings, and the contents of the library — can be damaged or lost in a number of ways. With the exception of loss by theft and mysterious disappearance, damage by fire is by far the most important single cause of loss to the property of libraries. Direct fire damage is often accompanied by related kinds of damage: that from smoke, for example, or from water used in fighting the fire.

Other kinds of physical losses to which libraries have been subjected are the effects of earthquakes and windstorms; attack by insects; the theft of books, art objects, and valuable or rare pieces of library property; and vandalism and the mutilation of books and other library materials.

Information on each of these types of damage and loss is available and will be presented in this chapter. Information about certain kinds of loss — e.g., the extent of loss through theft and mysterious disappearance of books — is relatively sparse. However, a great deal is known about the causes of fire and the kinds of conditions that tend to increase the probability of fire. The emphasis in this and subsequent chapters will be placed on damage resulting from fires, smoke, water used in extinguishing fires, and related factors.

## The extent of loss by fire

Records of the causes of fires in buildings and the extent of loss as related to different types of occupancies have been kept for many years. The two most prominent organizations interested in recording and publishing this kind of data are the National Board of Fire Underwriters and the National Fire Protection Association. Traditionally, with respect to both of these, libraries have been included as parts of more general categories. For the National Board of Fire Underwriters, libraries have been classed with the larger category of educational institutions. The National Fire Protection Association includes libraries in the category, "Public Buildings."

To understand why libraries are not regarded as a separate category in themselves for statistical purposes, it is necessary to know something about how fire rates are developed by the insurance companies for the purpose of establishing insurance premiums. Fire rating is different from any other type of rating in that there are wide variations in type of occupancy and construction between risks — i.e., the buildings to be insured. Insurance is based on the assumption of a large number of homogeneous risks, homogeneous in the sense that losses for a particular type of occupancy can be predicted with reasonable accuracy for that group. Because of the variations in potential susceptibility to loss, it can be seen that no truly homogeneous group exists. For example, the insurance company could not be expected to insure a library in a frame building on the same basis as a library in a modern fire-resistive building.

For this reason, a complicated rating schedule had to be devised reflecting all variations in the relative hazard presented by different kinds of construction and occupancy. Through this schedule, loss experience may be applied against basic rates which are used as the starting point in deriving final rates. The basic rates are the measure of the irreducible or unanalyzable hazard and are the same for broad general categories.

In its experience over the years, the insurance industry has found that educational institutions as a whole (including libraries) constitute the smallest category of risk in which sufficient homogeneity exists to make realistic basic rates possible. Thus, from the standpoint of insurance, libraries cannot be separated from other segments of this broad category either for rating purposes or for the gathering of loss statistics.

Figures on fire losses for the United States are presented in publications issued by the National Fire Protection Association (see Bibliography). Table 1 shows average annual fire losses for the five-year period from 1954 through 1958. Again, for NFPA purposes, libraries — except for special libraries in commercial, manufacturing, or scientific establishments — are included in the category, "Public Buildings."

Table 2 shows a breakdown of losses in "Public Buildings."

Although the incidence of loss in the several types of occupancy remains fairly constant, the total number of losses and their costs are increasing every year. The trend is indicated in Table 3.

## TABLE 1

### AVERAGE ANNUAL FIRE LOSSES

(Five-year Period—1954-58)

| Type of Occupancy | Number of Losses | Dollar Losses | Incidence of Fires (Percent) | Dollar Losses (Percent) | Dollar Losses (Average Per Fire) |
|---|---|---|---|---|---|
| Public Buildings | 16,380 | $ 68,438,000 | 2.0 | 6.9 | $4,180 |
| Residential | 566,920 | 307,351,000 | 68.7 | 31.2 | 545 |
| Mercantile | 73,300 | 190,166,000 | 8.9 | 19.2 | 2,950 |
| Manufacturing | 38,720 | 191,708,000 | 4.7 | 19.2 | 4,950 |
| Miscellaneous | 129,340 | 234,373,000 | 15.7 | 23.5 | 1,815 |
| Totals | 824,660 | $992,036,000 | 100.0 | 100.0 | $1,200 |

## TABLE 2

### FIRES IN PUBLIC BUILDINGS

(1954-58)

| Type of Occupancy | Number of Losses | Dollar Losses | Incidence of Fires (Percent) | Dollar Losses (Percent) | Dollar Losses (Average Per Fire) |
|---|---|---|---|---|---|
| Government Buildings | 1,720 | $ 3,168,000 | 10.5 | 4.6 | $1,840 |
| Hospitals, Institutions | 1,640 | 3,039,000 | 10.0 | 4.4 | 1,850 |
| Schools, Colleges | 4,440 | 26,691,000 | 27.2 | 38.8 | 6,000 |
| Churches | 3,660 | 18,228,000 | 22.3 | 26.8 | 5,000 |
| Theaters | 1,360 | 4,370,000 | 8.3 | 6.4 | 3,210 |
| Amusement Halls | 3,560 | 12,942,000 | 21.7 | 19.0 | 3,540 |
| Totals | 16,380 | $68,438,000 | 100.0 | 100.0 | $4,190 |

## TABLE 3

### ANNUAL FIRE LOSSES

| Period | Number of Fires (Annual Average) | Dollar Loss | Public Building Category | |
|---|---|---|---|---|
| | | | Number of Fires | Dollar Loss |
| 1941-45 | 650,800 | $396,800,000 | 10,500 | $35,460,000 |
| 1947-51 | 582,600 | 705,890,000 | 12,400 | 40,194,000 |
| 1954-58 | 824,660 | 992,036,000 | 16,380 | 68,438,000 |

Analysis of the questionnaires revealed that 155 libraries had reported the dollar amount of their fire losses. A breakdown of the number of library fires as related to these amounts is shown in Table 4.

## Causes of Building Fires

Table 5 lists the causes of building fires roughly in order of their incidence.

Fire protection engineering experience and information in the questionnaire returns indicate that of the causes of fire listed above, the following affect libraries most often.

Percentage breakdowns of library fires as related to these general headings can be made on the basis of information derived from three sources: The first is the assumption that the causes of fires in libraries would follow the pattern for all building fires (Table 5). The second is a National Fire Protection Association study[1] of forty fires occurring in museums, art galleries, libraries, and historical buildings between 1930 and 1961. The third source of information is the data collected during the present study on 359 library fires occurring between 1911 and 1961.

Table 7 shows a comparison of three percentage breakdowns.

As has been indicated, fires in libraries are related to poor housekeeping and operations, deficiencies in building maintenance (which would include defects or breakdown of the heating plant), failure of the electrical system and the misuse or neglect of electrical appliances, and a group of miscellaneous causes such as arson, lightning, the negligence of non-library persons — for example, those employed by an outside contractor — and "exposure" fires, i.e., fires resulting from proximity to another building (or a part of the same building occupied by another tenant) in which a fire had originated.

Examples cited in this chapter of actual library fires and conditions that increase the probability of fire are taken from information obtained in this study. These examples demonstrate that fires of all kinds do occur in libraries; that, although the record of libraries with respect to fire is good as compared with other kinds of institutions and establishments, there is room for a great amount of improvement.

[1] National Fire Protection Association, *Fire Record Bulletin FR60-1, Occupancy Fire Record—Libraries,* January, 1961.

## TABLE 4

### DOLLAR BREAKDOWN OF LIBRARY FIRE LOSSES

| Loss in Dollars | Public Libraries | College and University Libraries | Special Libraries | Government Libraries | Totals |
|---|---|---|---|---|---|
| Less than $1,000 | 53 | 14 | — | 1 | 68 |
| $1,000 to $9,999 | 27 | 7 | 1 | 1 | 36 |
| $10,000 to $49,999 | 14 | 8 | 1 | — | 23 |
| $50,000 to $99,999 | 5 | 4 | — | — | 9 |
| $100,000 to $499,999 | 6 | 2 | 3 | 1 | 12 |
| $500,000 to $999,999 | 4 | 1 | — | 1 | 6 |
| Over $1,000,000 | — | — | — | 1 | 1 |
| | 109 | 36 | 5 | 5 | 155 |

## TABLE 5

### CAUSES OF FIRES

| | Percentage of Total |
|---|---|
| Smoking and matches | 16.0 |
| Electrical (fixed service): fires due to misuse or faulty wiring and equipment | 9.3 |
| Defective or overheated heating equipment | 8.2 |
| Rubbish | 5.3 |
| Chimneys, flues: defective or overheated | 5.0 |
| Lightning | 4.8 |
| Lamps, lanterns, oil stoves | 4.5 |
| Open lights, flares, sparks | 3.9 |
| Sparks on roof | 3.6 |
| Children and matches | 3.6 |
| Electrical: power consuming devices | 3.4 |
| Flammable liquids | 2.9 |
| Exposure (external) | 2.4 |
| Spontaneous ignition | 2.0 |
| Grease, tar | 1.9 |
| Hot ashes, coals | 1.5 |
| Combustibles near heaters | 1.3 |
| Explosions | 1.3 |
| Gas and appliances | 1.0 |
| Incendiary (arson), suspicious origin | 0.9 |
| Torches: welding, cutting, plumber's | 0.8 |
| Sparks from machinery, friction | 0.4 |
| Thawing pipes | 0.3 |
| Miscellaneous | 7.5 |
| Unknown | 8.2 |
| | 100.0 |

## TABLE 6

### CAUSES OF FIRES IN LIBRARIES

HEATING PLANT
  Defective or overheated chimneys
  Defective or overheated heating equipment
  Hot ashes, coals
  Gas and appliances

HOUSEKEEPING AND OPERATIONS
  Combustibles near heaters
  Smoking and matches
  Spontaneous ignition
  Torches: welding, cutting, etc.

ELECTRICAL
  Fixed services, etc.
  Electrical devices and appliances

OTHER
  Lightning
  Incendiary fires; fires of suspicious origin

## TABLE 7

### PROBABLE CAUSES OF FIRES IN LIBRARIES

#### (In Percent)

| Source | Average Expectancy | NFPA Records on Libraries | Present Study Data |
|---|---|---|---|
| Heating Plant | 29.0 | 27.5 | 23.0 |
| Housekeeping and Operations | 37.0 | 27.5 | 27.0 |
| Electrical Failures | 24.0 | 12.5 | 29.0 |
| Others | 10.0 | 32.5 | 21.0* |
| | 100.0 | 100.0 | 100.0 |

*Almost two-thirds of these fires were caused by the negligence of outside contractors.

## Construction, operations, maintenance

The degree of combustibility of the structural components of the building, the nature of routine library operations, and the quality of maintenance all have a direct bearing on the probability of fire. With respect to the first, for example, the present study shows that the majority of library fires occur in those buildings classed as "ordinary combustible," which means construction of masonry walls with wood interiors. Seventy-six percent of the libraries studied were of this type of construction; these buildings suffered 85 percent of the fires reported. Fire resistive and noncombustible buildings made up 22 percent of the group and 11 percent of the fires occurred in those buildings. Only 2 percent of the libraries were in wood frame (combustible) buildings and 4 percent of the fires happened in this group.

Percentage figures on the points of origin of library fires, derived from the results of the questionnaire, throw some light on the relative importance of the other two key factors:

| Point of Origin | Percentage of Fires |
|---|---|
| Basements | 36 |
| Trash containers | 14 |
| Book stack areas | 12 |
| Offices and restrooms | 12 |
| Attics | 11 |
| Service areas (e.g., bindery, print shop, paint shop, carpenter shop, kitchen, garage, utility room, boiler room) | 6 |
| Points external to the building | 5 |
| Corridors | 3 |
| Elevator shafts | 1 |
| | 100 |

As used in this study, the term "housekeeping" has a broader application than its conventional meaning. Housekeeping is related to the operations of the library, as distinguished from maintenance or the structure of the building. Poor housekeeping, in general, is permitting conditions to develop and persist that would increase the probability of fire. It includes such practices as the improper storage of combustible materials, inefficient arrangements for the disposal of trash, carelessness in the handling of hazardous materials like gasoline, oils, and paints, and inadequate control of smoking.

A team of fire protection engineers, for example, inspecting a building and its contents for possible fire hazards, would make little distinction between *trash* — say, discarded papers and combustible packing materials — and loosely piled newspapers, unbound serials, pamphlets, or manuscripts awaiting processing to become part of the library's collection.

Numerous instances of dangerous housekeeping practices were observed during the course of this study. In one building, for example, 35,000 reels of microfilm, stored in ordinary (non-fire-resistive) metal drawers, were surrounded by stacks of unbound newspapers and other highly combustible materials.

A situation frequently encountered is that in which quantities of donated materials are improperly stored because staff time for processing is entirely absorbed in the handling of regular acquisitions.

In one library's boiler room, open paint cans and paint-soiled cloths — ideal conditions for spontaneous combustion — were found on a wooden table quite close to a gas-fired boiler. Two wooden doors leading from the boiler room to the reading rooms and stack areas normally were left open, which means that, had fire broken out, its path would have been unobstructed.

Lack of adequate space in many libraries tends to contribute to poor housekeeping and hence to increasing the possibility of fires. An extreme case of this was the librarian who stored a gasoline-powered lawn mower in a crowded basement area which also contained offices, records, and the shelf list.

At the same time, instances of poor storage arrangements were observed in many libraries in which there was no space problem. An example was the library basement room containing a recirculating air-conditioning system complete with water pumps, compressors, motors, and electrical accessories. Makeup air for the system

View of an extremely hazardous accumulation of trash and other combustible materials under a stairway leading from the basement display room of a children's library.

was taken from the same room. The remainder of the room was used for storage of lumber, cardboard boxes, wooden crates, and a variety of packing materials. The air-conditioning system served four rare-book vaults. There were no automatic devices for shutting off the system in the event of smoke or fire, which meant that, had a fire occurred in that room, the four vaults could have been filled with smoke. Here was a case of poor housekeeping, which, combined with poor building design and maintenance factors, produced an extremely hazardous situation.

Smoking in the library, except under tightly controlled conditions, is a very real danger. Careless smokers have started fires in libraries of every size and description. A new library of fire-resistive construction at a Louisiana university is a case in point. Fire was discovered in a group of government publications. Apparently an absent-minded smoker had rested a burning cigarette on the book shelf. Damage was not extensive in this case, but many of the publications were burned beyond the point of worthwhile salvage.

The medical library of a hospital at Moncton, New Brunswick, was destroyed in 1956 in a fire caused by someone carelessly tossing a cigarette into a wastebasket. (Analysis of this fire revealed that an important contributing factor was highly combustible acoustic ceiling tile.)

A fire was narrowly averted in a Wisconsin law library when a routine check of carrel desk drawers disclosed a smoldering cigarette.

A branch library in Wyoming, Ohio, was destroyed by an exposure fire. A cigarette was believed to be the cause of a fire originating in a bowling alley which shared the premises with the library.

A great many fires in libraries can be attributed to inefficient building maintenance, primarily in deficiencies and breakdowns of the heating plant. The relationship between failure of the heating plant and the incidence of fire can be observed in the following table which shows the percentage of fires occurring in each month.

| | | |
|---|---|---|
| January .......... 16 | May .............. 8 | September ....... 2 |
| February ........ 22 | June ............. 6 | October .......... 4 |
| March .......... 11 | July ............. 3 | November ........ 9 |
| April ............. — | August .......... 3 | December ........ 16 |

Note that 74 percent of the fires happened during the five winter months — November through March — which are only 42 percent of the year. This means that the probability of fire during those five months is almost twice as great as for the remaining seven months of the year.

There have been numerous examples of heating plant fires in libraries. During the winter of 1956, the heating system of a library

Aftermath of Moncton, New Brunswick, hospital library fire.

at Edwardsville, Illinois, was undergoing repairs. Briquette fires were kept going in two fireplaces to permit the repair work to proceed. Apparently the fireplaces were not designed for continuous use; wooden joists beneath the hearths finally ignited and burned undetected until three hours after the library had closed for the night. Several hundred books in the first-floor stacks dropped into the basement when the fire-weakened joists collapsed. The loss was estimated at $65,000.

A municipal library on the Mississippi Gulf Coast, operating in rented quarters, was completely destroyed in 1947 when a fire, apparently originating in the heating plant at the rear of the building, spread to the front — the location of the library.

The use of solid fuels in the heating plant creates an added fire hazard, in part because kindling materials are necessary. This often makes the adjacent area a collecting point for combustible materials. The ignition of rubbish near the furnace was probably the cause of a 1957 fire in the Colville, Washington, library. Two cases of library fires have been attributed to the careless handling of hot ashes from coal heaters.

Gas and liquid fuels are clean but, depending on the care taken, can constitute a hazard. In 1934 a heating plant gas explosion in Seminole, Oklahoma, killed three persons and injured two others. The building, which housed the library and municipal government offices, was so badly damaged that it had to be razed.

Defects in and deterioration of the electrical system are sources of many library fires. There are several specific causes: short circuits resulting from overloading; direct fires caused by damaged and defective wiring; defective lamp ballasts in fluorescent lighting fixtures.

Two examples of the latter can be cited. In October of 1960, the Library of the Waterways Experiment Station in Vicksburg, Mississippi, was completely burned out. Although the cause of the fire could not be precisely determined, an investigation showed that the probable cause was a defective fluorescent lighting fixture mounted against a combustible ceiling.

A similar fire occurred in 1961 at the Marine Biology Laboratory of the University of Hawaii at Honolulu. The private library facilities of the laboratory staff and the records of many years of research were severely damaged. Although the fire is believed to have been started by an over-heated drying oven igniting some flammable liquids in an adjacent chemistry laboratory, the precise cause was never established. It is considered highly significant that fluorescent fixtures were installed in the building, mounted directly against a low-density, combustible fibreboard ceiling, a condition extremely conducive to fire.

In the Parliament Building in Ottawa, Canada, in 1952, rain water entering a conduit serving dome flood lights caused a short circuit which started a fire. Although the library in the building was not directly touched by the fire, many thousands of books were damaged by water used in fighting the fire. Damaged wiring in the lighting system for the auditorium stage of the Colorado School for the Blind in Colorado Springs caused a fire in 1950 which destroyed the Braille books and maps in the school library. The total loss was $353,000.

Innumerable examples of fires of electrical origin could be cited — including those resulting from the added load imposed on antiquated electrical wiring systems by increased intensity of lighting. Other causes are defects in or the careless use of equipment such as electrical switch boxes, exhaust fans, heating controls, and electrical appliances. It is sufficient to point out that failure of the electrical system — the basic wiring system itself, related equipment, and extensions and appliances — is a major cause of fires in libraries.

Repair work carried on in regular maintenance activities and repair or construction work by outside contractors and service personnel tend to increase the hazard of fire, primarily because such work so often entails the use of blow-torches, welding torches, and the like.

The disastrous fire at the University of Montreal early in 1962, which destroyed the most complete library in existence on endocrinology and a cross-index system that took thirty years to build, is an example of this kind of loss. To quote from *The Montreal Star* of February 22, "Origin of the fire was not established, but was unofficially attributed to work above the library where men were using blow-torches. The heat and flames were believed to have spread through a ventilating system. . . . Fire and smoke engulfed five sections of the library and surged along and above the corridor to a dozen adjoining offices."

There are many other examples. Sheet-metal workers caused a major fire at Sydney, Nova Scotia, in 1959. The copper eaves of the county building were being repaired with the use of a plumber's torch. The interior of the vacant attic was accidentally ignited; the building, including the library, was a total loss.

Careless use of a blow-torch by the contractor engaged in rearranging and installing new stacks in the Ohio Historical Society Library caused a $100,000 fire.

## Arson: fires of suspicious origin

Arson as a cause of fires is somewhat different from other causes in that it is entirely unpredictable. Moreover, because of its very nature, a fire of incendiary origin often goes undetected; such fires usually result in large dollar losses.

The history of fires caused by arsonists in libraries dates back over a thousand years. The earliest known case occurred in the St. Gall Monastery in Germany in A.D. 937 when an angry student set fire to the library.

A Kansas City, Kansas, library in a school basement was set afire by a student in May, 1961. The student was failing in his school work; the school year was drawing to a close and the boy wanted to destroy the class records. This case, incidentally, is particularly significant because it represented an excellent test of the effects of fire in a closed book shelf. Although unplanned, the test provided completely objective information. The incident is discussed in further detail in Appendix A.

## Exposure fires and area fires

The term "exposure fire" refers to the situation in which a fire originating in one building spreads to another building, or, in the case of joint occupancy of the building, a fire spreading from one part of the building to another. By extension, the term would also

Some results of the 1962 fire at the University of Montreal library.

apply to the case of a village library in Ontario that was burned by the spread of a fire which had started in an adjacent lumber yard.

The meaning of "area fires" is self-evident. Classic examples of area fires are the great Chicago fire of 1871 and the burning of San Francisco as the result of the earthquake of 1906. In such disasters, libraries, obviously, were lost in the general destruction.

## Smoke damage

Records on fire losses are generally inadequate in one respect. The reported losses are not broken down into the separate amounts of damage caused by the fire, the smoke, and the water used for extinguishment. Smoke damage in many ordinary situations may not constitute significant losses. However, this is hardly the case where books are concerned.

Exposure to smoke is extremely harmful to a book. At the very least, a distinct and pungent burned odor permeates the volume, decreasing its appeal and usefulness to the reader. This is usually a long-lasting effect and, although it would be difficult to assign dollar values, the book undeniably has suffered damage. This odor alone is probably not permanently destructive. Commercial deodorizing firms today are able to remove all traces of smoke odor from certain materials without moving them.

In conditions of very thick smoke, there is the added problem of books becoming soiled. Soot may cover all of the exposed surfaces and even work in between the pages. Cleaning books affected by soot is especially difficult because the fine particles smudge readily. Books damaged in this way, although untouched by flames or water, may not justify the cost of restoration and would thus become a total loss.

The most dangerous aspect of smoke damage — one often overlooked — is the effect of high temperatures and acidic gases on the life of a book. It has long been recognized that, when exposed to heat, paper tends to become brittle. W. J. Barrow of Richmond, Virginia, an authority on the preservation of paper, reports that the normal tendency of paper to become brittle increases rapidly as the temperature is raised. Using as his criterion the ability of paper to resist tearing after repeated foldings, Barrow has established that a paper that normally could take 200 folds loses half its strength after being subjected to 100° C. temperature for 24 hours. At 120° C., the equivalent loss of strength required only 3.2 hours. For every 20° C. increase in temperature, the rate at which paper loses strength rises by seven times. Thus, a book might be exposed to hot gases and smoke for only a short time and, although never having caught fire or suffered noticeable scorching, yet might be rendered so brittle as to deteriorate rapidly in normal use.

## Water damage

The destructive effects of water on books are so great that librarians, contemplating the extent of damage resulting from a fire, understandably fear the water used in fighting the fire more than the fire itself.

Although during the extinguishment of fires a certain amount of damage to books by water is unavoidable, it is probably safe to say that, in general, a great amount of such damage is unnecessary. Ordinary fires are extinguished principally through the cooling action of water, which lowers the temperature of the burning material below the point where fire can be sustained. In extinguishing a fire with water, the most efficient method is to break the water into tiny droplets, emerging as spray or fog, which provides the maximum cooling effect relative to the amount of water used. Because this type of water fog has little carrying power, firemen must approach quite close to the fire for the technique to be effective. This, of course, is often an extremely dangerous procedure; in many cases, the firemen are forced to remain at some distance from the fire and are required to project water in solid streams.

Whenever solid streams of water are used, the quantities are likely to be excessive. Books will suffer damage from the direct impact of the stream and from prolonged exposure to soaking.

Water damage was the principal source of loss in the fire in the Michigan State Capitol building; the water inundated the library in the basement. Water was also the main cause of loss in the Parliament Building Library in Ottawa. The library was located beneath the building's dome, the area where most of the fire fighting was taking place.

Continued high levels of humidity can be as destructive to books as direct contact by water since humidity creates an environment favorable to attack by fungus.

As an example of the effects of extreme humidity, the Michigan State Library reported that, after its fire in 1951, many of the steel stacks had been warped and twisted from the pressure of soaked, bound newspapers. Crowbars had to be used to release the bound volumes. The water loss was intensified by the fact that much of the collection was soaked by 100 percent humidity without actually being touched by water from the hoses. (See Appendix F for a discussion of the effects of water on books, manuscripts, and related materials.)

The study disclosed that, very often, storage conditions are extremely poor. In one library, files of newspapers dating back to 1865 were stored in a basement room in which the floor was almost continuously wet. In another library, some of the more valuable books in the collection were stored in two sub-grade rooms built originally to serve as coal bins. Ground water seeping through the walls created a humidity condition highly conducive to the growth of mold and mildew. The problem in this case was further aggravated by the fact that almost all of the books were printed on sulfite paper, which is slightly acidic and tends to deteriorate more rapidly in the presence of moisture.

## Miscellaneous water damage

Results of the study showed that 153 libraries reported a total of 257 loss incidents due to water damage. The total dollar loss reported for 143 incidents (those for which dollar figures were available) was $611,000. Some of these were instances of damage caused by water during the extinguishment of fires. The others are divided into eight miscellaneous classes of damage: broken water and steam pipes; water entering the building during construction;

Water damage to books in the library of the Connecticut Historical Society following an August, 1955, flood of the Connecticut River.

condensate; seepage; storm-driven rains; leaking roofs; faulty drains and sewers; and floods — i.e., rivers overflowing their banks.

For example, several libraries have suffered the effects of floods. Two instances of flood damage occurred in New England as the result of tropical hurricanes which had swept up the Atlantic Coast and caused rivers to overflow. One Oregon library sustained a total loss when the Columbia river overflowed in 1948.

## Other acts of nature

Windstorms, hurricanes, tornadoes, and earthquakes have caused damage to libraries, but, understandably, no more than to buildings in general. Damage by lightning does not appear to be a serious library hazard except in a few isolated areas with a high frequency of lightning storms and in which building construction creates a higher-than-average susceptibility. The earliest known library fire attributable to lightning destroyed the monastery at Mont St. Michel in France about 1300. A bolt of lightning caused a fire in the Spanish Escorial Library destroying the bulk of that library's collection of Arabic books in 1674. To take a current example, lightning is reputed to have been the cause of a fire at Grambling College in Louisiana in early 1962 resulting in the loss of about 50,000 volumes.

Some California libraries have reported minor earthquake damage. Earthquakes caused damage to the Stanford library in 1906 and the Law Library in Eureka in 1954. California Building Codes have introduced design and construction requirements which have greatly reduced the probability of damage from earthquakes. Various areas in the United States have earth faults which could and have produced minor earthquakes. The incidence of earthquakes is shown on the seismic map which appears in Appendix C.

## Insect damage

According to the information obtained in the study, damage by insects is not a significant problem in libraries. Most of the relatively few cases of damage reported have been caused by termites attacking wooden parts of the building.

Insects unfamiliar to the United States have been discovered in shipments of books from foreign countries. To combat this problem, some major libraries, among them the Library of Congress, have installed fumigation chambers for treatment of all book shipments (except publishers' shipments) immediately upon arrival.

Moisture and darkness create a favorable environment for insects; light, general cleanliness, ventilation, and temperature control tend to inhibit insect life. The natural foods for certain species are such library material as paper, leather, wood, parchment, and

Damage to Stanford University Library resulting from 1906 earthquake.

glue. Cockroaches tend to appear whenever kitchens and related food operations are introduced into libraries.

Some of the common insects that may represent a problem in libraries are: book lice, silverfish, cockroaches, termites, larder beetle, white-marked spider beetle, Mexican book beetle, brown house moth, and drugstore beetle.

## Theft and mysterious disappearance

Theft of books and other library property is a major problem throughout the library world. The study revealed a wide range of attitudes among librarians toward this problem. Some librarians appear to be concerned about theft only with respect to money or equipment, such as typewriters and audio-visual devices, or some of their more valuable books. Others are fully aware of the extent of their losses through theft, accept this condition as a routine operational expense, and arrange for funds in their budgets to cover the cost of replacement.

For various reasons, many libraries have neglected to take physical inventories of their collections over extended periods of time. Determining the extent of loss by mysterious disappearance of books in such libraries would be a difficult task. For this and other reasons — primarily the lack of sufficient library staff time — accurate figures on losses of books by theft are difficult to obtain. However, from the facts reported in the course of this study, it can be estimated that about $5 million worth of books are vanishing from library shelves every year. A confirmation of this statement is an estimate derived from a recent study on circulation control methods. Analysis of the results of selected library inventories showed that losses of books through theft and mysterious disappearance range from .06 percent to .30 percent of the annual circulation rate.

## Vandalism, including mutilation

Except for the mutilation of books, vandalism appears to be no more or less common in libraries than in other buildings, although the rate of occurrence in libraries affiliated with schools is perhaps higher. A startling illustration of vandalism has been reported by a Kansas college. Apparently as a prank, three students broke into the library and systematically shuffled 120,000 catalog cards into complete disorder. This bit of misguided humor resulted in the expulsion of the students from the college, a three-month refiling job for the library staff, and costs of about $1,200. A similar incident occurred in a Missouri branch library. In this case, vandals dumped the entire card catalog on the floor and then smeared the cards with glue and shellac.

It is probably safe to say that every librarian is acquainted with the problem of people writing in library books or mutilating them by excising single pages or entire sections. Unfortunately, such damage is not readily detectable at the time the book is returned to the library. Mutilation by persons who have access to the stacks is even less capable of detection. A costly instance of mutilation has been reported from California. In this incident, a patron removed all of the pages pertaining to Ireland from all of the encyclopedias in the San Bernardino Public Library.

One major library reports that, through vandalism of buildings and grounds, mutilation of books, and theft of books, it loses roughly $40,000 a year.

# CHAPTER 2

## The Prevention of Losses

In her 1946 book, *Insurance for Libraries,* Dorothea M. Singer cited a number of opinions too prevalent among librarians:

"Nothing much ever happens to libraries.

"Books do not burn easily; even if a fire should start, it would spread very slowly.

"Books — unless of special value and carelessly guarded — are rarely stolen.

"Library buildings are well kept, and liability or other claims seldom arise."[1]

The data derived from this study do not support these opinions, however widely they may be held by librarians. Obviously, as buildings with contents, libraries in general are no safer from harm than other buildings.

The idea that books do not burn easily is a dangerous half-truth. When they are tightly packed on the shelves, they do burn at a slow rate. However, in a situation of multi-tier stacks with unrestricted passageways and openings in the floors permitting vertical drafts, intense fires can build up in the stacks very quickly.

Although librarians are generally aware of the occasional disappearance of their books, the theft of library materials, taken on a nationwide scale, is a much larger problem than many librarians appear to realize.[2]

Some libraries are well cared for; others are not. Very often, in the same library, good housekeeping practices were observed in the areas open to the public while service areas and others without public access were veritable fire traps.

In short, the assumption that, from the standpoint of the probability of loss, libraries are inherently different from and hence less vulnerable than other establishments is not only false; it is a dangerous assumption and one that constitutes an abrogation of a major facet of management responsibility.

[1] Dorothea M. Singer, *The Insurance of Libraries* (Chicago: American Library Association, 1946), p. 3.

[2] See Joan Van Every, "Is It Worth Doing Anything About Book Losses," *Library Journal,* LXXXV (September 1, 1962), 2842-46.

The librarian as the principal executive officer of the library is responsible for the operations of the library. This necessarily includes whatever policies and procedures are introduced to protect the library against loss. Of course, the librarian often acts with the consent, approval, and support of the trustees, which means, in many cases, that the latter must be educated to the necessity for effective measures of protection.

The preservation and protection of the assets of a library are a responsibility of the library administration. Fulfilling this obligation depends largely upon the *attitudes* of the librarian and the board of trustees. As might be expected, the study showed that attitudes toward protection ranged from utter complacency to a high level of interest in positive programs.

What does it mean to say that the library administrator should have a "favorable attitude"? Essentially it means a willingness (1) actively to assume the responsibility for the preservation of the property; (2) to recognize the need for positive protective measures; (3) to analyze the situation with respect to loss possibilities; and (4) to take appropriate action.

The first two elements of a favorable attitude need no further comment. The third and fourth provide the framework for what might be called "an organized program for the physical protection of the library and its contents." (Many of the suggestions and recommendations presented in this chapter are discussed in greater detail in Chapter 5, "Fire Protection In Library Planning," because they apply to new buildings as well as existing buildings.)

There are a number of general factors that affect the relative susceptibility of the building to damage. These are (1) the location of the building; (2) the manner in which the building is used, i.e., the nature of its occupancy; (3) the construction — that is, wood frame, partially fire resistive, or completely fire resistive; (4) the size of the building, both in height and area; (5) the size of the internal areas; (6) the proximity of other buildings and the characteristics of the immediate neighborhood (from the standpoint of exposure hazards); (7) the internal arrangement, e.g., the style and the materials used in construction of partitions; (8) the nature of materials used in the interior finish, for example, the relative degree of combustibility of wall and floor surfaces, etc.; (9) the number and arrangement of open spaces creating vertical drafts such as stairways and elevators; and (10) the quality and characteristics of the electrical, heating, air conditioning, and plumbing systems.

In addition, there are a number of supplementary considerations that may affect the extent of damage in a particular loss occurrence. These are such factors as (1) the degree to which more hazardous areas (garage, shipping and receiving room, kitchen, bindery, heating plant, print shop, paint shop) in the building have been segregated; (2) the installation of particularly hazardous equipment, materials, and processes; (3) the number and accessibility of exit facilities; (4) the susceptibility to damage (e.g., collapse, combustibility, etc.) of furniture, fixtures, and equipment; (5) the extent to which specific loss-control devices (fire detection equipment, alarm systems, sprinklers) have been installed, and (6) the quality of the library's program of inspection, emergency procedures, and evacuation.

The most efficient way for the librarian to initiate measures for the protection of the library's property, as well as the safety of employees and patrons, is to arrange for a systematic program of inspection. Several types of inspections should be made.

The most important of these is a general inspection of the entire building, including the internal structural arrangement and the contents, primarily with respect to the possibility of fire. This inspection would, in effect, be an analysis of the general factors listed above as related to the particular library in question.

Ideally, the over-all inspection should be made by a professional team of competent, reliable fire protection engineers. However, as one would expect, the ideal is usually expensive, and often not readily available. For those libraries that can afford this type of expert consulting service, the reliability and competence of fire protection engineers in a particular locality can be determined by means of inquiries to The Society of Fire Protection Engineers (see Glossary).

In many cases, this type of general inspection can be effectively conducted by representatives of insurance companies (often at no cost) in conjunction with arranging for insurance. Increasingly, in recent years, agents of many of the larger insurance companies have become skilled in the techniques of inspecting buildings and their contents for purposes of identifying potential hazards. Also, many insurance companies have found it advantageous to employ qualified engineers to make periodic inspections of insured property. Here again the service is usually offered free of charge.

A third group capable of providing the librarian with a realistic appraisal of the library's condition is made up of inspectors whose assignment is to ascertain whether a library fulfills the requirements of various codes, such as the building code, the electrical system code, and the fire prevention code. This subject is discussed in detail in Chapter 5.

More specialized analyses and inspections that should be made are (1) an inspection of the electrical system by engineers trained in that specialty, (2) surveys of the library by experienced members of the municipal fire department, (3) perhaps an examination of the library's relative vulnerability to burglary, vandalism, etc., by the police department, and (4) inspections that can be carried out by the librarian himself, or members of the staff.

It is immediately apparent that the purpose of inspection of all types is to discover whatever hazardous conditions might exist in the library. Moreover, it is evident that the librarian as such would be ill-equipped to identify many such conditions; this is the reason for the recommendation that outside experts be called in to make inspections in their specialized fields. However, there are a great many protective measures that the librarian can take with the assistance of his immediate staff and others; this subject will be taken up in Chapter 3.

A full-scale analysis by professional fire protection engineers, as was mentioned above, would result in observations and their implicit recommendations of the following kind:

Exit facilities and fire escapes might be inadequate; for example, there should always be more than one exit. There might be a need for segregating the more hazardous areas in the building from the rest of the library, especially service areas (garages, kitchens, the bindery, etc.), through construction of fireproof partitions or fire walls (see Glossary). Additional dampers and suitable cut-offs might be required in the ventilation and air conditioning systems to prevent the spread of smoke and toxic gases.

Based on the information gathered in this study and the accumulated knowledge and experience of the fire engineering profession, a number of specific hazards and corrective measures, not necessarily peculiar to libraries alone, can be listed as being especially important to the librarian. These are things the librarian should be aware of, even though the particular action taken may be limited to instructions to contractors, or discussion of such problems with fire protection engineers or other consultants.

It should be noted that each library presents its own set of problems with respect to the possibility of fire and other kinds of damage. Moreover, and this is especially important, within each library, the kinds of corrective actions taken must be related to each other; that is, the achievement of a condition of safety in the particular library does not necessarily entail the introduction or installation of all possible protective measures, devices, or equipment.

In any case, the discussion here must be carried on at the general level; each librarian, preferably with some expert assistance, must evaluate his own situation and take whatever steps are necessary to prevent damage, loss, or injury to the property and lives for which he is responsible.

Review of numerous library fires and, incidentally, the results of the fire tests at Norwood show that open multi-tier stacks with

# FOUR-HOUR RATING

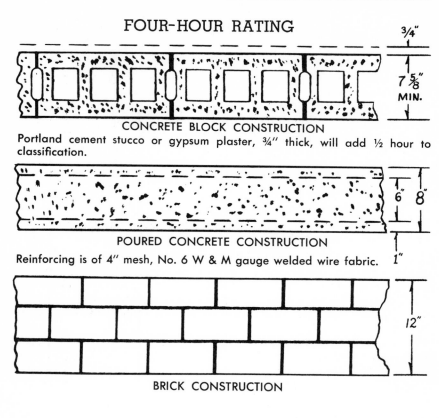

### CONCRETE BLOCK CONSTRUCTION

Portland cement stucco or gypsum plaster, ¾" thick, will add ½ hour to classification.

### POURED CONCRETE CONSTRUCTION

Reinforcing is of 4" mesh, No. 6 W & M gauge welded wire fabric.

### BRICK CONSTRUCTION

# TWO-HOUR RATING

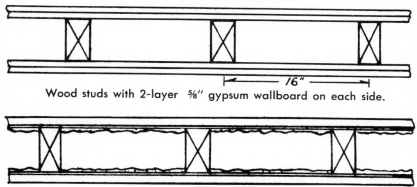

Wood studs with 2-layer ⅝" gypsum wallboard on each side.

Wood studs with 1" fibered gypsum plaster on metal lath.

Typical fire partition sections.

openings in the floors present a special fire hazard. Such openings tend to produce a flue-like effect in a fire and this, combined with the large volume of open space in ordinary stack arrangements, tends to promote the more rapid burning and spread of the fire. This means that, in those libraries with multiple levels of stack

*Courtesy of Remington Rand Division of Sperry Rand Corporation*
A typical multi-tier steel stack arrangement. The continuous metal floors at each level will retard the upward propagation of fire and smoke for a time. However, the open stairway will act as a chimney and fire and smoke will travel to all levels above the point of origin.

tiers, the vertical openings in the floors should be closed, making continuous floors on each level.

The same rule applies to open stairways, in the stacks as well as elsewhere in the library, and other vertically open spaces such as elevator shafts. In a fire, open stairways and elevator shafts

*Courtesy of Remington Rand Division of Sperry Rand Corporation*
A typical example of multi-tier construction with concrete floors at each level. Here the vertical, unprotected steel tier members support the shelving and all floors and tiers above. Experience of fires in similar construction shows that buckling of unprotected steel supporting members because of fire could result in collapse of the tiers above.

An abandoned three-level, open, multi-tier stack structure from which the shelving has been removed. The slots between the glass floor panels show how flames, heat, and smoke could propagate upward through the entire structure.

have the same effect of causing the fire to spread more rapidly. Thus, these spaces should be enclosed with fire resistive materials.

A second principle of fire protection engineering is that, in general, large, open spaces promote the rapidity and spread of burning. The rule is to break up such spaces with fire resistive barriers such as fire walls and fire doors (see Chapter 5). In this regard, however, the modern tendency in library construction toward large open spaces does not necessarily increase the hazard provided other pertinent factors are favorable.

In the past some libraries were constructed with glass floor panels in the stacks. The Boston Public Library Annex, for example, built in 1918, used two- by three-foot glass floor panels, three-quarters of an inch thick, supported on iron frames. In 1961, a stack attendant jumped from a chair in a book stack aisle and plunged through the floor on which he was working, and through the next one below for a total drop of fifteen feet.

An investigation by the library's consulting engineers led to the conclusion that the glass panels would safely support the static loading of book trucks but were unsafe against the impact of a person falling or jumping from a height of one or more feet. Replacement of the floor by steel or concrete was recommended.

From the hazard standpoint, there is some evidence that glass may develop "fatigue" or weakness with age; moreover, large glass panels would probably break from the impact of water dispensed in fighting a fire, especially if the glass had been heated by rising gases. This would increase the draft and the difficulty of fire fighting and would also endanger the lives of firemen.

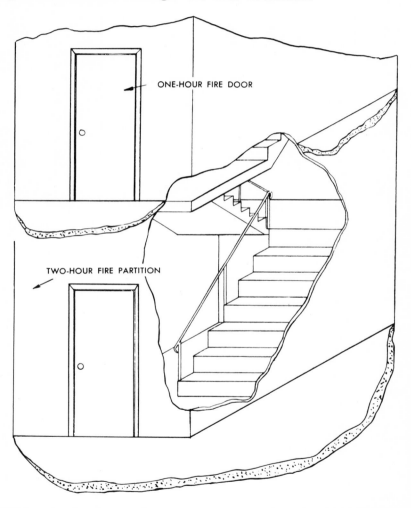

Typical enclosed stairway with continuous floor at each level. Similar enclosures around all openings in floors, i.e., book lifts, elevators, conveyors, isolate each floor as a separate fire area which in many cases obviates the need for certain types of fixed fire protection systems.

In short, librarians in buildings with glass floors (or slate floor-ing) should be aware that there are certain hazards inherent in this type of floor construction and that they might well have their situation reviewed by competent engineers to ensure that all neces-sary measures had been taken to minimize the hazard.

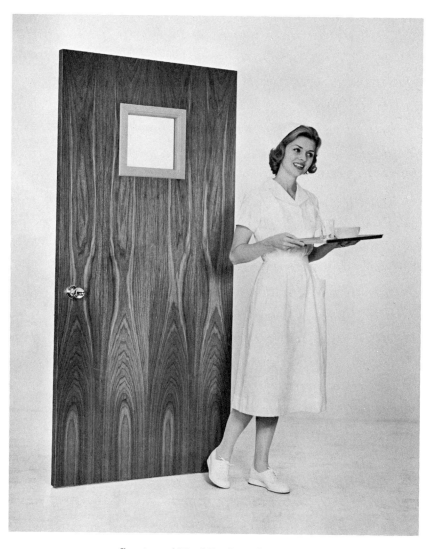

*Courtesy of Wood Products Division, Weyerhaeuser Company*
This walnut fire door has a mineral core and is available with a glassed opening not exceeding 100 square inches in size. It has the same classification and application as the all-wood door.

*Courtesy of Wood Products Division, Weyerhaeuser Company*
Fire doors can be attractive. The all-wood Cherry door shown above is listed by Underwriters' Laboratories, Inc., for use in Class B openings. Such doors have a one-hour fire rating and are applicable to enclosed stairways extended upward through book stacks, and openings in corridor or room partitions. The core of the door consists of fire retardant treated wood particles, bonded with phenolic adhesive under pressure and heat. The faces are three-ply veneer panels available in a wide range of domestic hardwood as well as many imported woods.

There is evidence that U-bar shelving, as opposed to solid shelving, tends slightly to increase the fire hazard. This is because, in a fire, open shelving permits air and hot gases to reach the bottom edges of books causing them to catch fire in a shorter time than would otherwise be the case. Such shelving also provides a draft passage between shelves, especially where books are shelved loosely. A second point: Open shelving of the U-bar type allows dust to collect at the lower shelf levels where it may produce a housekeeping problem, increasing the fire hazard. This is not to say that U-bar shelving necessarily should be replaced. Again, the decision depends upon other relevant factors. If other more important requirements of fire safety have been met, the implicit suggestion that U-bar shelving should be replaced with other types may be ignored.

Combustible acoustic ceiling tile creates an unusually hazardous condition, especially in combination with fluorescent lighting fixtures (see Chapter 5).

A special problem arises in many cases in which the library occupies a building jointly with other kinds of establishments. The study revealed a great variety of such joint occupancies, many of which, because of the possibility of direct exposure to fire or smoke damage, could represent a threat to the library. Here again, competent engineering inspection might result in a recommendation for the erection of fire walls to separate the library portion of the building from the other occupancies.

The list of establishments occupying a building jointly with a library, as reported in the questionnaires, is interesting. Here are a few of them presented roughly in descending order of hazardousness: bowling alley (because of the high degree of flammability of lane and floor surfaces), mercantile shop, maintenance shop, mechanics' shop, restaurant, tavern, feed store, computer laboratory, residential dwellings, and print shop.

An inspection by qualified electrical engineers might result in the recommendation that the entire electrical system be replaced. As a matter of general interest, the estimated average useful life of an electrical wiring system is about twenty years. Wire insulation ages at a uniform rate under normal conditions of usage. Under abnormal conditions, such as overloading or subjection to high temperatures, aging may be accelerated. It is certainly the case that after twenty years a thorough investigation of the system should be made.

The installation of temporary electrical wiring should be avoided; moreover, if the basic electrical system requires repair or renovation, the librarian should not attempt this kind of work himself, but should assign the job to competent electricians or electrical engineers.

A too-common practice is to use over-sized fuses to reduce the annoyance of repeatedly replacing blown fuses. This, of course, is an open invitation to electrical fires. The real causes of blown fuses — overloaded or faulty circuits — are too often overlooked. The best solution to this problem is modernization of the electrical system to prevent overloading. If this is not practicable, steps must be taken to prevent over-fusing. One method is to use special fuse holders which will not accept fuses of greater-than-specified capacity. The holder, which is screwed into the ordinary fuse receptacle, is locked in place so that it cannot be removed; its purpose cannot be nullified by inserting a coin or other device to bypass the fuse mechanism. Another useful device is a circuit breaker. When overloaded circuits cause the lights to go out, the current is restored simply by pressing a button. The temptation to use larger fuses is diminished; momentarily overloaded circuits protected by circuit breakers are annoying but not unduly hazardous.

The installation of fluorescent lighting has introduced a special hazard, not generally known. By way of background, fluorescent lighting is produced as an incidental effect of an electrical discharge in a gas-filled tube. Depending on the length of the tube, initiating the discharge of electricity requires considerable voltage. For example, in 96-inch tubes, at least 625 volts are required for starting. After the tube has been started, its resistance falls off sharply. A current regulating device is included for control purposes.

Starting voltage and current regulation are supplied by ballasts. These are inductive devices wound on an iron core, usually built into a pitch-filled case. Normally they operate at a temperature of about 194° F. Studies have shown that ballast temperatures under some conditions may go as high as 260° F.[3] Abnormally high temperatures shorten the life of ballast insulation; it has been established that, because of the loss of insulation protection, the ballast may fail at anytime. Failure of the ballast insulation produces local hot spots; the temperature may rise to 390° F. or higher. The results may be the ignition of nearby combustible materials, dripping pitch, even a violent explosion of the ballast case, with the potential danger of personal injury.

An internal short-circuit in a ballast which is about to fail does not allow the passage of a sufficient load of electricity to blow the fuse or trip the circuit breaker, which is ordinarily used to protect the circuit serving a fluorescent fixture. Several fixtures are usually served by the same circuit which is protected by a fuse or circuit breaker not sufficiently sensitive to react to the small overload caused by a defective ballast.

The solution is relatively simple. Each ballast should be individually fused. Fuse ratings are available (from 0.5 to 6.25 amperes) to match various combinations of ballasts and lamp-power combinations. Like the special fuseholders mentioned earlier, these

3 *Illuminating Engineering* (September, 1959), 513-15.

special fuses will not accept a replacement fuse of a higher rating. In addition to this protection, ballasts are available with thermal cutouts which require manual resetting; also there are ballasts with thermal cutouts which will be automatically reset once the heat has been dissipated.

At present, although some municipal building codes make individual fusing of ballasts mandatory, there is no uniform policy among fixture manufacturers on providing adequate protection against failure of fluorescent-fixture ballasts. The hazard is recognized, but individual fusing, or other built-in protection, is not provided unless specified when the fixtures are purchased.

In any event, all fluorescent ballasts should be individually fused. The cost is under one dollar per fixture. This expense is low considering the degree of hazard otherwise presented.

The relationship between the library and the local fire department is an extremely important part of the general protection responsibility of the librarian. For many libraries, the decision as to what kinds of internal protective measures should be taken will depend, at least in part, upon the capability and quality of fire-fighting personnel and equipment available in the community.

Certain conclusions are obvious: as is the case with libraries, the great majority of fire departments are located in small communities; a great many of them will be faced with limitations in their number of personnel, the extent of training that may be provided, the type or quantity of equipment available, and other handicaps.

These limitations make a difference to the librarian in two respects: First, the librarian, in designing and implementing his program of protection, should have some acquaintance with the relative ability of the fire department in his community to cope with emergencies in the library. Second, arranging for a visit to the library by personnel of the department can acquaint the firemen in advance with the situation they will encounter in the event fire does occur.

A request for inspection by members of the fire department, perhaps periodically such as annually or semi-annually, and immediately after extensive alterations or rearrangements, is an especially advantageous course to pursue. In most cases, this service would be performed at no cost to the library. Of course, it is in the interest of the fire department to assist wherever possible in the reduction of losses by fire. Thus, in many departments, there are highly skilled personnel with extensive experience in estimating the probabilities of fire in a particular building.

Firemen would establish the relative accessibility to the fire department of the building itself, as well as that of the various areas and rooms within the building; firemen would also ascertain whether an adequate supply of water was available to fight the fire. Such inspection would be useful in (a) checking the condition and adequacy of existing fire fighting equipment in the library and (b) making recommendations on the type and quantity of such equipment to be introduced.

In light of the fact that more and more libraries are adding cooking and eating facilities for the staff, it should be noted that kitchens and related areas offer a special hazard because of the possibility of grease fires and fires caused by defective electrical appliances. A general inspection by the fire department certainly should include an examination of equipment and conditions in such areas.

An inspection by the fire department provides an opportunity for the librarian to acquaint the firemen with an important fact about library property: the serious damage that can be caused to books through the excessive use of water. Thus the librarian should submit an advance request that in the event of fire the firemen exercise as much care as possible with respect to the amount of water used. The specific suggestion is that, where possible, the firemen use techniques and equipment for dispersing the water in the form of fog or spray.

It may happen that because of limitations on their time, the members of the local fire department would be unable to provide this type of inspection service. In such cases, it is not unreasonable to suppose that the department could offer suggestions to the librarian about what persons in the community were qualified to carry out such inspections. These might be officials of municipal government or representatives of private agencies, whose services could be obtained on a contract basis.

In the general framework of analyzing the over-all situation, there are two main points that should be mentioned even though they appear to be almost obvious. First, a general principle of fire protection is that property be separated physically into smaller units wherever feasible. If this principle were followed, a single fire would then destroy only part of a particular kind of property. In a library, for example, a collection of rare books might be stored in two separate vaults to avoid the possibility of losing the entire collection. Whether such a procedure is practicable in a particular library would depend, of course, on the specific conditions in that situation.

Second, unusually rare or irreplaceable items should be given more consideration in arrangements for physical protection than less expensive or more readily replaceable materials.

## Protecting the card catalog

The library card catalog warrants a careful study of measures for its security. Regardless of how much insurance may be carried, its loss would result in a period of serious confusion. Card by card it would have to be reconstituted, a tedious and time-consuming process under even the best of circumstances. The information in vital library records, such as the catalog, should never be exposed to complete loss.

The most complicated reconstitution of the catalog would occur if it were destroyed, with little or no destruction of the book stock, because the catalog would then need to be re-established in its entirety. Loss of the book stock without damage to the catalog, in the unlikely possibility that that should happen, would be less of a problem, because the book collection would be started anew, with new cataloging for the items purchased. (The old catalog would serve as an important guide to building the new collection.) The effect of partial destruction of a catalog, with or without accompanying loss of books, obviously will vary with the extent of the damage; however, it is probable that if more than a small portion is damaged, it may be more efficient to reconstitute the catalog as a whole rather than to attempt to salvage what remains, for the problem of sorting, assembling sets, and editing would soon equal or surpass those of full reconstitution.

No fully satisfactory method of protecting the catalog appears to exist. Several methods, with variations, are possible, but none can be undertaken without a considerable expenditure of time and money, either at the outset and on a continuing basis or when the actual reconstitution is needed. The critical problem is that a library's card catalog is a dynamic, changing bibliographical asset; normally the catalog is a different instrument at the end of a working day than it was at the beginning. It exists in time as well as in space, and cannot be protected and replaced in the same way as a static item, such as a book or a piece of furniture or equipment.

*Protection by fire resistive vaults.* Solely from the standpoint of physical protection, perhaps the ideal method is to house the catalog in a fire resistive vault. This may range in scope from a single "safe" for a catalog cabinet to a series of such safes, and in large libraries, to an entire insulated room, not unlike a large bank vault. The latter would not only house the catalog but would provide space where the public and the library staff could consult it. Individual safes or fire resistive cabinets pose problems of ease of access (open vault doors would seriously hamper use), rapid closing of the vaults in the event of fire, the extra space taken up by the thick, insulated walls of the cabinets and the heavy weight on the floors. A room-size vault for the catalog complex no doubt would need to be a part of the original construction of a library building, and might conflict with future expansion and with the concepts of open, modular planning in contemporary library construction. Both types of vaults are expensive, and neither, in the last analysis, is entirely fireproof. Some savings in insurance premiums could, however, be obtained through this type of protection.

*Protection by duplication of the catalog.* Some library systems maintain complete catalogs of the main library at branches, as well as for the branches at the main library. Where this is done, the loss of the catalog at any single location would be less serious; reconstitution would be expensive, but the data would be available, assuming that the catalogs at all locations were kept up to date on a frequent and regular basis. Those libraries maintaining an "official" as well as a public catalog are in an advantageous position, providing that the two catalogs are sufficiently separated and are protected from simultaneous hazard. Reconstitution through the shelf list, and through individual branch and departmental catalogs, depends largely on the completeness of the catalog information contained in each. In most cases, the information would be insufficient because so many shelf list cards would lack indication of the added entries.

The maintenance of two full catalogs, each in a separate location, is so costly a solution that few libraries can seriously consider it.

*Protection by microfilming.* The most frequently used method of specific protection for the catalog has been microfilming. This method has advantages and disadvantages. Among the disadvantages are cost and the problems of keeping the records current. This may become a more acceptable technique as continuing technological advances in filming and reproduction of cards are accomplished.

In protecting the catalog by microfilming, there are two possible alternatives to be considered. The least expensive, and perhaps the best solution in a modern fire resistive building where the risk may be considered small, is to microfilm the cards by the least expensive method available, in order to have a record from which the catalog can be reconstituted in the event of loss. The other alternative, and the more expensive of the two, is to microfilm the catalog so carefully that the microfilm can be used to reproduce the cards directly by the use of such equipment as Xerox Copyflo.

In the first instance, automatic equipment can be used and less care needs to be exercised in the microfilming than in the case when it is desired to reproduce the cards directly from the film. In the latter instance, planetary equipment is usually recommended, and the process requires more time and is therefore more expensive. Cards which might be eventually reproduced by Xerography can be no better than the film from which they are made. The quality of the latter is influenced (a) by the care of the operator and (b) by the clarity of the material on the card. Catalogs of any age or size normally contain cards of widely varying quality: new, old, soiled, clean, dog-eared, handwritten in ink of varying shades and colors, typed, or printed, on cards which sometimes are of different heights. Card reproduction by electrostatic printing can now provide for back-to-back duplication of a card with information on both recto and verso when such cards are separated from those for which only the recto is needed, or when the former are in the majority. But since the original filming must usually be done as a mass production operation, it is exceedingly difficult, if not impossible, to arrive at photographic specifications which will provide for satisfactory reproduction of all variations in card quality. Color differentiation (e.g., subject headings in red) on the original cards will, in any case, be lost.

In both cases, a major problem is created by the constantly changing nature of the catalog. Most microfilming cannot accurately record a catalog as of a given date; few catalogs can be filmed from beginning to end in a single day, and yesterday's filming becomes out of date with today's filing.

When a filming of the entire catalog has been completed, it is relatively simple to develop a routine for filming subsequent additions on a periodic basis. Establishing the frequency of this subsequent filming is the crux of the problem. Most libraries wish to keep the catalog as up to date as possible, so new cards and changes to old ones cannot usually be held any length of time for filming as a group. Consequently, filming is necessary at the same frequency with which filing is done, often daily, and usually at intervals of not more than a week. This filming provides the needed duplicate record of all that is in the catalog, but, as the process continues, the number of alphabets of filmed cards increases, creating a multitude of supplements not only to the original film of the catalog, but to previous supplements as well. With the passage of time, this accumulation of hundreds or even thousands of separate alphabets would result in reproduced cards in a wide variety of conditions, which, in reconstituting the destroyed catalog, would pose an interfiling and editing problem of immense proportions.

A more attractive alternative is that of filming the entire catalog at intervals of, say, five years, and providing for the intervening additions and changes in some manner other than filming. A library may "gamble" and assume that the most recent complete filming will provide for most of the catalog so that supplementing it is unnecessary. The smaller the catalog, or the more frequent the complete filming, the more feasible this is. For a larger catalog or less frequent filming, the most recent complete film could be supplemented by a "catalog" of main entry cards in a separate location and kept up to date with the principal catalog. This supplementary "catalog" could be discarded at the time of the next complete filming, and so on.

If microfilming is undertaken as a protective measure, whatever the variation decided upon, it is obvious that the film itself, in turn, must be protected, through storage in a vault, a separate location, or some other suitable manner. Microfilming is equivalent to partial insurance as long as the film is given adequate physical security. Catalog cards can be reproduced from microfilm at reasonable cost, but the insured value of the catalog must also include provision for substantial labor costs involved in refiling and probable editing of the reproduced cards.

*Other methods.* The existence in book form of all or part of a library's catalog is another form of duplication to be considered. While it is doubtful that a library would wish to put its catalog into book form solely for protective purposes, the existence of a book catalog created for other reasons as well undoubtedly could reduce insurance premiums and aid in recreating a new card catalog. Whatever factors may lead to a book catalog, the original cost may seem more reasonable when viewed also as a part of the library's insurance program.

A divided catalog can also be a protective safeguard. However the division of cards is made, the section containing main entries with tracings can provide for reconstituting the remainder. The value of the subject section in recreating the main entries depends entirely on the extent to which these cards carry full information. Most libraries with divided catalogs have not wished to separate the parts geographically, which is an obvious necessity if such division is also to serve the purposes of protection against possible loss or damage.

Still another protective measure has become available in recent years, though in the near future its use will be limited to the very large or the special library. Electronic data processing equipment can also serve insurance purposes. Catalog information stored in a computer can, if programmed with this function in mind, reconstitute a complete catalog in card or book form more effectively than any other method.

*Protecting the shelf list.* Along with other functions, the shelf list serves as the library's inventory control of its stock. While the catalog conceivably could serve this same purpose, its inherent nature virtually precludes any practical use in this way. Consequently, the shelf list might attain its greatest value precisely at the time of a disaster, for only from this record could a library determine with any accuracy the losses in its book stock. The methods of protecting a shelf list do not vary, for the most part, from those for the catalog itself. A library must provide for both. Under ideal circumstances, either record could be reconstructed from the other, but most libraries have not cataloged their collections with this in mind. Reconstitution of a catalog from a shelf list would also require protection of author and subject authority files, and libraries considering a shelf list also as an insurance device might do well to consider the possibility of using as a shelf list card a complete duplicate of the main entry card, from which full catalog information could be reconstructed.

*Summary.* The economics of microfilming or comparable record duplicating techniques depend upon the value of the records involved. How essential are they to library operation? If the records are vital, and reconstitution after a loss would be almost impossible, duplication should be a matter of necessity rather than economics. The cost of restoration, expensive at best, should be estimated realistically, with adequate debits included for the loss of library usefulness during the period of reconstitution.

## Repairs and alterations

Repair work and construction work in or about the library, whether carried out by employees of the library or outside contractors, create special hazards as was shown in the discussion of causes of fires (Chapter 1). Such work should be carefully supervised in the interests of fire prevention, not only by the persons responsible for the work but also by the librarian or a designated member of the staff. Following is a brief check list which will serve as a guide to the librarian in controlling the activities of contractors (or others on similar assignments) performing work in existing library buildings. If the work to be done is designed in advance by an architect or engineer, most of the contingencies may be covered in the architectural-engineering specifications governing the work.

# CHECKLIST FOR OUTSIDE CONTRACTORS' WORK

1. Does the contractor carry adequate compensation, liability, contractual, and surety insurance to protect the library against any losses or claims? (See Chapters 8-12.)

2. Does the contractor use only well-kept materials and equipment to avoid accident to others?

3. Does the contractor plan the work in advance with the librarian to minimize interruptions to the normal operations of the library?

4. Does the contractor rope off, barricade, or otherwise isolate work areas which might be hazardous to visitors and staff? Are precautionary signs provided?

5. When work is being performed above floor level, does the contractor take the proper precautions to protect people from falling objects?

6. When working on water or steam piping, are the library's resources removed from the immediate vicinity, or otherwise protected against exposure?

7. When rearranging or installing stacks, is the work programmed and conducted in such a manner as to avoid overturning or collapse?

8. When painting, does the contractor store paints, thinners, solvents, etc., in a designated safe place where they will not constitute a fire hazard? Is he required to store drop cloths, wiping cloths, waste, and paint-saturated cloths in covered metal containers, or remove them from the premises at the end of each work day, to avoid spontaneous ignition fires?

9. Is the contractor tidy about his work and does he remove debris to avoid accidents?

10. Does the contractor store materials and supplies neatly so as not to obstruct passageways used by visitors and staff?

11. When the work requires the use of open flame, such as cutting, welding, or blow torches, are combustible materials removed beforehand from the work areas? If not, are combustibles protected from flying hot metal particles by surrounding the work area with flame-retardant tarpaulins or other fire resistive materials? Does the contractor keep a fire extinguisher ready at hand when performing such work? Is such work performed only under the supervision of a competent person and with authorization from the librarian or his designated representative?

12. When work ceases for the lunch hour and at the end of the day, is the contractor required to examine the entire work area closely to make certain that no conditions have been created which might result in fire or other loss at a later hour?

# CHAPTER 3

# Fire Defense Measures

There are several categories of protective measures that can be carried out by the librarian or by the library staff under the supervision of the librarian. These have to do with: (1) inspection, (2) housekeeping and operations, and (3) preparation for emergencies.

## Inspection

A comprehensive inspection of the library can be made by members of the library staff through the use of the check-off inspection form presented at the end of this chapter. Depending on the size of the staff in a particular library, one or more persons should be assigned to make periodic (perhaps monthly) inspections of the premises using this form or a modified version of the form adapted to the particular situation. This checklist is designed in the form of a questionnaire; the appropriate corrective action is implicit in each question.

A closing-time inspection should become a routine procedure to be carried out by various members of the staff. This would ensure that doors and windows (including fire doors) are properly closed and locked, that no incipient fires are present.

The general recommendation that good housekeeping practices be observed is almost too obvious to be mentioned. However, during the course of the study, a great many departures from safe housekeeping practices were observed and it cannot be assumed that such practices will be corrected simply through this recommendation. Here again, the check-list for inspection provides the librarian with a handy enumeration of those things against which he can measure his own practices.

## Operations

Under the general heading of operations, perhaps the most important factor is the relative effectiveness of supervision both of the staff and of the general public. Considering that the greatest single cause of fires in libraries is smoking, it is evident that the librarian must adopt a strict procedure for its control.

It must be assumed that in some libraries smoking simply cannot be permitted at all. In others, smoking must be prohibited in certain areas: the stacks, and especially hazardous service areas such as garages, storage rooms, shipping and receiving rooms, etc. Probably the ideal solution to the problem of smoking in libraries is to combine strict observance of stated and posted regulations about smoking in certain areas of the library with a provision for permitting smoking in certain specified areas — a smoking lounge for the patrons and similar, perhaps more liberal, allowances and space for the staff.

The comments on control of smoking apply in part to the prevention of theft, mutilation, and other forms of malicious mischief performed by people using the library. Ideally, the total library should be under continuous observation by a member or members of the staff, watchmen, guards, or custodial personnel — that is, every day for twenty-four hours a day. However, such an extreme procedure would be extraordinarily expensive, if not impossible, in many libraries. Fortunately, total surveillance is not necessary to ensure a reasonably safe condition in the library. The amount of supervision necessary depends upon the conditions imposed by other pertinent factors.

So far as direct supervision is concerned, one technique that has come into recent use for surveillance of every area (at least theoretically) of the building, is the use of closed circuit television. TV camera units are available at a cost of about $600. The camera can be located wherever desired and connected to any standard television receiver, using coaxial cable costing 10 to 15 cents per foot. The signal is transmitted on a locally unassigned channel. The total cost may be doubled if such accessories as remote-control devices are required and if maximum picture quality is to be achieved. Under such conditions the signal is transmitted at video frequencies; the TV receiver requires modification and its cost would be about $350. There is no limit to the number of cameras that can be used with a single receiver through a central switching arrangement. For greater control, several monitoring receivers can be used for observation at a number of different points in the library. Such systems can be designed for any degree of flexibility depending on the internal arrangement of the library. In a multiple-camera situation, a single control center, containing all power equipment, is feasible. In this type of system the camera housing may be as small as three inches square and ten inches long.

Even with remote-control TV, obtaining effective surveillance would not necessitate complete coverage of the library. The mere existence of such remote-control supervision would be sufficient to act as a deterrent to patron carelessness or deliberate acts of mischief. An added feature: connecting the television system to an intercom microphone-speaker system would permit observation to be combined with warnings, either to alert people of danger or as admonishment.

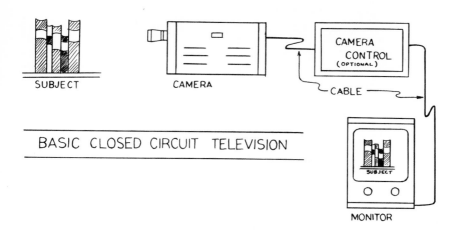

BASIC CLOSED CIRCUIT TELEVISION

*Courtesy of General Dynamics/Electronics*

The optional camera control in the basic TV circuit may be a video switcher which will permit pictures from as many as eight cameras to be viewed on one monitor.

## Preparation for emergencies

The entire library staff should be encouraged to develop the habit of watching for signs of danger — the sight or smell of smoke, the accumulation of combustible trash, the deterioration of electrical appliances or wiring, a patron sneaking a cigarette in the stacks — in short, any of the conditions enumerated in the checklist inspection form plus any others that common-sense observation would disclose as hazardous in the particular situation.

Second, the staff should be given systematic instruction and practice in the following kinds of emergency procedures: the method and technique for sounding the proper alarms; the location of internal fire fighting equipment such as fire extinguishers, hose lines and standpipe systems, and related equipment, and the techniques for their use; and the details of an organized plan for evacuation of the building by staff and the general public. The specific details of such training must, of course, be developed for the particular library. However, some of the elements of an effective training program are self-evident and some may be provided through a cooperative arrangement with the local fire department.

Third, the library can and should formulate a written policy which would include specific instructions to the members of the library staff on their responsibilities and procedures in the event of emergency. By way of assistance in the development of such a written emergency plan, a brief essay on first-aid fire fighting and a model set of fire drill regulations and evacuation instructions are presented at the end of this chapter. The evacuation plan is adapted from a set of regulations issued to the staff of the Minneapolis Public Library, but with appropriate modifications, it should be applicable to most libraries.

There are a few miscellaneous general rules and suggestions which may be stated here: (1) Exit doors should not be capable of being locked against emergency egress. Some type of safety device should be installed, such as "panic hardware," i.e., a bar arrangement on the door so that a person falling against or pushing the bar automatically opens the latches and permits the door to open outward even though, when not in use, the lock mechanism prohibits entrance from the outside. (2) Fire doors should be closed after each passage. They should never be permitted to be propped open. If required to be left open for normal daily operations, they should be equipped with automatic closing devices which would be actuated by a rise in temperature (fusible link) or by means of connection to the fire alarm system.

(3) Because time is so important in preventing the spread or growth of fire, a valuable procedure is the development of a "fire brigade" made up of members of the library staff. Even with an automatic detection system and prompt giving of alarms, some time must elapse before firemen can reach the scene; fire brigades fill this time gap. It must be emphasized that the primary responsibility for coping with fires rests in the fire department, but a fire brigade with a relatively small amount of instruction and practice can provide immediate and extremely important defense measures. The staff members' first responsibility is to turn in an alarm to the fire department; second, to evacuate the visitors and all employees not given fire defense assignments. Then the fire brigade can attack the fire. In no case should an attempt be made to fight the fire without having alerted the fire department first.

# SELF-INSPECTION FORM FOR CONTROL OF FIRE HAZARDS IN LIBRARIES

The form is designed so that a "no" answer indicates an unsatisfactory condition requiring corrective action. Space is provided at the end of the form for making notes on unsatisfactory conditions found.

A. Housekeeping and operations          YES    NO

In general, is housekeeping good? _____ _____

Have accumulations of combustible trash been eliminated? _____ _____

Are all areas free of accumulations of dust? _____ _____

Are oily mops, cleaning fluids, sweeping compounds, paints, oils, grease, and cleaning equipment stored in fire resistive areas or metal cabinets? _____ _____

Are covered metal trash containers provided at central collection points? _____ _____

Are metal wastebaskets (not wire mesh) provided in offices and public areas? _____ _____

Is all trash either stored in a safe location or removed from the building before closing each day? _____ _____

Are storage areas maintained in orderly condition? _____ _____

Are "No Smoking" signs conspicuously posted in all hazardous areas? _____ _____

Do library employees and patrons abide by "no smoking" regulations? _____ _____

Are an adequate number of deep ash trays, and other safe receptacles — for sand, water, etc. — available for safe disposal of all smoking materials where smoking is permitted? _____ _____

Are smoking materials kept separate from other combustible trash? _____ _____

Are decorations and draperies fire resistive? _____ _____

Are stack areas kept free of stored materials unessential to stack functions? _____ _____

Are outside contractors required to observe fire safety rules and regulations in their work? _____ _____

Does the librarian require that someone make an inspection of the entire library at closing time to ensure that no conditions exist which might cause fire afterwards? _____ _____

B. Personnel

Has the staff been instructed in the procedure to be followed in the event of a fire? _____ _____

Are fire instructions posted in all areas?          _____  _____

Is the telephone number of the fire department posted near all places where it is likely to be needed?          _____  _____

Are fire drills being conducted at proper intervals?          _____  _____

C. Heating and air conditioning

Is all heating equipment, including flues and heating pipes, in safe condition?          _____  _____

Has heating equipment, including that in bookmobiles, been checked by a qualified person or agency within the past year?          _____  _____

Is proper and adequate clearance being maintained between heating equipment and combustible materials?          _____  _____

Are motors, fans, etc., clean and well lubricated?          _____  _____

Has air conditioning equipment been checked within the past year?          _____  _____

Are screens and filters in air ducts clean?          _____  _____

Are ashes stored in metal containers or other safe places?          _____  _____

Are facilities for storing fuel safely segregated?          _____  _____

D. Electricity

Has it been established that all fuses are of proper size?          _____  _____

Are extension cords in good condition and safely located?          _____  _____

Are all ordinary extension cords under 10 feet in length?          _____  _____

Are extension cords installed so they are not readily subject to damage?          _____  _____

Are covers on all electrical controls and electrical equipment in place?          _____  _____

Is wiring installed in proper manner (not nailed or fastened over nails, or hot pipes, or loose, etc.)?          _____  _____

Are all electrical appliances in good, safe working order?          _____  _____

Are electrical heating appliances, such as hot plates, glue pots, etc., equipped with a pilot light to warn that they should be turned off at closing time?          _____  _____

Are fluorescent lighting fixtures properly spaced, or otherwise protected from direct contact with combustible ceiling materials?          _____  _____

E. Exiting facilities

Are all emergency exits unlocked for egress? ___ ___

Are doors in stairway enclosures kept closed? ___ ___

Are all exit aisles kept clear? ___ ___

Are all exits properly identified and lighted? ___ ___

Are stairways kept free from storage of combustible materials, including the spaces beneath the stairs? ___ ___

Is panic hardware on doors in good operating condition? ___ ___

Is access to doors clear? ___ ___

Are floors and stair treads in good condition? ___ ___

Are handrails provided at stairs and are they in good condition? ___ ___

F. Protection features

Are all fire extinguishers in their proper location? ___ ___

Have all extinguishers been serviced within the past year? ___ ___

Are extinguishers readily available in all areas? ___ ___

Are all extinguishers accessible? ___ ___

Are extinguishers mounted so that they can be easily removed and used by female staff members? ___ ___

Are nozzles on extinguishers free from obstruction? ___ ___

Is all standpipe hose in proper location? ___ ___

Does all standpipe hose appear to be in good condition? ___ ___

Is unobstructed access maintained to all standpipes? ___ ___

Are sprinkler heads unobstructed? ___ ___

Are sprinkler-system valves open? ___ ___

Has sprinkler system been thoroughly inspected within the past year? ___ ___

Has any new construction or installation in areas with sprinkler protection been properly protected with new sprinkler heads where required? ___ ___

Does sprinkler system appear visually to be in generally good condition? ___ ___

Has fire pump been tested regularly? ___ ___

Are all fire alarm devices in good condition? ___ ___

Have proper tests of fire alarm systems been made? ___ ___

Have you invited the local fire department to visit and familiarize its members with the conditions to be encountered in the event of fire, and have they been cautioned regarding injudicious use of water? _____ _____

Does the local fire department have means of gaining ready access to the library building(s) in the event of fire? _____ _____

Are manual or automatic alarm systems arranged to give an alarm at the fire department and have they been regularly tested? _____ _____

G. More hazardous areas

Are maintenance shops, etc., clean? _____ _____

Are combustible materials in maintenance shops safely stored? _____ _____

Are flammable liquids, including paints, properly stored with no open containers? _____ _____

Are all oily rags, etc., removed from premises daily or stored in closed metal cans? _____ _____

Is adequate ventilation maintained in work and storage areas? _____ _____

Are paint residues regularly removed from paint spray booths, exhaust fans, and ducts? _____ _____

Are fire doors in working order and unobstructed? _____ _____

Are the proper types of extinguishers provided where needed for flammable-materials (Type B) and electrical (Type C) fires? _____ _____

Are filters, hoods, and ducts over kitchen equipment regularly cleaned to prevent grease fires? _____ _____

H. List here any unsatisfactory conditions found and corrective action taken.

# FIRST-AID FIRE FIGHTING

The librarian should designate a person (and an alternate) for each major area of the library to act as captain for emergency operations. (This will vary, of course, with the size of the library and the number of personnel.) This person should be responsible for the operation of whatever first-aid fire fighting equipment is available in his area. He should also be responsible for instructing other staff members in his area in their emergency assignments.

Most if not all staff members should be trained in the use of portable fire extinguishers. Fire extinguishers have labels with instructions for their use. Personnel should be familiar with these instructions; when a fire emergency makes the operation of a fire extinguisher necessary, there is no time to read instructions. Wherever possible, training should include the use of extinguishers on actual fires. This provides the user with knowledge of how to operate the unit, the techniques for applying the extinguishing agent, and the size and type of fire that can be controlled or extinguished by a given extinguisher. Training classes can be arranged with the local fire department or, in many areas, with representatives of extinguisher manufacturers.

Visual aids may be used to supplement the training program. Posters and folders showing basic principles of extinguisher operations are available from equipment manufacturers and the National Fire Protection Association. Also, there are many excellent motion picture films and slides available for training purposes. Organizations from which films may be obtained are listed in the NFPA pamphlet, "Fire Control Film List" (see Bibliography).

## ABC's of fire extinguisher use[1]

The National Fire Protection Association has given advice on safe methods of fighting small fires with portable fire extinguishers. Of great significance is advice about safety precautions: when and how to use various types of extinguishers, and how to select, maintain, and mount portable extinguishers. (See chart of characteristics of extinguishers, page 76.)

How to fight a small fire safely:

- Take time to *think;* quickly size up the situation.

- Get *everyone* out; call fire department at once.

- *Keep near door* so you can have an escape.

[1] With special acknowledgment to the National Fire Protection Association, this has been adapted from: R. N. Finchum and Glenn C. Boerrigter, *School Fires: Prevention, Control, Protection* (Washington, D. C.: U. S. Government Printing Office, 1962).

- *Stay low,* out of heat and smoke.
- Aim extinguisher at *base* of fire.
- Stay *outside* small rooms: shoot stream in.
- Ventilate *only after fire is out.* But if fire gets large, *get out;* close doors!

For ordinary combustibles, use:

- Pressurized water — operates usually by squeezing handle or trigger. Read instruction label. (Contains *water* or water with anti-freeze chemical.)
- Pump tank — operates by one hand pumping handle while other holds nozzle. (Contains *water* or water with anti-freeze chemical.)
- Soda-acid — operates by turning extinguisher upside-down. Has handle on bottom for inverting. (Contains *water,* soda mixture, acid — no anti-freeze.)
- Dry chemical — multi-purpose — operates by squeezing handle or trigger. Read label. (Contains a *powder* commonly designated "A, B, C.")

For flammable liquids, use:

- Carbon dioxide ($CO_2$) — operates usually by squeezing handle or trigger. See instruction label. (Discharges as a *heavy gas* that smothers fire.)
- Dry chemical — operates usually by squeezing handle or trigger. See instruction label. (Contains one of two general types of *powder* — not to be mixed. One is for Class B, C fires; one for Class A, B, C fires.)
- Foam — operates by turning extinguisher upside-down. (Contains *water* and ingredient to make a heavy foam that smothers fire.)

For electrical equipment fires, use: nonconducting extinguishing agent, such as —

- Carbon dioxide ($CO_2$).
- Dry chemical (B-C type).
- Dry chemical (multi-purpose).
- Vaporizing liquid.
- Do not use soda-acid, foam, or other *water-type* extinguishers until electric power has been shut off.

Be sure your fire extinguishers are reliable:

- Look for the Underwriters' Laboratories label or the Factory Mutual Approval Seal. These labels mean that each extinguisher has met exacting requirements of construction and performance.

- Inspect extinguishers periodically. Being mechanical devices, they should be serviced from time to time. Refill immediately after *any* use.
- Keep extinguishers within reach for anyone to use — and practice how to use them *before* a fire starts.
- Have the right type of extinguisher handy at the right place.
- BEWARE! Do not risk your life on "beer can" size extinguishers (tin cans, "bombs," aerosol containers, plastic bottles) usually holding less than a pint of liquid or 12 to 16 ounces of dry powder. To depend on such gadgets of such small capacity, limited range, and unknown reliability is dangerous.

## FIRE DRILL REGULATIONS
### (Minneapolis Public Library)

1. Pull appropriate fire alarm box in the building.
2. First-aid fire fighting equipment should be put into use by building personnel.
3. Personnel on each floor should acquaint themselves with the locations of fire extinguishers, fire hoses, and fire alarm boxes for their own information.
4. Captains on each floor will detail appropriate persons to see that all employees and members of the general public have evacuated the premises. This includes stack and workroom areas as well as lavatories.
5. Use stair exits, not elevators. All doors should be closed on leaving. (Only those persons unable to use a stairway may use the elevator.) In general, personnel in work areas may use the stack stairs, while the general public and staff engaged in desk service will use the corner stairs.
6. The captains for the building are as follows:

   | | |
   |---|---|
   | 1st floor | Mr. A_____ |
   | 2nd floor | Mr. B_____ |
   | 3rd floor | Miss C_____ |
   | 4th floor | Mr. D_____ |
   | Mezzanine & Basement | Mr. E_____ |
   | Museum | Mrs. F_____ |
   | Shops & Maintenance | Mr. G_____ and Mr. H_____ |

   Captains will appoint others to clear each floor and assign one person to each exit.
7. Personnel should proceed away from the building. Stay away from 4th Street ramp entrance.

## EVACUATION ROUTE

### 4th Floor

Extension office
Bookmobile office
Coordinators
Athenaeum
Order department
Cafeteria
} will all use the stairs on the Nicollet Avenue and 4th Street corner.

Catalog department
Processing room
Bindery
} will use the stairs on the Hennepin Avenue and 4th Street corner.

### 3rd Floor

County Library office
Visual Aids workroom
} will use the stairs on the Nicollet Avenue and 4th Street corner.

### 2nd Floor

Children's department
Sociology
Visual Aids
} will use the stairs on the Nicollet Avenue and 4th Street corner.

Art
Music
Office
Lounge area
} will use the stairs on the Hennepin Avenue and 4th Street corner. Someone from Art shall be delegated to clear the lounge area.

### 1st Floor

All departments
} out the main entrance into the arcade and exit by least crowded door. Someone selected by Mr. A_____ shall clear the lounge area.

Mezzanine Area and Basement
} will use the stack stairs to the 1st floor and exit with the 1st floor staff.

Bookmobile Delivery Office
} will exit up stairs to 4th and Hennepin side.

### Museum

Planetarium
Black light exhibit
} will exit through arcade to Nicollet side of the building.

Display room
Exhibit area
    (basement)
Work areas
Small lecture room
} use public stairs to Museum lobby and out on 4th and Nicollet.

Auditorium                    } out on the Hennepin side of the arcade.

Shops (basement)

Printing                      ⎫
Display shop                  ⎬ will use stairs on the 4th and Nicollet
Paint shop                    ⎭ side.
Carpenter shop

## SPECIAL ASSIGNMENTS

Switchboard                   Call Fire Department by telephone: 123-1234. This is in addition to the alarm which was first sent in.
Direct public out of building on intercom.

Maintenance                   Engineer on duty go to 4th Street ramp entrance and unlock door for Fire Department. Take care of mechanical duties as outlined by Mr. J_____'s office.
Bring freight elevator to basement level for the use of the firemen.

# CHAPTER 4

# Fire Protection Equipment

A completely automatic system for protection of the library building would include:

(1) some type of automatic detection device to sound local alarms (within the building) for purposes of evacuating the building and initiating first-aid fire fighting and also to transmit an alarm to the fire department;

(2) a system (connected with the detection system) that would actuate cut-off mechanisms in the ventilation system and automatically close fire doors;

(3) an automatic system to extinguish or control the fire actuated simultaneously with the detection device and the transmission of alarms.

Insofar as one departs from this ideal of a complete protection system, reliance must be placed upon human factors such as alertness, training, and experience. To illustrate this: if the library has no automatic detection system, it must rely upon the detection capabilities of its staff or custodial personnel. If the library has no automatic alarm system, members of the staff must be depended upon to transmit alarms to others in the building and to the fire department. Staff members must make sure that fire doors and other cutoff devices are manually closed in case of emergency, unless these are connected with the alarm system for automatic closing. If there is no automatic extinguishing equipment (leaving aside the actions of the fire department and the rapidity with which firemen may reach the scene), the library must depend upon its own personnel to operate quickly and efficiently whatever first-aid fire fighting equipment is available (portable fire extinguishers, hose lines and standpipe systems, etc.).

## Detection of fire

It is obvious that the amount of time that elapses before a fire is detected will have a bearing on the extent of loss. In most large losses, the factor of delayed detection is usually the critical factor. Results of the study showed that the great majority of all library fires — 71 percent — occurred between 9 p.m. and 9 a.m., the period during which most libraries are closed and probably unattended.

Another 18 percent happen between 5 p.m. and 9 p.m., another period when many libraries are closed. The remaining 11 percent of library fires, occurring between 9 a.m. and 5 p.m. — that is, the hours when the library would be expected to be open and occupied by people — have resulted in relatively few major losses. The major losses sustained during this period occurred in unattended libraries; for example, college libraries closed for holidays.

Detection of incipient fires can be accomplished through the human senses (hearing or seeing fire, smelling smoke, feeling heat) or through mechanical/electrical devices, or both. There are two objections to complete reliance upon detection through the senses; that of staff or custodial time limitations (e.g., no watchman could be expected to be everywhere all the time), and ordinary human fallibility. Thus it follows that any adequate program of physical protection must include the installation of automatic fire detection devices. Highly efficient detection systems are available. These are of several general types: devices that are sensitive to smoke, to combustion gases, or to these two in combination, to a rapid rise in temperature, to excessive heat, or to flames.

The sensitivity and response time of fire detection installations can be adjusted over a wide range. Each type has certain inherent advantages or disadvantages in this respect. A compromise must be reached between the point where a device is so sensitive that extraneous or natural effects will result in a false alarm, and a sensitivity so low that its response to an actual fire is sluggish or unreliable. A high degree of reliability in a detection system can be achieved through proper selection, installation, supervision, and regular testing and servicing.

Detection systems are designed to cover as broad an area as may be desired, operate on a twenty-four-hour basis, and initiate necessary emergency actions such as sounding a local alarm, transmitting an alarm to the fire department, and actuating a fire extinguishment system. Of course, as opposed to human capabilities, such devices are not subject to errors of judgment. Barring improper installation or defective equipment, the device should carry out the prescribed action. Incorrect action — poorly planned coverage, for example, or transmitting an alarm to an unattended station would be errors of design or planning, not a fault of the system.

There is no single detection device that would be best for all situations. The sensitivity, response times, and other characteristics vary; the proper selection of a detection system must depend upon the peculiarities of the particular situation if maximum protection is to be achieved at a minimum cost. Several types of detection systems are described briefly in the following passages.

## Fire detection devices

Detection of a fire by a mechanical device requires that a sensitive element in the device be actuated by some effect produced by that fire. In most devices the actuating effect is heat. In what are called "fixed-temperature" detection devices, the standard actuating temperature is 165° F. In addition there are those called "rate-of-rise" detectors. These are designed to operate whenever the surrounding temperature rises more than 15° F. to 20° F. per minute.

Both of these have certain advantages. Detection devices are generally designed to respond within two minutes after a fire starts. Thus, a rate-of-rise system would probably respond more rapidly than a fixed-temperature system to rapidly spreading fire. On the other hand, a slow, smoldering fire would probably actuate a fixed-temperature system more quickly than a rate-of-rise system. The obvious conclusion is to combine both types of elements in a single system, which slightly increases the cost, but this would be a well-justified additional expense.

There are "spot" detection devices and "area" detection devices. The former may be illustrated by equipment with a thermostatic attachment that actuates alarms when the temperature reaches a certain point, or by equipment with the fusible elements (containing metal that melts at a low temperature, say 135° F. to 165° F.) which when fused release a spring or other device to set off an alarm.

Area detection devices may be illustrated by those actuated by the stimulus of radiant heat or flickering light from flames. This type of device is appropriate to large, relatively open areas where the sensitive element can "see" or "feel" the fire. One such device (the Teletherm detector manufactured by American District Telegraph Company) consists essentially of two connected thermocouples. One of these is exposed to direct or reflected thermal radiation from a fire; the other is shielded and thus acts as a compensating element. As a general principle of physics, it is known that whenever certain dissimilar metals are in contact, electric currents are set up which depend upon the nature of the metals and the surrounding temperature. Thus, in the application here, two such thermocouples continuously exposed to the same temperature will generate the same voltage (amount of current), and no electric current will flow between them. Gradual temperature changes will affect both equally. In the present installation any sudden temperature rise will affect the exposed thermocouple first. The imbalance will cause a current to flow through a relay and turn in an alarm. Small areas may be covered by up to twelve pairs of thermocouple junctions, wired together; this will provide for a coverage range of from 250 to 3,000 feet per unit.

## CLASSIFICATION OF FIRE DETECTION SYSTEMS

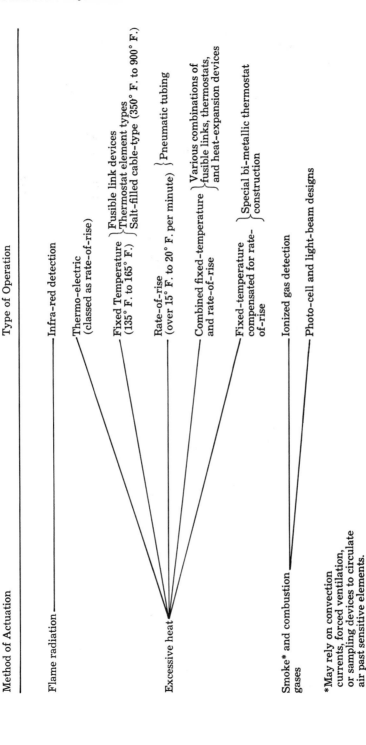

Method of Actuation

Type of Operation

Flame radiation ————————— Infra-red detection

Thermo-electric
(classed as rate-of-rise)

Fixed Temperature ⎱ Fusible link devices
(135° F. to 165° F.) ⎰ Thermostat element types ⎱ Pneumatic tubing
Salt-filled cable-type (350° F. to 900° F.) ⎰

Excessive heat

Rate-of-rise
(over 15° F. to 20° F. per minute)

Combined fixed-temperature ⎱ Various combinations of
and rate-of-rise ⎰ fusible links, thermostats,
and heat-expansion devices

Fixed-temperature ⎱ Special bi-metallic thermostat
compensated for rate- ⎰ construction
of-rise

Smoke* and combustion ————— Ionized gas detection
gases

Photo-cell and light-beam designs

*May rely on convection
currents, forced ventilation,
or sampling devices to circulate
air past sensitive elements.

*Courtesy of American District Telegraph Company*
The Teletherm Heat Detector uses a 72-junction thermocouple element in the form of a ring surrounded by chrome reflectors for maximum concentration of reflected radiant heat. The unit is suitable for protection of large areas; smaller styles are available for smaller areas.

A large installation is available with seventy-two thermocouple units set up with a 360-degree parabolic reflector which focuses heat radiation on the thermocouples. This system would cover an area with a 105-foot radius, about 8,600 square feet, for each installation.

## Thermostatic fire detection

There are two general types of devices employing the thermostat principle. One unit contains bi-metallic strips, which expand at different rates, and electrical contacts. The strips which are similar to those ordinarily used to regulate heating systems are self-resetting after the high temperature which had originally caused them to actuate an alarm is reduced to normal levels. A second type of thermostatic device contains a spring-loaded mechanism which is released when the temperature reaches a pre-determined point, a point at which solder of carefully controlled composition melts. For fixed-temperature devices, temperature settings are available ranging from 125° F., to 350° F. as required. Settings commonly used are 135° F. and 160° F.

## Optical fire detection

Optical detectors operate in response to the visual characteristics of flames. The light produced by a fire is subject to wide, sudden, and frequent changes in intensity; this flickering light is

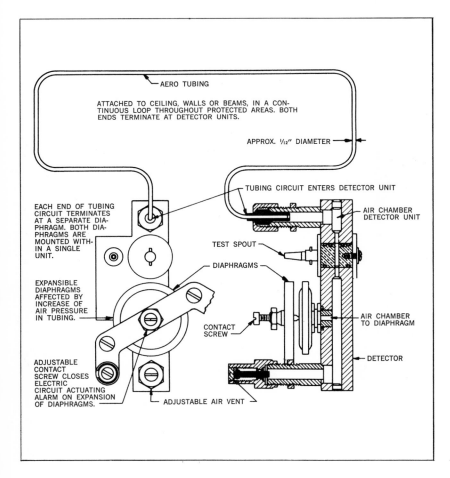

*Courtesy of American District Telegraph Company*
**Details of the detector unit of an Aero automatic fire alarm system supplied by ADT Company for protection of industrial and institutional properties.**

used to actuate an optical fire detection device produced by several manufacturers (among them the Fireye Division of General Electronics). The flicker of a flame corresponds to frequencies of about 5 to 25 cycles per second. The effect of such flickering light on a photo-sensitive device causes the device to actuate the alarm. A brief delay is built into the system to prevent false alarms being given by flashes of light from sources other than fires. Because their flicker-frequency rate is too high, ordinary electric lights operating at 60 cycles per second would not affect the device. Optical detection equipment is best suited to large, open areas; in the stack areas, for example, the cost of numerous detectors required to "see" all of the possible points at which fires could occur, would exceed that of other methods of equivalent reliability.

## Pneumatic fire detection systems

Thermostats have been designed that use the expansion of air for actuation; these are fundamentally rate-of-rise systems providing area coverage. Small-diameter (as small as ⅛- to 1/12-inch) tubing extends back and forth through the areas to be protected. A rough

*Courtesy of American District Telegraph Company*
This gallery in the Art Institute of Chicago is protected by an Aero system. The tubing, one-twelfth of an inch in diameter, is so skillfully installed that it goes unnoticed.

*Courtesy of Notifier Corporation*
This fixed-temperature, automatically resetting thermostat is shown actual size. It is
economical when installed in areas not exceeding 20 by 20 feet. When the temperature at the thermostat reaches 135°F., electrical contacts operate to initiate the
alarm. The unit may be installed flush with the ceiling in new construction.

guide is to provide about one foot of tubing for every fifteen square
feet of ceiling area. The tubing is connected to a diaphragm which
carries a set of electrical contacts. Slow changes in the over-all
temperature cause air in the tubes to expand or contract. A small
leakage hole in the system permits air to enter or leave at slow
rates. This controlled leakage is inadequate, however, for any sudden rise in temperature at or above the specified 15° F. to 20° F.
per minute. When this occurs, pressure is built up on the diaphragm,
the contacts operate, and the alarm is sounded. For protection of
small areas where it would be impractical or unsightly to install
sufficient tubing, rosettes are available which are equivalent to
25, 35, or 45 feet of tubing, respectively, depending upon the area
involved.

Pneumatic systems can add fixed-temperature operation to their
inherent rate-of-rise characteristics by including a sealed chamber
or chambers at critical points. At the set temperature, rupture of a
disc or operation of a fusible link allows expanded gases in the
chamber to surge into the tubing and actuate the alarm.

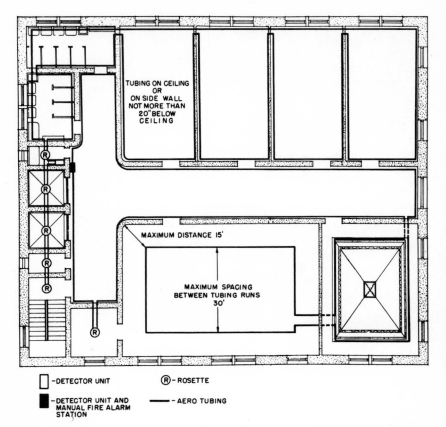

TUBING ON CEILING
OR
ON SIDE WALL
NOT MORE THAN
20"BELOW
CEILING

MAXIMUM DISTANCE 15'

MAXIMUM SPACING
BETWEEN TUBING RUNS
30'

☐ –DETECTOR UNIT    ⓡ – ROSETTE

■ –DETECTOR UNIT AND    —— – AERO TUBING
MANUAL FIRE ALARM
STATION

*Courtesy of American District Telegraph Company*

Layout of a typical Aero Heat Detection system. Expansion of air in small-diameter tubing, when subjected to heat from fire at a given rate of rise, exerts pressure against a diaphragm in the detector unit which causes electrical contacts to operate alarm circuits.

## Ionized particle fire detectors

One detection device (manufactured by the Pyrotronics Corp.) is sensitive to the gases given off by fires. The device consists essentially of a small ionization chamber containing a minute source of radium. The emitted alpha particles ionize the air and permit a very small flow of current. When gaseous products of combustion enter the chamber, the current is decreased and, through a built-in amplification system, this difference actuates the alarm circuit. The device can be set for a high level of sensitivity and, when located in the path of convection currents or in a forced ventilation duct, it can detect fires at an early stage. As with all detectors, care should be taken to avoid excessive sensitivity to preclude false alarms. The device is relatively new and has not as yet been extensively installed. The cost per detector is somewhat higher than other detection devices but the authors believe that in some installations the ionic detection system may be competitive in cost and also highly desirable.

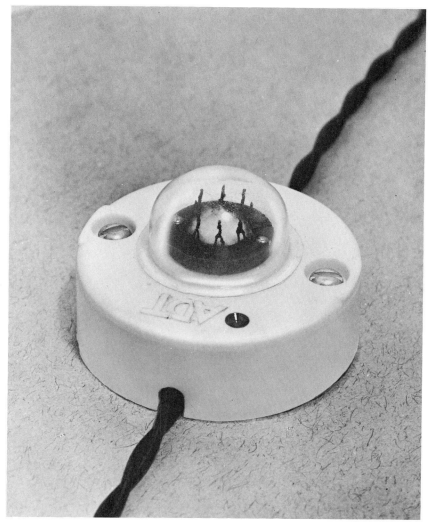

*Courtesy of American District Telegraph Company*

Teletherm detector for small areas. Small-room detectors are made in several sizes, depending on the number of thermocouples required to protect a given area. Up to 3,000 square feet per detector can be protected, and various types and sizes of detectors may be combined in a single circuit.

*Courtesy of Fire Devices, Inc.*

The Spot Fire Lowecator is a brass shell sealed to a phenolic base containing a diaphragm which causes electrical contacts to close and actuate an alarm when the air pressure in the shell is increased by a temperature rise in the protected area, generally 15°F. in one minute. It also incorporates a fixed temperature release (usually 136°F.) and is used frequently in conjunction with pre-action sprinkler systems. The rate-of-rise feature can be factory set to suit conditions, such as the starting up of building heating systems, and resets automatically when temperatures are restored to normal. Once the fixed temperature feature operates, the unit must be replaced.

## Fire detection by smoke

A limited number of devices are available for detecting fire by exposure to smoke. These are usually regarded as auxiliary or special precautionary measures. The devices consist of a carefully regulated light source, a photo-electric cell as a receiver, and a control unit. Mirrors are used to blanket the protected area with light beams in a criss-cross pattern. A reduction in light to the receiver of as little as 15 to 20 percent will operate the alarm. Smoke detection units are especially useful when installed in ventilating

*Courtesy of Pyrotronics, Inc.*

A typical Pyr-A-Larm installation. Several libraries are protected by this equipment. A smoke detection system can be applied to air ducts and air conditioning systems to warn of smoke originating either inside or outside the duct system.

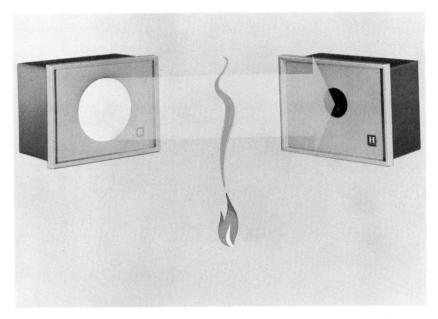

*Courtesy of Minneapolis-Honeywell Regulator Company*

Projector sensor elements of a smoke detection system applicable to large areas. One set may supervise an area up to 200 feet long by approximately 30 feet wide, depending upon conditions of air circulation and physical layout.

or air conditioning ducts. Normally, the device acts to shut down ventilation and/or air conditioning systems, to stop circulation of the smoke to other areas, while at the same time sounding an alarm signal.

*Courtesy of Pyrotronics, Inc.*

The Pyr-A-Larm is a fire detector of the ionization type which senses invisible combustion gases to initiate an alarm. Visible smoke, flame, or heat are not necessary for operation. The device is suitable for large areas and may also be located in air conditioning ducts.

## Burglar alarms

In those libraries with especially valuable collections or in which other factors make the likelihood of burglary a problem, the installation of a burglar-alarm system as an adjunct to the fire detection system may be deemed advisable. Various burglar-alarm systems are available; these can alert someone to the entry to the premises by a person or the movement of persons within a building after it is closed. The devices operate on photo-electric principles, or changes in electrical capacitance when a human body is present, or on ultra-sonic phenomena. Such devices are highly effective in guarding against theft or burglary. In addition, they may prevent the deliberate setting of a fire, or other acts of malicious mischief.

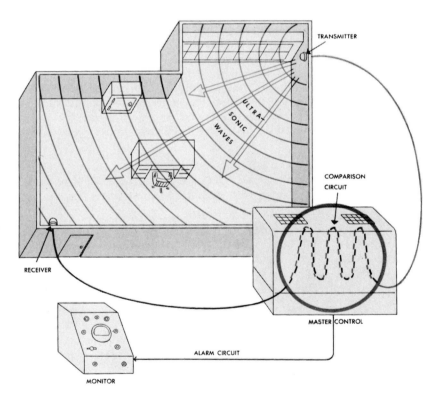

*Courtesy of Walter Kidde & Company, Inc.*
The ultra-sonic intrusion detection system transmits sound waves throughout the protected area. The sound waves are beyond the range of the human ear. The system is carefully designed so that sound waves echoing from fixed objects do not produce an alarm. Any slight movement in the area throws the frequency of the sound waves out of balance and the alarm circuit is operated. The operating principles are depicted in the above diagram. The system will detect an open flame.

## Fire alarms

It is readily apparent that a fire detection system must either sound an alarm, or initiate extinguishment of a fire, or both. The particular action depends upon the operating principle used for detection. Most detection systems are electrical systems, i.e., electrical contacts are opened or closed to operate alarm circuits. In other devices the action is mechanical: a weight is tipped, a cocked-spring is released. Alarm devices are available that when exposed to a pre-assigned temperature, will cause a spring-wound bell to begin ringing. A similar device sounds a warning by the escape of stored gas through a whistle or siren. These two kinds of devices are relatively limited in their application because the alarm given is strictly local and of short duration. Alarm devices to convey warnings over a wide area are almost necessarily electrical in nature.

There are two general types of alarm systems: local alarm systems (those in which the entire alarm operation occurs within the building) and those with connections to points outside of the building. Local alarm systems are useful primarily for warning occupants to evacuate the building. Many local alarm systems are nothing more than manually operated stations with no provision for automatic detection. The building codes of many cities call for the installation of such manually operated local alarm systems as a minimum requirement.

Local alarm systems are clearly inadequate in an effective program of protection against fire. Because of the possibility of human error, it cannot be assumed that, although local alarms are sounded, an additional alarm has been transmitted to the fire department.

The first rule to be observed in the design of an adequate alarm system is that every alarm device be connected to fire protection headquarters. In most cases, this point is the municipal fire department, although some major universities have extensive fire-fighting facilities of their own.

There are several ways of transmitting alarm signals to the fire department. The first is to connect the local system in the building to a municipal fire alarm box located in the library building itself. Where this is not practicable there are two alternative procedures. Many cities have established what is called "central station supervision." This is a contracted service for both fire and burglary protection. Alarms are transmitted to the central station, a guard is dispatched to the premises, and simultaneously the alarm is given to the fire department or police headquarters. If such service is not available, the librarian can have the alarm system in the library building connected to the fire and police departments by means of a telephone wire leased from the local telephone company.

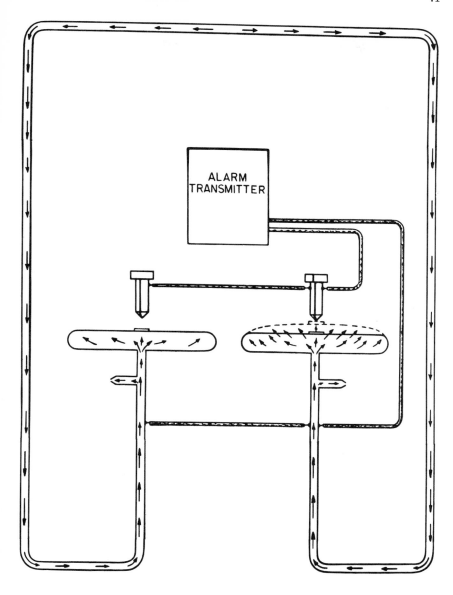

*Courtesy of American District Telegraph Company*

This diagram shows how the AERO automatic fire alarm system works. Both ends of the tubing circuit installed in each fire area terminate in air chambers within the detector unit. The walls of these air chambers are flexible metal diaphragms. When fire starts, the temperature in the immediate area increases rapidly. Air inside the tubing expands rapidly, too, and presses against the walls of the air chambers; the metal diaphragms bulge, as shown, until they come in contact with metal post. Instantly an electrical circuit is closed, actuating the alarm transmitter.

*Courtesy of American District Telegraph Company*
A typical ADT central station, where personnel are on twenty-four-hour duty to receive signals from fire and burglar alarm systems, watchmen's reporting systems, and various supervisory systems. Operators notify police or fire headquarters over direct wire connections, and also dispatch uniformed ADT guards to investigate.

The reliability of full-scale automatic detection and alarm systems is ensured by a form of artificial "supervision" of electrical circuits. This supervision is accomplished by connecting the equipment in such a way that a small electrical current is constantly passing through the wiring. Standard operation (closing a set of contacts by actuating a fire alarm box or fire detection device) increases the current, closes a relay, and sounds the alarm. Any abnormal condition, such as an open circuit or a wire being grounded, would cause a "trouble bell" to be sounded. Power for the trouble signal is supplied by a separate circuit so that failure of the alarm system would not incapacitate the trouble bell as well. This arrangement is called "single supervision." If the power to the trouble bell is also supervised to make sure that it is in operating readiness, the system is doubly supervised.

The installation of an electrically supervised system does not in itself ensure reliability. The system must be properly maintained and inspected from time to time as with any complex electrical mechanism.

Apart from automatic transmission of alarms directly to the fire department (that is, a direct connection from the detection-alarm system without the need for human intervention), there are two general methods available: transmission by telegraph and telephone. For many years the predominant method of reporting fires has been a system employing the principle of the telegraph. Telegraphic equipment had been extensively installed in most cities before telephones came into widespread use. Thus the great majority of street fire-alarm boxes are components of telegraph systems. In the alarm boxes, the transmitter consists of a precision clock-work mechanism which, when tripped, causes a code wheel to open and close electrical contacts thereby sending a numerical signal to the fire department. The numerical signal identifies the location of the box and fire fighting equipment is dispatched accordingly.

Tripping the transmitter may be done manually or by electrical signals from a local alarm system. Fire-alarm telegraph systems have been brought to a high degree of reliability and at present are more useful in connection with automatic local devices (i.e., automatic detection and alarm systems in the library) than are telephone systems.

The conventional response to an emergency situation — especially the detection of fire — is, or should be, for a person to pick up the telephone and call the fire department. Today, 95 percent of fire alarms in the majority of cities are transmitted over the conventional telephone. Of course, the reliability of transmitting an alarm in this manner depends upon human factors. Whatever automatic alarm features may have been introduced into the protection system of a particular library, the number of the fire department should be clearly posted near every telephone that may be used to place an emergency call.

In an attempt to make telephone alarms less dependent upon strictly human participation, many cities have established reporting systems using street telephones with direct lines to fire and police departments. These systems are equivalent to telegraph systems except that, like private telephones, they make it possible for inaccurate information to be transmitted. Street-telephone systems represent an improvement over private calls in that, even if no intelligible information is given, the location of the instrument can be determined and an investigation can be made immediately.

A further improvement in telephone alarm systems is available in some localities. This system utilizes leased telephone circuits for transmission of an alarm signal from the property protected to a central fire-alarm headquarters (e.g., the fire department), or to the headquarters of a commercial organization which provides this type of service under contract to the property owner.

*Courtesy of The Gamewell Company*
A typical municipal fire alarm box. Any type of fixed fire detection or extinguishing system installed in libraries may be arranged to operate the box automatically, thus assuring rapid response by the fire department.

## Portable fire extinguishers

Statistics on fire experience have shown that in industrial establishments where portable fire extinguishers are commonly available, more than one-third of all reported fires are successfully controlled by such extinguishers alone. Even this is an inadequate measure of the value of portable fire extinguishers because a great many small fires are never reported.

Portable fire extinguishers constitute the most important piece of equipment in what may be called "first-aid fire fighting." To be useful at all, portable fire extinguishers must meet three fundamental requirements: the extinguishers must be located properly, be in good mechanical condition, and be appropriate to library use. All members of the staff should be familiar with the location of all fire extinguishing equipment in the library.

Public buildings such as libraries are classified as "light hazard." (Examples of building occupancies classed as "ordinary hazard" and "extra hazard" are restaurants and paint shops, respectively.)

In "light-hazard" buildings, a general rule is that enough extinguishers be provided so that one is within 100 feet of a person no matter where he is. Although local building and fire codes frequently provide specifications in this respect, a second general rule is that an extinguisher be provided for each 2,500 square feet of area on each floor. An additional point: even though the practice might require more than the minimum number of extinguishers, a third rule is that such equipment should be located at the approach to all exits.

Inspections of fire extinguishers should be made at least annually. Such inspections can be made by representatives of the manufacturer, by private agencies providing this service on contract, or by inspectors from the fire department.

A 2½-gallon fire extinguisher weighs from 35 to 40 pounds. In a particular situation, if women are expected to use such equipment, it is recommended that smaller-size extinguishers be obtained and located within easy reach.

There are various types of fire extinguishers; they vary in effectiveness depending upon the type of fire under consideration. In 1956, a classification system was established by Underwriters' Laboratories that assigns certain types of extinguishers to certain types of hazards. Briefly, the system sets up three classes of fires — Class A (wood and paper fires), Class B (inflammable liquids), and Class C (Class A and Class B fires with the added hazard of electrical shock). The chart on page 76 shows the characteristics of the various types of portable extinguishers available including their suitability to the several different types of fires.

In the past, because libraries are primarily a Class A risk, water-type (soda-acid) extinguishers have been almost mandatory. However, plain water extinguishers pressurized with air are now available and are to be preferred over the soda-acid type. These can be recharged at the nearest service station or even with a tire pump. In addition, units in which the extinguishing fluid is expelled by

# CHARACTERISTICS OF PORTABLE FIRE EXTINGUISHERS

| | | Water Pail | Anti-freeze Type | Carbon Dioxide | Dry Chemical |
|---|---|---|---|---|---|
| SUITABILITY | Class A Fires (wood, cloth, paper, rubbish) | Yes | Yes | No* | No*† |
| | Class B Fires (oil, gasoline, grease, paint) | No | No | Yes | Yes |
| | Class C Fires (electrical equipment) | No | No | Yes | Yes |
| Nominal Capacity and Weight Fully Charged | | 10 qt., 23 lb. 14 qt., 31 lb. | 2½ gal., 40 lb. | CO₂ — Wt.<br>5 lb. — 16 lb.<br>15 lb. — 41 lb. | Chemical — Wt.<br>10 lb. — 23 lb.<br>20 lb. — 40 lb.<br>30 lb. — 55 lb. |
| Square-Foot Rating Against Class B Gasoline Fire | | — | — | 5 lb., 2 sq. ft.<br>15 lb., 5 sq. ft. | 10 lb., 7 sq. ft.<br>20 lb., 12 sq. ft.<br>30 lb., 17 sq. ft. |
| Means of Expelling | | Throw | Cartridge or stored pressure | Internal pressure | Cartridge or stored pressure |
| Extinguishing Agent | | Water | Special salt solution | Carbon dioxide | Treated sodium bicarbonate |
| Yearly Inspection Required | | Empty | Weigh cartridge or check pressure | Weigh semi-annually | Check pressure in medium |
| Operation | | Throw | Press lever or invert and bump | Press lever | No uniform method |
| Square-Foot Approximate Area Served | | 750 sq. ft. | 2,500 sq. ft. | Locate at special hazards | Locate at special hazards |
| Maximum Travel Distance | | 35 ft. | 50 ft. | — | — |

* These extinguishers have no quenching power and are not recommended against Class A Fires. They may be useful in knockdown and control of small fires.

† Special multi-purpose dry chemical based on silicone treated mono-ammonium phosphate is recommended for Class A fires as well as Classes B and C. Some units are more effective than water extinguishers for the same over-all weight.

| Foam | Pump Tank | Soda Acid | Vaporizing Liquid‡ | Pressurized Water-Filled |
|---|---|---|---|---|
| No* | Yes | Yes | No* | Yes |
| Yes | No | No | No | No |
| No | No | No | Yes | No |
| 2½ gal., 35 lb. | 2½ gal., 40 lb. | 2½ gal., 35 lb. | — | 2½ gal., 35 lb. |
| 2½ gal., 5 sq. ft. | — | — | — | — |
| Carbon dioxide from chemical reaction | Hand pump | Carbon dioxide from chemical reaction | Hand pump | Stored pressure |
| Water with foaming agent | Water | Water | Chlorinated‡ hydrocarbon | Water |
| Discharge and recharge | Empty | Discharge and recharge | Partially discharge | Weigh cartridge or check gauge |
| Invert | Pump | Invert | Pump | Press lever |
| Locate at special hazards | 2,000 sq. ft. | 2,500 sq. ft. | Locate at special hazards | 2,500 sq. ft. |
| — | 50 ft. | 50 ft. | — | 50 ft. |

‡ These agents have toxic properties and should not be used in enclosed areas.

means of gas cartridges are available but these are less convenient to recharge. Extinguishers employing carbon dioxide, the ordinary dry chemical solution, and vaporizing liquids can control small fires and achieve a reasonable degree of flame-suppression, but there is always the possibility of re-ignition. These types are generally considered to be unsuitable for deep-seated fires and should be used on Class A fires only when prompt follow-up action with water can be taken so that the fire, when put out, will stay out.

*Courtesy of The Fyr-Fyter Company*
The air-pressurized water extinguisher is excellent and highly economical protection for ordinary combustibles such as wood, paper, rags, etc. It is easy and simple to operate and can be recharged by the library staff using a service-station air hose.

A new type of dry chemical extinguisher was offered for sale beginning in the summer of 1960. The extinguisher uses a silicone-treated compound of mono-ammonium phosphate as the extinguishing agent, rather than sodium-bicarbonate. This development represents a significant improvement over previous dry-chemical extinguishers because, although the former units had demonstrated a

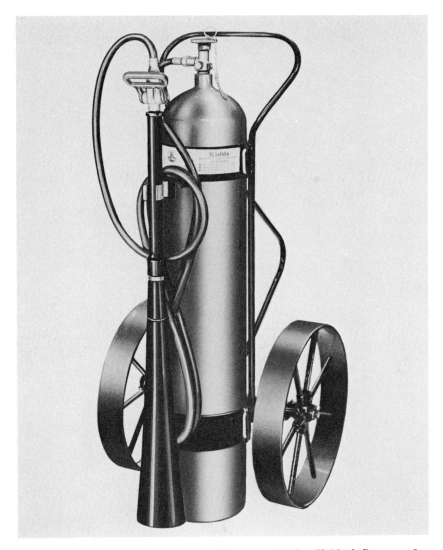

*Courtesy of Walter Kidde & Company, Inc.*
A typical wheeled carbon dioxide extinguisher of 50-pound capacity. These are suitable for fires involving fuel oils, paints, printing inks and solvents, and electric equipment.

high flame "knock-down ability" (that is, the characteristic of suppressing flames rapidly), they were ineffective against Class A fires because they did not prevent re-ignition. The new agent begins to soften at about 300° F. and provides a coating which adheres to hot surfaces excluding air and prevents further burning. The material thus deposited can later be washed off with warm water.

In the absence of specific fire tests on books and the restoration to usefulness of books on which the new dry chemical has been used, firm recommendations cannot be made at this time. Librarians however should be aware that such an extinguisher is available and

*Courtesy of The Fyr-Fyter Company*
Carbon dioxide extinguishers are available in several sizes. They are effective on both flammable liquid fires and those involving electric equipment. They are suitable in areas where food is prepared because the gas is inert.

that it shows promise of being applicable to the library situation.

Certain types of fire extinguishers are not recommended for library use. The first is a vaporizing liquid pump extinguisher using carbon tetrachloride as the extinguishing agent. It is now known that carbon tetrachloride in contact with fire breaks down into phosgene, an extremely dangerous gas. Other agents of this type have been developed and are perhaps better suited for fighting fires, but still are too dangerous for use in the interiors of buildings.

*Courtesy of The Fyr-Fyter Company*
The wheeled dry chemical extinguisher contains 150 pounds of agent (small hand units are also available) which is expelled by nitrogen stored under pressure in the cylinder on the right. Similar units are available using carbon dioxide or foam as the extinguishing medium. These would have application in library paint shops, bookmobile garage shops, and around boilers fired with fuel oil.

The second is a chemically expelled extinguishing agent of the foam and soda-acid type which, again, is not suited for library use. Once these extinguishers have started operating, the entire contents of the tank must be expelled. Because the water is mixed with various chemicals, there is the possibility of extensive damage to books. Pending further information on all portable units, the only standard extinguishers that can be recommended for use in libraries are those using clear water with the flow under complete control.

Unfortunately, the extinguishers now on the market are equipped with small, solid-stream nozzles which, although they permit the operator to stand at a greater distance from the fire, tend to increase the probability of water damage. If the nozzles were designed to break the water into spray, the operator would be forced to stand closer but the extinguishing effect would be greatly increased. The question of producing such an extinguisher has been discussed with several manufacturers. No special difficulties are foreseen; if sufficient consumer demand were forthcoming — that is, the probability of sufficient sales to institutions such as libraries where water damage is an important factor — such extinguishers would probably soon be offered on the market.

## Hose lines and standpipe systems

Many building codes require that certain buildings be provided with standpipe systems. These consist of separate water pipes extending upward through the building at pre-selected locations. There are two general types. One, which may or may not be filled with water at all times, is intended for use by the fire department only. It has provisions for pumping water into the system from fire hydrants and for attaching fire department 2½-inch or 1½-inch hose on each floor. The other type is of the same basic design except that it is always supplied with water under pressure and has 1½-inch hose permanently attached on each floor for use by occupants of the building.

At least two trained persons are required to handle the larger hoses because considerable pressure is exerted by the water at the nozzle. Loss of control under pressure of a 2½-inch hose nozzle can be dangerous: the hose line may whip around and cause personal injuries. In those buildings in which hose lines larger than 1½ inches have been installed, the staff should be instructed that such hoses are to be operated only by experienced firemen.

Another factor is the type of nozzle used. Hose lines in libraries normally carry simple straight-stream nozzles. As is the case with fire extinguishers, these nozzles increase the likelihood of water damage. When the only way to start water flowing and control the flow is by turning the valve at the hoseline station, water damage can be expected while the hose is being advanced to the fire and,

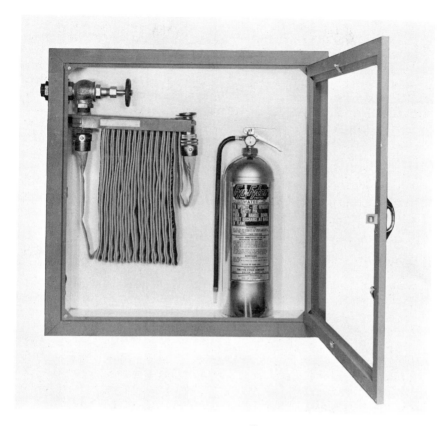

Courtesy of The Fyr-Fyter Company

A typical fire hose cabinet found in many libraries. The hose shown is linen and must be examined frequently to avoid deterioration from exposure to moisture. The fog nozzle is recommended for use in libraries as it will help to minimize water damage.

following extinguishment of the fire, until the valve can be closed. Semi-automatic racks (listed by Underwriters' Laboratories) do not release the water until the last loop of hose leaves the rack. This reduces the potential water damage but, of course, does not eliminate it.

Normally, 1½-inch linen hose has been provided for use by building occupants. If subjected to high humidity or wetted by leaking valves, it deteriorates rapidly. Consequently, it must be examined frequently and at least once a year it should be re-folded on the rack to avoid constant crimping at the same spot and breakage of threads. Today, hose constructed of synthetic fibres is available which is not subject to such failures.

The value of fire hose for use by building occupants is questionable for certain types of occupancies. Many fire departments will not use building hose because they have learned through experience it is often undependable because of neglect. The experience of the federal government with respect to fire hose installed in office buildings, post offices, court houses (which contain libraries), and similar structures indicates that it is virtually never used in fire situations. In addition, the maintenance of the hose and hose racks represents an expense in excess of the value of the protection provided. In those buildings with large post-office workrooms or storage areas (measuring over 200 feet on the narrowest side) containing heavy concentrations of combustibles, standpipes designed for the use of fire departments and building occupants of the areas concerned are required. The same philosophy could be applied to libraries except where otherwise governed by local codes.

## Fixed systems for extinguishment

As was indicated earlier, fixed extinguishing equipment constitutes the third part of a three-phase, automatic, interconnected system of protection against fire: detection, transmission of alarms, and extinguishment. The installation of a fixed system for extinguishment approaches the ideal of complete protection on a twenty-four hour basis.

There are three general types of fixed automatic systems: (1) sprinklers, (2) systems employing total flooding of an enclosed area with carbon dioxide gas, and (3) those which flood an area with a dry chemical compound. Of these systems, only sprinklers have any potential application in libraries, and the value of sprinkler systems in libraries can be asserted only with certain reservations which will become clear in the following discussion.

Fixed extinguishing systems have been used in all types of building occupancies as an effective means of reducing losses from fire. The equipment goes into action as soon as a fire is detected. Alarms are sounded simultaneously with actuation of the system. Following extinguishment of a fire, the systems must be shut off manually and restored to service. Failure to shut them down at the proper time and failure to restore them to service upon the rekindling of a fire have, in some cases, resulted in greater over-all fire damage.

As the term implies, automatic systems begin to operate immediately; there is no delay for the arrival of building or fire department personnel. This immediacy of action has advantages and disadvantages. Quick action serves to decrease fire damage and permits more time for evacuation of the building. Automatic systems, however, cannot be as selective as human beings. The systems would tend to apply their extinguishing agents to larger areas than might actually be required. A human operator, for example, might extinguish a small fire with a portable fire extinguisher; an automatic sprinkler system might apply much more water than was needed, which could result in greater over-all damage.

## Sprinkler systems

Automatic sprinkler systems are the most widely used type of fixed protection systems; they have established remarkable fire control and extinguishment records. Statistics accumulated by the National Fire Protection Association on 67,457 fires occurring from 1925 through 1959 in buildings protected by sprinkler systems show that such systems performed satisfactorily in 96.2 percent of the fires with 57.2 percent practically or entirely extinguished and 39 percent held in check. These figures also show that this performance record was made with relatively few sprinklers operating in each case. The point is illustrated by the following table.

| Number of Sprinklers Operating | Cumulative Percentage of Fires Extinguished or Held in Check |
|---|---|
| One sprinkler | 38.1 |
| One or two sprinklers | 55.3 |
| One, two, or three sprinklers | 64.6 |
| One, two, three, or four sprinklers | 70.9 |

The effectiveness of sprinkler systems, as well as other fixed systems of extinguishment, is also reflected in the fact that their installation normally produces substantial reductions in fire insurance premiums. Moreover, such fixed systems often have an effect on requirements imposed by building codes. That is, if a sprinkler system is planned for installation in a new building, certain provisions of the code covering construction may be modified with a resulting reduction in construction costs.

To arrive at a realistic appraisal of the relative applicability of sprinkler systems in libraries, it is necessary to understand their operating principles, the types of systems available, and their advantages and disadvantages. A sprinkler system consists of a network of piping connected to a source of water. Depending upon conditions in the particular situation, a sprinkler head normally is installed so that it covers floor areas ranging from 65 to 200 square feet. Whenever the temperature at a sprinkler head exceeds a pre-established point (usually about 160° F.), a soft metal in the head will melt causing the head to open and discharge water in a circular solid-cone pattern over the protected area. This discharge will normally continue until the system is manually shut off. Those heads opened by a fire must be replaced in the process of restoring the system to service.

All sprinkler systems are equipped with audible local alarms to alert the occupants of the building or passersby. Of course, in addition, the alarms should be automatically transmitted to the local fire department. Automatic alarms to the fire department are necessary not only for the obvious reasons but also because the likelihood of accidental water damage is reduced: fire department personnel can prevent extension of the damage that would othewise result from accidental sprinkler-head operation, or from a break in the piping which might occur when the building is unoccupied.

The installation of an automatic sprinkler system increases the possibility of non-fire-caused water damage although incidents of this kind are rare. Most cases of mechanical damage to sprinkler heads are caused by carelessness and could be avoided. Breaks in sprinkler heads are usually caused by freezing. Libraries, generally in heated buildings, would not normally experience such incidents. Proper care and maintenance of the system virtually eliminates the possibility of any accidental water damage.

There are three primary types of sprinkler systems with possible library application: "wet-pipe," "dry-pipe," and "empty-pipe." The wet-pipe system is far more common, much simpler, and somewhat less expensive than the other two systems.

The lines in a wet-pipe system are filled with water under pressure, usually the pressure provided by the source of the water supply. Ordinarily the piping can be concealed in the ceiling with only the sprinkler heads exposed. Wet-pipe sprinkler systems are inappropriate to buildings or areas of buildings that might be subject to freezing, and in most libraries this would not be a problem. However, it should be noted that small rooms or otherwise unheated areas may be protected by such systems provided the piping is filled with an anti-freeze solution in accordance with National Fire Protection Association standards.

A dry-pipe system is similar to a wet-pipe system except that the pipes in the former are filled with air under pressure which holds the sprinkler valve closed to water. Air pressure is ordinarily supplied through an orifice by an air compressor and tank. When a sprinkler head is actuated, air is released at the head at a faster rate than the rate at which the pressurized air is admitted to the system. Thus the internal air pressure continues to drop until the dry-pipe valve opens and permits water to flow into the system. Because the original cost and maintenance costs of dry-pipe systems are higher than those of wet-pipe systems, the former are recommended only for buildings and areas in which there is a high probability of freezing. Again, the pipes in a dry-pipe system can be concealed in the ceiling but this requires the use of special "dry-pendant" sprinkler heads which cost many times more than standard

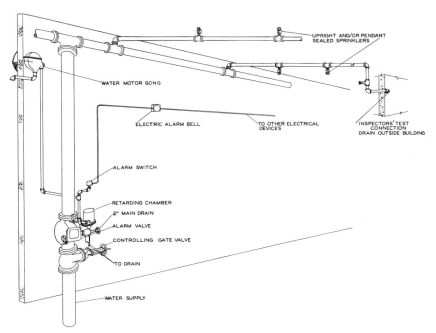

UPRIGHT AND/OR PENDANT
SEALED SPRINKLERS

WATER MOTOR GONG

ELECTRIC ALARM BELL

TO OTHER ELECTRICAL
DEVICES

INSPECTORS' TEST
CONNECTION
DRAIN OUTSIDE BUILDING

ALARM SWITCH

RETARDING CHAMBER

2" MAIN DRAIN

ALARM VALVE

CONTROLLING GATE VALVE

TO DRAIN

WATER SUPPLY

*Courtesy of "Automatic" Sprinkler Corporation of America*

The wet-pipe sprinkler system always has water in the pipes ready to discharge once the heads fuse. Piping in the dry pipe system is filled with air under pressure which holds the water valve closed until the pressure is released through fused heads. Dry pipe systems are generally installed in unheated areas subject to freezing. Both systems sound alarms on the premises and may be arranged to transmit fire alarm signals to a remote point.

heads. (Dry-pendant sprinkler heads are also used in wet-pipe systems.)

An empty-pipe system is suitable for installation in those libraries in which the problem of water damage may be especially critical. This system, usually called a "pre-action system," consists of two separate but inter-connected systems — one a fast-operating fire detection system (usually electrical), and the other a closed-head, empty-pipe sprinkler system. The latter is essentially the same as standard types of sprinkler systems except that the pipes are filled with neither water nor pressurized air. The system has a special valve, normally kept closed, which opens automatically when a fire is detected and permits water to flow into the pipes to the sprinkler heads. However, no water is discharged until the sprinkler head is actuated by the heat of the fire.

The pre-action system has two important advantages: It is an empty-pipe system, which means that the problem of accidental water damage from the sprinkler system is eliminated. Second, and more important, the companion fire detection system will normally detect a fire at a temperature lower than that required to actuate a sprinkler head. This produces an earlier alarm and makes it possible to locate and extinguish the fire before it has become hot enough to melt the sprinkler heads above it, thus preventing the discharge of any water at all.

Pre-action systems are more expensive than standard systems, primarily because of the added, companion detection system. The additional cost is often justified, however, in those areas in which it is determined that sprinkler protection is absolutely essential and

*Courtesy of "Automatic" Sprinkler Corporation of America*
The standard upright sprinkler head has a top plate which deflects water downward in a spray pattern. The two-piece soldered link at the right parts when the surrounding air is heated to the melting temperature of the solder. This allows the two-arm strut to drop out and open the water orifice. Similar heads are available for installation in the pendant position. Ordinary fusing temperatures range from 125° to 165°F. Higher temperatures to 360°F. are used where ambient temperatures are above average, such as near skylights, ceiling suspended heaters, or in boiler rooms.

Example of installation of sprinkler heads in ceiling of library reading area.

in which it is also the case that water damage would be inordinately destructive and costly.

There is another system, not yet identified by name, presently under laboratory testing and evaluation. This modification of standard systems appears to have great advantages both in controlling fires and in protecting against water damage.

The system is similar to a pre-action system in that it combines a detection device with an empty-pipe sprinkler system. However, detection is based on special devices sensitive to the presence of a flame or heat. The sensing devices perform two functions: they automatically cause the special sprinkler-system valve to open when a flame is detected, and they automatically close the valve when the flame is extinguished. A variable time delay is engineered into the system so that it would continue to operate for a brief period after the devices no longer "see" the flame or "feel" the heat. The system automatically resets itself so that it will be ready to operate if the fire is not completely extinguished and flames appear again, or the fire causes another increase in temperature. If this system proves to be reliable under the wide range of operating requirements that must be met for unqualified approval by organizations responsible for setting protection standards, then it will be placed on the market.

*Courtesy of "Automatic" Sprinkler Corporation of America*
**Automatic spray sprinkler head — pendant type.**

The system could prove to be of great value in the protection of libraries.

In general, the key advantage of sprinkler systems is their proven capability on a twenty-four-hour basis to detect, control, and in many cases extinguish fires before they have caused extensive damage. In addition, sprinkler systems may discharge less water in extinguishing a fire that might otherwise be used. This is because the particular sprinkler heads that open are immediately above the fire; they discharge water only into the actual combustion zone. To illustrate this: the 15 to 20 gallons of water per minute normally discharged from a single sprinkler head can often do a far more effective extinguishing job than 250 gallons per minute discharged in a hit-or-miss manner from a fire hose.

## "Mist" or "water fog" sprinklers

For years the method of designing sprinkler systems has been based upon standards which prescribe a fixed pipe size, a fixed sprinkler head discharge orifice size (½ inch) and a minimum water pressure of 15 pounds per square inch at the uppermost head in the system. In practice, this has generally resulted in a discharge rate per sprinkler head of approximately 0.17 gallons per minute per square foot of area covered by the discharge pattern at the uppermost heads. Consequently, in multi-story buildings protected by sprinklers, those heads in the lower stories would deliver more water when operating. Also, as most sprinkler systems installed in libraries and similar occupancies are supplied directly from public water systems in which the pressure fluctuates, the amount of water discharged from a sprinkler head will increase with an increase in pressure and much of the water is wasted. This is one of the reasons for the desirability of insurance against sprinkler water damage.

In recent years, there has been a tendency in the fire protection profession toward favoring hydraulically calculated sprinkler systems. This is a decided improvement over the arbitrary system used in the past and is based on sound engineering principles. On the basis of experience, or future testing, it can be determined how much water should be required for controlling or extinguishing a fire involving a given combustible or flammable material under given environmental conditions — such as building arrangement, ventilation, and other factors. This calls for a water supply from an automatically operated fire pump on the premises delivering water at a high constant pressure through piping of a calculated size (smaller than normal) to sprinkler heads with a predetermined orifice size. In some cases this type of installation has been made (effecting savings in pipe size) using sprinkler heads with ¼- and ⅜-inch orifices which deliver a finely divided heat-absorbing water

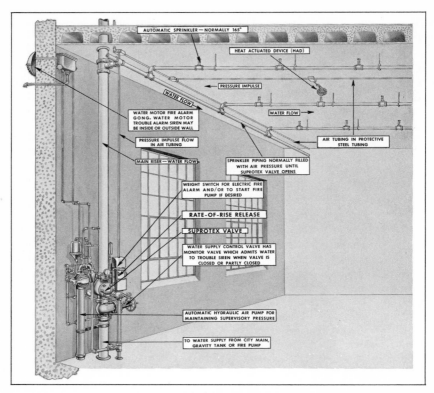

*Courtesy of "Automatic" Sprinkler Corporation of America*
The pre-action sprinkler system normally has no water in the pipes. An associated heat detection system may be the rate-of-rise (shown right) or utilize thermostats or other devices operating at temperatures below the fusing temperature of the sprinkler heads. When the heat detection system operates, it causes the sprinkler system valve to open, admitting water to the piping and sprinkler heads, and sound an alarm on the premises. Fire alarm signals may also be transmitted to a remote point. Water is not discharged until the air temperature reaches the fusing temperature of the sprinkler head, normally 165°F. The pre-action system is suited to library areas in which sprinklers may be required because action can be taken to control or extinguish a fire before it reaches such proportions as to require sprinkler operation.

mist at a rate as low as 0.10 gallons per minute per square foot.

It is probable that this method of design has application in libraries and that it would reduce the cost of sprinkler protection and minimize water damage. It is known that when water is broken up into fine droplets, more surface area is exposed and the rate of heat absorption is higher than with larger droplets. Thus the efficiency of the use of water increases, more of it is converted to steam which has a fire smothering effect, the temperature at the burning surface is reduced more quickly, and less water is wasted in run-off.

## RATE-OF-RISE OPERATION

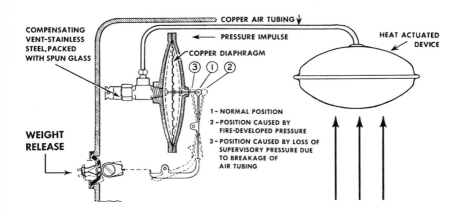

COPPER AIR TUBING

COMPENSATING
VENT-STAINLESS
STEEL, PACKED
WITH SPUN GLASS

PRESSURE IMPULSE

COPPER DIAPHRAGM

HEAT ACTUATED
DEVICE

③ ① ②

1 - NORMAL POSITION

2 - POSITION CAUSED BY
FIRE-DEVELOPED PRESSURE

WEIGHT
RELEASE

3 - POSITION CAUSED BY LOSS OF
SUPERVISORY PRESSURE DUE
TO BREAKAGE OF
AIR TUBING

## HEAT ACTIVATED DEVICE (HAD)

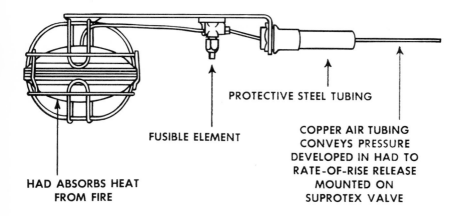

PROTECTIVE STEEL TUBING

FUSIBLE ELEMENT

COPPER AIR TUBING
CONVEYS PRESSURE
DEVELOPED IN HAD TO
RATE-OF-RISE RELEASE
MOUNTED ON
SUPROTEX VALVE

HAD ABSORBS HEAT
FROM FIRE

## Pros and cons of sprinkler systems

Librarians, traditionally, have resisted the installation of sprinkler systems in libraries because of the possibility of water damage
to their collections. This concern is genuine and largely justified.
Since sprinklers can be set off accidentally (or deliberately, as in the
case of vandals or pranksters), the potential hazard from water
damage does exist. Whether or not a librarian should object to the
installation of a sprinkler system in his library is not a question that
can be answered simply.

Unfortunately, because of the unquestioned effectiveness of

sprinklers, a tendency has developed in certain fire protection groups to regard such systems as the universal solution to the fire protection problem. This is an unfortunate development because it is important to recognize that sprinklers represent only one approach to a solution. Each building and its contents make up a unique situation with respect to fire protection; each case must be evaluated individually to determine protection needs and the most practical and economical ways to meet those needs. In short, if a library building, or certain areas within that building, because of the peculiarities of the particular situation, are especially vulnerable to fire, then the logical course is to make them less vulnerable by methods calculated to obtain an acceptable level of protection at minimum cost without necessarily subjecting the books to the additional danger of damage presented by sprinkler systems.

It should be noted that sprinkler systems are not generally required nor installed in office occupancies, even though there may be wood furniture, combustible floor coverings, and wood wall paneling, as well as much paper in the open or stored in steel or wood files. The fire hazard in ordinary offices is considered to be low; for this reason, sprinklers are not generally required in offices. By extension, it would appear that sprinklers should not be required in those areas of libraries with comparable fire loadings.

In general, the observations made by the fire protection engineers engaged in the present study did not indicate that library stack areas were especially hazardous. Neither do fire tests conducted to date show that such areas are especially hazardous. As has been stated repeatedly, a great many factors in combination determine the relative degree of fire hazard present in any building situation. These have been described in detail earlier in the book but, in the framework of the immediate question, it may be stated that the presence of all or most of the following conditions in the library would tend to eliminate the need for introducing an additional hazard by the installation of an automatic sprinkler system:

1. A building of fire resistive or noncombustible construction in a location with good public fire protection.

2. Division of the building into relatively small fire areas by use of fire walls and fire doors.

3. Elimination of vertical draft conditions and prevention of propagation of fire upward by means of horizontal barriers such as fire resistive continuous floors, and enclosure of stairways and elevator shafts.

4. Minimum use of combustible materials in interior finish and furnishings.

5. Installation of a central-station detection and alarm system properly supervised and maintained in good working order.

6. Installation of protective devices such as automatic closing of fire doors and cut-off of air circulation ducts, and first-aid fire fighting equipment kept in good working order.
7. Careful supervision of library operations including control of smoking and good housekeeping practices.
8. An effective system of periodic inspection of the entire premises for unsafe fire conditions such as defective electrical wiring or deficiencies in the air conditioning or heating systems.

Except where local codes may insist upon sprinkler systems in basements and work areas, there are no definite rules on what conditions would require the installation of sprinklers. Again, each case must be appraised and evaluated on its own merits. However, at a general level, it may be stated that the following kinds of building situations represent a sufficient departure from the conditions listed above to call for serious consideration of sprinkler protection:

1. Library buildings of wood frame construction.
2. Libraries located in areas not protected by an organized fire department or located more than five miles away from the nearest fire department station.
3. Library buildings with highly combustible interior finish.
4. Libraries located in basements or other building areas such that access is difficult for effective fire fighting.
5. Library buildings of combustible construction located in areas subject to a high incidence of arson. (Depending upon circumstances, a fire detection system alone might be acceptable in buildings of noncombustible construction.)
6. Those rooms or areas in library possessing greater-than-ordinary hazards such as storage and work areas, carpenter shops, paint shops, printing shops, bookmobile storage and servicing rooms, garages, etc.

## Carbon dioxide extinguishment systems

With certain qualifications, the second and third major types of fixed extinguishment systems — carbon dioxide and dry chemical — are not recommended for general use in libraries. The advantages and disadvantages of each type will be discussed in conjunction with their respective descriptions.

Like sprinkler systems, carbon dioxide extinguishing equipment operates in connection with fire detection units or heat-actuated devices. The extinguishing agent is carbon dioxide gas ($CO_2$), which is dispersed through a system of pipes and which smothers the fire by depriving it of oxygen. Actuation of the system produces a two-stage response: first, an alarm is sounded which warns human occupants that the area must be evacuated. Shortly afterward, large amounts of carbon dioxide gas are released into the affected area.

As a fire extinguishing agent in the library, carbon dioxide has certain important advantages. The gas is perfectly clean, leaves no residue, and cannot damage the books in any way.

The main disadvantage in carbon dioxide extinguishing systems is the potential hazard to human life.[1] Carbon dioxide in itself is a harmless gas. However the amount of gas which must be dispensed in a given enclosed space to extinguish a fire is so great that it reduces the supply of oxygen in that area to such a level that life cannot be sustained.

The atmosphere normally contains about 21 percent oxygen and 79 percent inert gases, mostly nitrogen. Carbon dioxide is included with the inert gases and makes up about 0.05 percent of the air. If the percentage of carbon dioxide is increased to 3 or 4 percent, humans will experience a shortage of breath. Brief exposures to this amount will cause no serious after-effects. A proportion of about 9 percent is the maximum that humans can tolerate without losing consciousness within a few minutes. Above 9 percent, loss of consciousness is quite rapid. At proportions of about 20 percent, death will follow from asphyxiation in twenty to thirty minutes unless the person is removed to a source of fresh air.

To achieve minimum effectiveness, a carbon dioxide extinguishing system must fill the protected space with enough $CO_2$ to make a concentration of at least 34 percent. This amount of $CO_2$ is sufficient to reduce the oxygen content to 14 percent, the point at which many materials — including paper — will not burn. This much carbon dioxide in the air is extremely dangerous to human life.

Present standards for total-flooding $CO_2$ systems take account of both surface and deep-seated fires. The storage of paper materials, i.e., library storage, is classed as a service with a deep-seated fire requirement; the protection design calls for a concentration of 65 percent $CO_2$. This results in a reduction of the oxygen content to about 7.2 percent — a lethal condition. This quantity of $CO_2$ must be continued until complete extinguishment of the fire is accomplished. Otherwise there is the possibility of re-ignition. This means that the carbon dioxide gas must be retained in the space for a comparatively longer period than might be the case with other kinds of extinguishing agents. Thus there is a secondary limitation on the use of carbon dioxide systems: the spaces protected must be able to confine the gas for the necessary period of time.

Proper design of a system requires that the amount of carbon dioxide gas provided be twice that ordinarily needed to fill the larg-

---

1 Although neither case involved fire, at least two deaths can be attributed to the operation of $CO_2$ systems in enclosed rooms. One case was that of a welder whose torch actuated a thermostat. The other appears to have been an accidental manual operation of the system by an uninformed person.

est area protected. This is a safety feature; it allows for a second flooding in case the first fails to extinguish the fire completely.

In general it may be stated that systems of extinguishment employing total flooding of building areas with carbon dioxide cannot be recommended for libraries. The advantages of such systems in the protection of property are far outweighed by the hazard to human life.

In those special cases in which such systems are considered to be necessary, it is imperative that adequate alarm systems be installed to ensure that complete evacuation of persons from the protected areas has been accomplished before the discharge of carbon dioxide gas has begun.

## Dry chemical systems

The second type of automatic extinguishing system regarded as unsuited to libraries is a dry-chemical system. The term "dry chemical," as used in reference to fire protection systems, is a finely pulverized sodium bicarbonate powder to which has been added small amounts of free-flow and water-repelling agents. This dry chemical is a highly effective fire extinguishing agent with about two-and-one-half times the repressive power of carbon dioxide.

The main objection to the use of dry-chemical equipment in fixed (pipe) extinguishment systems is that it is not suited to Class A fires, which are the kind that would occur in most areas of the library. The equipment is not suitable because the chemical used in the system often does not prevent re-ignition. This type of system, however, is highly recommended for protection against Class B fires — ignition of flammable liquids such as gasoline and oil. Although at least one library has installed a dry-chemical fixed system, the manufacturer regards the system as obsolete and of limited utility.

As was noted earlier in this chapter, portable dry-chemical extinguishers are useful in libraries for special locations such as oil-fired boiler rooms or areas in which flammable liquids are used or stored.

# CHAPTER 5

# Fire Protection in Library Planning

Planning the design and construction of a new library must necessarily be a cooperative, group effort. Such a group may, at different times during planning and construction, include the librarian-administrator, the architect, several engineering specialists (structural, mechanical, electrical), representatives of insurance companies, officials of the municipal building department, fire protection engineers, and the contractor. Two of these — the insurance consultants and the fire protection engineers — are too often omitted from the project.

The necessity for utilizing the talents and skills of *all* of these specialists is apparent in the great variety of factors to be considered in planning a new library. Although not exhaustive or detailed, the following list illustrates the broad scope of planning needed:

Location and site
Proposed height and floor area of the building
Functional arrangement of the interior
Projections of library growth and expansion
Compliance with building codes and other codes
Space and facilities for ancillary services
Operating and maintenance costs
Structural and internal fire safety
Safety of personnel and patrons
Insurance needs and costs
Esthetic considerations
Required date of completion
Civil defense considerations

In ordinary practice, the architect and librarian will arrive at a desired design for the building in conference with the structural, mechanical, and electrical consultants who will then prepare detailed designs in their respective fields. When mutual agreement is reached, preliminary drawings are prepared. When doubt exists as to what may be required by the local building code, representatives of the municipal building department are consulted to reduce the probability of later changes contingent upon the issuance of a building permit.

Normal procedure, as outlined above, is essentially inadequate because detailed designs often fail to take full advantage of the flexibility which is an inherent part of modern codes.

A second point: detailed designs are very often completed before insurance requirements have been considered. Such oversights can result in expensive changes in the plans or increases in premium costs over the life of the building.

Third, it should be recognized that from 20 to 25 percent of the cost of a building may be absorbed by special features of construction required for protection against fire. This fact makes highly desirable the participation in planning of competent fire protection engineers. (The selection of reliable fire protection consultants has been discussed in connection with inspections of existing buildings, Chapter 2.)

## Local codes and regulations

Certain legal requirements imposed by municipal governments must be met in construction of new buildings. These requirements are incorporated in the form of published codes and standards, the three most common of which are the building code, the fire prevention code, and the electrical code.

The building code, in general, governs the construction features of the building; the fire prevention code covers the installation, maintenance, and use of various types of protective equipment and processes; the electrical code sets standards for electrical installations. There is, of course, some overlapping, particularly between the building and fire prevention codes. In some cities, a separate code covering exits is included in the building code.

The building code imposes limitations on the size and height of buildings, depending upon the kind of construction. In some localities, the code may restrict the building to a certain type of construction. The building code also states the requirement for light and ventilation and sets minimum design load criteria. Most building codes cover the installation of heating and air conditioning equipment although occasionally the latter is governed by a separate code.

There are several model building codes which have been widely adopted, although many cities, especially the larger ones, have compiled their own codes. The four most widely used model building codes are (1) the National Building Code, promulgated by the National Board of Fire Underwriters; (2) the Uniform Building Code, sponsored by the International Conference of Building Officials; (3) the Basic Building Code, prepared by the Building Officials' Conference of America; and (4) the Southern Standard Building Code, the work of the Southern Standard Building Code Congress. The particular code in effect in any area can be determined by contacting the local building or engineering department.

If the library is being erected in an area in which no building restrictions apply, almost any of the nationally recognized codes might be used. There are individual differences among them in organization and specific restrictions, but all ensure a reasonable degree of safety. It would probably be advisable to select the code used by the nearest large city, modifying it to exclude obviously inapplicable requirements.

The fire prevention code, in general, covers the use of the building (nature of occupancy) and the installation of devices and equipment not normally regarded as being part of the basic structure of the building. The code usually requires that fire extinguishers be provided, prohibits the accumulation of combustible trash, and requires that the premises be open to the local fire inspector.

The original model fire prevention code was prepared by the National Board of Fire Underwriters about 1905 and this code with subsequent revisions has been widely adopted. Some cities have adopted separate standards published by the National Fire Protection Association and the National Board of Fire Underwriters. These standards cover the installation, maintenance, and use of particularly hazardous materials and processes.

The National Electrical Code, under continual revision by a committee of the National Fire Protection Association, is approved by the American Standards Association as an American Standard. It has also been adopted as the Standard of the National Board of Fire Underwriters. This code has been given almost universal recognition and acceptance.

Codes necessarily must be written to apply to broad categories of occupancies and uses. Accordingly, in some respects, the provisions of a particular code may be inadequate to safeguard the library properly. Conversely, some code provisions may appear to be unreasonable or unduly restrictive. The former condition is met by recognizing that codes set up minimum standards. Thus, good library design should go as far beyond such minimum standards as is justified by the library's needs and the availability of funds.

Restrictive provisions are another matter. Some restrictions are plainly written in the interest of public health and safety. With respect to others, officials administering the code regulations are often empowered to grant reasonable variances upon satisfactory proof that the spirit of the code is not violated.

The librarian should be aware that codes are not necessarily perfect or even up to date. Building construction and fire prevention techniques are constantly being improved; changes in codes to reflect such improvements may not have kept pace. Despite this possibility, the code need not be an obstacle to good, functional design.

It is often the case that design modifications may be introduced that will vitiate the restrictive effects of certain code provisions and even permit better methods at lower costs. Here is another situation in which expert consulting assistance may prove to be worth more than its cost.

## Location of the building

A number of protection and loss considerations should be examined in choosing a site for the new building. One obvious example is the prospect of locating the building in an area known to be subject to a high incidence of earthquakes. In such areas, the prevailing building code will probably have made provision for construction measures to diminish the likelihood of earthquake damage.

A factor often overlooked in searching for an appropriate building site is the availability of organized fire department services. This is not ordinarily a problem for existing older libraries which are usually located in downtown areas. However, in contemplating the site of a new library or branch, the fact that fire department facilities and services in many communities and subdivisions are inadequate or entirely lacking should not be overlooked.

A third factor to be considered is the availability of water for fire-fighting purposes. The trend toward locating new buildings in the outlying sectors of metropolitan areas has significance in this respect. In many newly developed areas, the capacity of the water distribution system is grossly inadequate; as a result, the fire department is severely handicapped in its efforts.

A fourth factor is the possibility of damage to the library because of exposure to fires or explosions occurring in adjacent or nearby buildings. Obviously a library building in a congested area, surrounded by other buildings of non-fire resistive construction, is more susceptible to exposure damage than a building with considerable open space around it. In those cases in which a number of different building sites are being considered, insurance companies can provide a valuable service. Representatives of those companies expected to submit bids for insurance contracts on the new building will be able to evaluate the site conditions to the benefit of the librarian as well as to their own advantage.

Codes governing new construction and fire codes require the construction of certain types of walls and other features when buildings are to be located within specified minimum distances from lot lines or other buildings. There are several devices to provide against exposure damage. These are listed roughly in order of their protective capabilities. The most effective barrier is a blank masonry wall. The others are wired glass windows in metal frames, glass-block window panels, open sprinkler heads outside over the windows, and fire shutters (metal panels covering window openings). The last of these offers only limited protection. Shutters are only effective when they are closed. All-metal shutters are ineffective because they usually conduct heat quite rapidly. Tin-clad shutters have slightly greater protective value but, in general, it may be stated that shutters are obsolete.

In general, the more fire resistive the building, the safer it is from serious fire damage and other structural damage. Although the decision must depend upon the particular situation, it is possible that a higher degree of over-all safety could be provided by combining construction of lower fire resistance with complete defense measures such as an automatic sprinkler system, a combination that also might result in considerable savings in cost.

An interesting sidelight on the question of building construction is the fact that a building in which the basic structural members are composed of laminated or "mill" timbers with masonry walls will have greater structural stability in a bad fire than a building of non-combustible construction with *unprotected* steel structural members. When subjected to high temperatures, the exposed load-bearing steel members can be expected to fail (collapse) in a surprisingly short time. Load-bearing steel can retain its full strength under high temperature conditions only if it is insulated by encasement in concrete or other materials having equivalent resistance to fire and heat.

## Use of the building

The problem of joint occupancy of a building by the library and other kinds of establishments has been discussed earlier (page 33). However, the library administrator, in planning new quarters, may find it necessary to share the building with others. Joint occupancies are covered by certain building code provisions. Depending upon the particular kinds of occupancies concerned, these provisions may require the construction of fire resistive separating walls, or a more costly type of construction, or both.

## Types of building construction

Buildings are constructed of various types of materials and with varying degrees of resistance to fire loss. According to the codes, there are four general classifications of buildings:

*Fire resistive:* buildings constructed of reinforced concrete or of steel and masonry with steel structural members encased in concrete or other fire resistive material.

*Non-combustible:* buildings constructed of steel and masonry or steel structures with exposed structural members.

*Ordinary:* buildings with outer walls constructed of masonry with interior joists, framing members, and floors of wood.

*Wood frame:* buildings in which the entire basic structure is of wood.

There are various subdivisions within these main groups, primarily depending upon the degree of resistance to fire provided for the structural members. There are also subdivisions based on combinations of these four.

It should be remembered that these classifications are based only on the structural features of the building, not on the contents. The fact that a fire resistive building may contain highly combustible materials does not affect its classification.

An axiom of fire protection is that reduction of the total loss possible in a single loss occurrence entails the reduction of the amount of property exposed in that occurrence. In a building this is done by reducing the size of a fire area (the area in which a fire may be contained). In effect, the building is split into several fire areas by means of fire walls. Building codes provide specifications

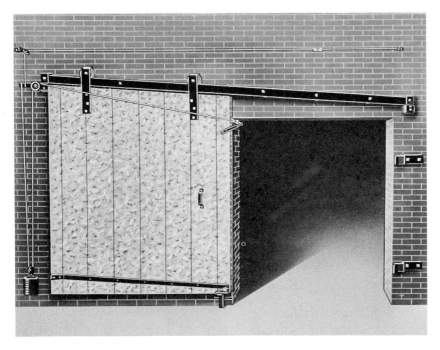

*Courtesy of Richards-Wilcox Manufacturing Company*
This metal-clad, sliding fire door is held open by the counter balance weight at the left. Once the fusible link releases the weight (from heat above the door or coming through the opening) the door rolls down the inclined track to close. Sliding doors on horizontal tracks are closed by dropping weights. Generally, weights should be encased in pipe or other suitable materials so that operation is not impaired by storing material under them. Needless to say, fire doors are useless if they are wedged open or if material is placed against them or in the openings. They should be examined frequently to ensure that they will close if called upon to do so.

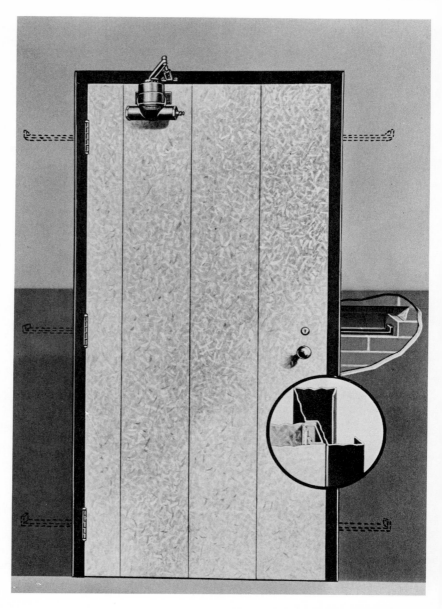

*Courtesy of Richards-Wilcox Manufacturing Company*
A fire door equipped with a self-closer has greater reliability as people cannot "forget" to close the door. Where it is desired that doors remain open for daily traffic, hold-open closers are equipped with a fusible link which releases when subjected to heat and allows the door to close. Frames are specially constructed to prevent passage of flame with the door closed and are firmly anchored in the wall for stability.

for the permissible size of fire areas based upon the type of construction, height of the building, and the nature of the occupancy.

The height, for example, has a close relationship to the possible loss; the higher the building, the more difficulty is encountered in fighting fires on the upper floors.

In planning new construction, it is useful and practicable to raise regular partitions to the status of fire walls, especially if the partitions are designed to be constructed in the same location for all floors. Such partition fire walls greatly improve fire protection at a low cost. To qualify as a fire wall, the construction must conform to standards set forth in the fire prevention code as to the fire resistance rating required. (In the fire protection engineering profession, fire walls and other types of fire barriers, e.g., fire doors, are classified according to the number of hours they can prevent the propagation of fire from one side of the barrier to the other.)

The effectiveness of fire walls is vitiated unless any breaks in them (such as fire doors) are closed during a fire emergency. Various devices can be used to accomplish the closing of doors. For example, there are fusible link mechanisms, actuated by the direct heat of a fire, which automatically release the door and cause it to close, but these usually lack rapidity of response. The best method is to design fire doors so that they are self-closing; if they are open in the normal course of operations, they can be arranged to be held (and closed automatically) by release devices connected to the fire alarm system.

If the design of a new building calls for large, open areas — this is a distinct trend in modern library construction — the over-all fire safety measures taken must compensate for the increase in the single fire risk thus presented.

## External access to the building

Access refers to the ability of fire department personnel, or other emergency forces, to approach and enter a building to cope with emergency situations. The need for ready access to the library building by such emergency forces continues on a twenty-four-hour basis, but is most urgent during nighttime, weekends, or other hours when the library is unoccupied.

Unless arrangements are made in advance — such as providing keys to the fire department — fire fighting forces, arriving at the scene of a fire and confronted with locked doors, must resort to forcible entry.

In many smaller libraries with wood doors and ordinary glass windows, breaking in would cause no great difficulty and would probably result in only slight delay. In some of the larger libraries, however, in which physical security for especially valuable materials has been a paramount consideration, special problems of entry may arise. Cases were observed during this study in which only a single door made of heavy metal was provided and in which every window was securely barred. In one instance, the doors themselves were objects of art; forcible entry alone would cause serious damage. Many modern buildings are being constructed with few windows or none at all. In such designs, planning for emergency access takes on even greater significance.

## Vertical draft openings

The lack of enclosures for stairways, elevator shafts, and other vertical openings is a feature of building construction contributing to the seriousness of fires. The large loss of life (95 pupils and teachers) in the 1958 fire at Our Lady of the Angels School in Chicago can be attributed in part to the school's open stairways.

In spite of this type of fire experience, many new libraries are being constructed with open stairways, often for purely esthetic reasons. From the standpoint of safety, proper enclosures not only provide safer means of exit; they also prevent the open spaces from serving as flues for fire, smoke, and toxic gases.

Building codes require the enclosure of vertical openings in all but a few special situations. The problem should be given serious consideration even in those cases in which this provision of the code is not mandatory, both for existing buildings and in planning for a new building.

## Exit facilities

Although loss of life in library fires has been quite low,[1] this fact should not affect planning for adequate exit facilities. The minimum requirements for exits are outlined in local codes which are usually based on the Building Exits Code published by the National Fire Protection Association (NFPA Pamphlet No. 101). In general, the provisions of this code should be adopted as minimum requirements for any new library, although local codes may impose additional regulations.

Section 1008 of this code reads as follows:

"Every building or structure, section, or area thereof of such size, occupancy and arrangement that the reasonable safety of numbers of occupants may be endangered by the blocking of any single means of egress due to fire or smoke, shall have at least two means

---

[1] Two students were killed when fire destroyed the library of Dakota Wesleyan University at Mitchell, South Dakota, in 1888. A library attendant died from smoke inhalation in a 1934 fire at a Pittsburgh, Pennsylvania, branch library. Later that year, three people lost their lives in a gas explosion in the Seminole, Oklahoma, library.

*Courtesy of New York Daily News*
View of apartment-building fire showing flames pouring out of two first-level windows.
This is an example of the extreme hazard of fire escapes exposed to ordinary glass
windows, a condition observed in several library situations.

of egress remote from each other, so arranged as to minimize any possibility that both may be blocked by any one fire or emergency condition."

This section has the following footnote:

"Chapter 2 generally requires at least two exits but specifies conditions where one means of egress is all that can reasonably be required in the interests of public safety."

The code specifies maximum travel distances to the nearest exits and outlines the basic requirements for these exits including specifications for enclosures, widths, and the installation of hardware.

Traditional library design and practice, based on control of book withdrawal and prevention of theft, channeled all patron traffic past the charge-out desk to a single exit. For this reason, many libraries were constructed with only one public exit. If the building did have other exits, they were usually kept locked.

The very practical question arises as to how control of withdrawals and theft can be reconciled with considerations of safety. It is certainly the case that no *required exit* (that is, required for reasons of safety) should be locked against egress while the building is occupied. The hours after closing present a slightly different problem, although, as everyone knows, people have been inadvertently locked in buildings by custodians who assumed the building empty.

Several procedures and devices have been developed to solve this problem. Some libraries have provided secondary (emergency) exits in closely supervised areas. Supervision prevents unauthorized use of the exits without impairing their emergency usefulness.

A simple and inexpensive solution is to provide a key on the inside of the doorway. The key is placed in a well-marked box with a break-glass front. The box can be electrically connected with a fire alarm or police alarm circuit and this warning posted near the box. Thus the likelihood is diminished that a person would actually break the glass to get the key unless a true emergency existed.

Special door mechanisms have been designed for preserving the security of emergency exits. The doors may be left unlocked to permit normal traffic from either side. When locked, they permit egress only; use of the door sounds a mechanical alarm which alerts the authorities that unauthorized egress has occurred. Experience has shown that such mechanical alarms are not adequate deterrents except in small, well-supervised buildings.

To be fully effective, the security egress lock should be supported by a full-scale electrical alarm system which would ensure that the alarm is *heard* and that corrective action could be taken.

In one application of this principle, some librarians have arranged for an electrical alarm to be sounded at the charging desk. This will alert the staff that the door was being improperly used, but would not guarantee that the offender would be apprehended.

One "fail-safe" system supplements the door alarm with a proximity device, e.g., a photo-electric beam or ultrasonic detector. A person breaking the beam or approaching within a prescribed distance from the doorway automatically triggers an alarm and alerts the staff before the unauthorized exit. The door is immediately (although temporarily) locked against egress by an electrical signal.

A modification of this system provides for locking by remote-control means a second door in the same passageway to prevent unauthorized use of the exit.

## Interior arrangement

From the standpoint of fire protection, open multi-tier stacks constitute a hazard; at the same time, most librarians now agree that the traditional reasons for vertical openings in the stack areas

*Courtesy of Best Universal Lock Company, Inc.*
The Exit Lock is adaptable to any existing door which should be available as an emergency exit, yet which the librarian does not wish to be used for surreptitious exiting. Operation sounds a bell integral with the lock and can also be arranged to sound an alarm and identify location of the specific door on a control panel located at the charge-out desk or other attended locations. The lock may be key-operated without sounding an alarm.

*Courtesy of Best Universal Lock Company, Inc.*
The Security Indicator for the exit lock allows central supervision of numerous locks.

have been discarded. Following the already stated principles of minimizing the size of fire areas, closing off vertical openings, and avoiding the use of unprotected steel structural elements in construction, the recommended arrangement would be free-standing stacks on concrete floors which are structural parts of the building. The term "free-standing" is used loosely and would include those situations in which the stacks had been braced by being attached to the floor and to the ceiling.

Stacks should be completely cut off from level to level and should be separated by vertical partitions depending upon the size of the fire areas under consideration. Adequate fire separations can be provided at a low unit cost and little loss of storage space by using metal-gypsum sandwich spacers along the center line of a standard range of steel shelving, combined with fire doors at the ends. A sketch of this construction is shown on page 112.

Stacks provided for storage only should be separated from shelves open to the patrons.

In many libraries, stack areas are combined with reading rooms. A typical arrangement in a reading room with a fifteen-foot ceiling is that of having one tier of stacks on the floor with an additional mezzanine stack level. Such an arrangement produces no special hazards.

However, in those relatively rare situations in which the ceiling height might make the addition of a third tier of stacks possible, the hazard introduced by this addition would be somewhat increased unless extensive further work was done with respect to the enclosure of stairways and vertical cutoff barriers.

To repeat a point made in connection with protective measures to be taken in existing buildings: In all cases, the service areas (garage, bindery, kitchen, carpenter shop, print shop, heating plant, paint shop, receiving and shipping room, etc.) should be segregated from the library proper — particularly the collections — by walls of the stature of fire walls.

*Courtesy of Remington Rand Division of Sperry Rand Corporation*
An example of free-standing stacks with each level cut off by continuous floors which are structural parts of the building. This is preferred construction from the standpoint of fire safety, providing all openings between floors, such as stairs, book lifts, etc., are enclosed with fire resistive construction.

The almost universal pattern in libraries of shortages of space for book storage has, in some libraries, led to the installation of sliding and pivoting book shelf arrangements (compact book storage). A characteristic of this type of book storage is narrow aisles. No philosophy or techniques of fire protection have been yet developed to cover such installations; it is probable that for some time to come each case must be evaluated on its own merits. From the viewpoint of potential fire hazards there is no intrinsic objection to such methods of high-density book storage, but the problem of

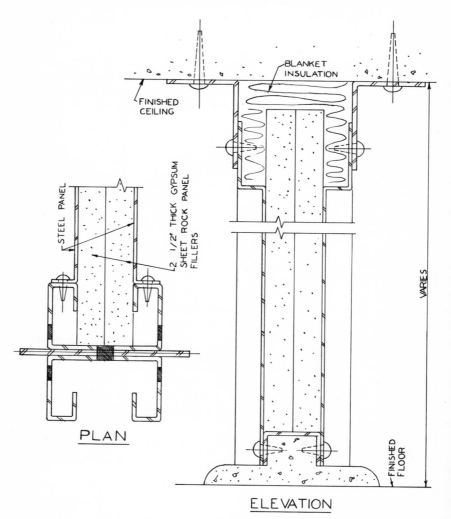

Design of fire separation: stack section.

*Courtesy of Remington Rand Division of Sperry Rand Corporation*
A single tier of stacks with a mezzanine level in the David Sarnoff Research Laboratory Library, typical of many libraries. Three rate-of-rise heat detectors can be seen on the ceiling.

achieving rapid access to all points in the library in case of fire must be treated separately.

In this connection, the width of aisles in the stack areas has a bearing on fire safety. Many libraries have adopted standard spacing between stacks — 54 inches on centers — leaving aisles about 36 inches wide. Storage stacks are spaced closer together, about 48 inches on centers. The main requirement for space is that library staff be able to work in the aisles. The building code defines the minimum width of exit passageways as 22 inches. The width of long-range aisles should be no less than 22 inches; however, short aisles leading to exit aisles of adequate width might safely be less than 22 inches.

## Interior finish and trim

Building codes often include classifications and specifications for interior finish and trim, that is, the composition of finish materials — paint, varnish, wax, etc. The basis for classification is usually a surface flame-spread test, such as is described in Standard E84 of the American Society for Testing Materials (ASTM). Flame spread — the rapidity with which flame advances over a surface — is measured on a scale derived from a formula based on the arbitrary assignment of 0 to transite (cement asbestos) and 100 to red oak. Limitations are placed by codes on the use of materials rated above 100; materials with very high flame-spread ratings are prohibited in areas to be occupied by human beings.[2]

Typical flame-spread ratings are:

| *Material* | *Flame-spread Rating* |
|---|---|
| "Fiberglass" acoustic tile | 10-20 |
| "Tectum" slabs | 15 |
| Vinyl wall fabric (on unpainted plaster) | 15-25 |
| Impregnated Northern pine | 20 |
| Fire resistive paint on Douglas fir | 25 |
| "Zonolite" acoustic plaster on combustible base | 30-40 |
| Vinyl wall fabric (on painted plaster) | 30-40 |
| Untreated Northern pine | 165 |
| Untreated cellulose insulating board | 225 |
| Veneered wood | 515 |
| Canvas in folds | 640 |

Flame-spread ratings for a given material may vary with different methods of installation. For a more complete listing, see NFPA *Fire Protection Handbook,* Twelfth Edition.

As interior-finish building materials are submitted for Underwriters' Laboratories approval, they are tested and the results appear in UL publications giving flame spread ratings, relative fuel contribution, and a smoke index.

Paints, varnishes, lacquers, shellacs, and waxes are flammable compounds and should be handled accordingly. The degree of flammability of paints may vary with the materials used in manufacturing. Once applied to interior building surfaces in the usual manner, paint does not materially contribute to flame spread as the thin coats rapidly transmit the heat of a fire to the under-surface. In older buildings, in which several coats of paint have been applied over the years, heat transmission is slower. As a result the paint surface is subjected to higher temperatures, vaporizes, and adds

2 During World War II a great many service clubs were built in military installations. Some were constructed of wood frame; others were more durably built of concrete blocks. Interior decorations were often quite elaborate with many thin wooden partitions and with the trim heavily varnished or waxed. Repeated experiences with fires showed that they traveled along these highly flammable surfaces with such rapidity that frequently the interiors were gutted before fire fighting could be started.

fuel to the fire. On highly waxed wood paneling, the flame spread would be much more rapid than on a painted surface.

Plastics are being used in many applications in libraries. Radios, television sets, and reproduction equipment may be housed in molded plastic cases. Rigid sheet plastic is used as decorative panels, as diffusers for fluorescent lights, and, in some cases, as suspended ceilings beneath lighting fixtures. Thin sheet plastics are used as protective jackets for books: heavier sheets (often polyvinyl chloride), textured and colored, are applied to walls. There are plastic floor tiles, rugs made of synthetic (plastic) fibers, and, quite often, furniture and table work tops covered with plastics. Plastic-base paints are also used. The combustibility of plastics varies with their chemical composition. Some burn until consumed; others burn with a feeble flame which may or may not propagate away from the point of ignition. A third group of plastics burn only so long as a flame is applied to them. All plastics will decompose in a fire.

Any fire produces gaseous products of combustion which are toxic and result in more fire fatalities than all other causes. An analysis of combustion products from a library fire would indicate the presence of carbon dioxide, carbon monoxide, ammonia, hydrogen sulfide, sulfur dioxide, and hydrogen cyanide. These are the common gases. Others which might be present include nitrogen oxides, phosgene, acrolein, hydrogen chloride, acids, peroxides, and other halogen compounds. Specific toxic gases present may unite chemically to form others. Smoke may contain irritating particles of tar. Polyvinyl chloride plastic decomposes in fire and releases hydrogen chloride. This in turn combines with moisture in the air, or on the skin, to form hydrochloric acid. In some past fires, damage to machines and metallic surfaces etched by the acid has far exceeded the actual fire loss. Other acids may be formed through decomposition of plastics differently compounded.

Originally, a building may have had acceptable interior finish (e.g., fire resistive paint), but over a number of years, factors such as seasoning and perhaps the later use of less flame resistive finishing materials may have increased the fire hazard. Planning should take account of the necessity for preserving the safe character of the interior finish over time.

A significant illustration of this point appears in the use of acoustic ceiling tiles. In the past, acoustic tiles were manufactured from low-density fibrous materials which proved to be highly combustible. Not only do the tiles have a high flame-spread rating, but the cement holding them tends to soften readily under heat which causes the tiles to drop to the floor during a fire; this second effect further promotes the spread of fire.

In recent years, the field of acoustic treatment of rooms has seen marked improvements in safety. Rooms now may be finished with noncombustible acoustic materials — special types of plaster or noncombustible ceiling tiles, or both.

## Furniture, equipment, machinery

On a purely statistical basis, the chances of fire increase with the amount of combustible material present. This would indicate that steel book carts should be preferred over wooden ones; that metal cases be used for the card catalog; that, throughout, metal furniture is superior to wooden furniture. However, the statistical fact exaggerates the practical situation: in general, it may be stated that the suitability for its intended purpose should be the basis for the selection of furniture rather than the slight differences in the degree of hazard presented. It is known, for example, that, except in the center of a blaze, the cards in a wooden card catalog case will be less subject to damage than they would in a metal one. The transmission of heat in metal cases has caused serious charring damage to cards in metal drawers.

The electrical services in a new library building should be designed with ample capacity for the addition of new circuits (see Chapter 2). When fluorescent lighting is used, each ballast should be individually fused. Protection against circuit overloading should be provided by circuit breakers as opposed to simple fuses. Special emergency circuits supplied directly from the electrical service entrance point should be used exclusively for fire detection and alarm purposes, exit lights, and exit lighting. If it appears that additional lighting is needed for exits, the library administrator might consider emergency power arrangements supplied by batteries or a standby generator.

Broken or defective water, steam, and drain pipes present special problems in libraries because of the possibility of water damage to books. In planning a new building, water pipes should be located so that in case of failure, books will not be exposed to damage.

Garage areas for bookmobiles and other library vehicles should be separated from the ordinary library areas by fire walls with four-hour ratings. The same rule applies to the storage of such equipment as gasoline-powered lawn mowers. Safe storage spaces should be provided for flammable fuels, lubricants, paint, etc.

Most air conditioning and ventilating systems include a device to filter recirculated air. Some systems use adhesive coated stationary filters or traveling screens in oil baths. The adhesives and oils normally furnished by reputable manufacturers of filter systems have flash points (the temperature at which ignition occurs) not lower than 350°F., a relatively safe figure. There are other so-called fire resistive adhesives and oils with flash points at about 460°F. which provide a greater degree of safety at a much higher cost.

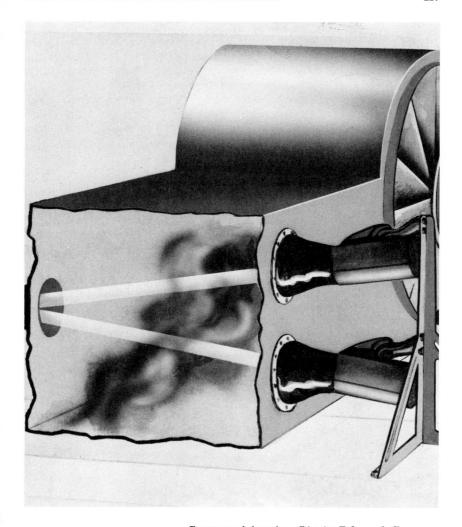

*Courtesy of American District Telegraph Company*
When smoke in the air duct interrupts the light beam of the photo-electric detector, an alarm is sounded and fans are automatically shut down. Other functions may be incorporated as warranted by local conditions.

Oil bath filters present the greater hazard because of the larger quantities of flammable liquids used. The fire safety of filters can be impaired through improper maintenance and the substitution of cheaper oils with much lower flash points. Such filters call for automatic systems of protection — sprinklers or carbon dioxide systems. The alternative would be to use non-flammable filter media which recently have become available.

When a fire occurs in one part of a building, the air circulating system can spread smoke to other parts thus increasing the possibility of smoke damage. Smoke spreading throughout the building makes evacuation of personnel more difficult. It also increases the difficulty of determining the exact location of the fire itself. Thus, it is important that an air circulating system be capable of being shut down quickly in an emergency.

There are several ways to do this. The best plan is to interconnect the fan motors with the fire detection system. The shutdown action then is immediate and automatic.

A second method is to use a smoke detection device in the air circulation system. A third is the use of thermostats in the circulating ducts to shut off the motors, but this is not recommended because considerable damage could occur before the ducts were hot enough to actuate the thermostats.

Whether or not automatic protection is provided, there should always be a conveniently located station from which the circulating system may be manually shut down by the librarian or members of the staff. Many libraries lack such manual trip stations; others have all such controls located in the building utility areas where they are readily accessible only to maintenance personnel.

The ducts in air circulating systems can permit the spread of fire as well as smoke. For this reason, dampers with fusible links should be required at the points at which the ducts pass through fire walls. However, such dampers are not a safe substitute for fan cutoff devices because the former do not operate rapidly enough.

# PART TWO
# Insuring the Library

# CHAPTER 6

## The Librarian as Insurance Administrator

The primary purpose of this discussion of insurance is to assist the library board of trustees and the librarian in the formulation of a comprehensive insurance program for the protection of the library and in the effective administration of such a program by making full use of all of the facilities that the insurance industry has to offer. This cannot be accomplished by attempting to train the librarian to become an insurance expert; thus, for the present purpose, a textbook of insurance is not called for. Nor would a manual which simply presents an array of policy forms and conditions serve any useful purpose. The librarian should, however, be aware of general insurance practices so that he may deal effectively with representatives of the insurance industry and he should be familiar with some of the unusual problems he might be required to face. He should also know what to look for in the way of assistance and counsel from people in the insurance business.

The ultimate responsibility for an adequate insurance program, of course, rests with the library's board of trustees but, as in other matters, the primary function of the board is to develop a set of broad guiding principles within which the librarian has full authority to make specific decisions and take appropriate action. The librarian, in turn, after working with the board to help formulate the guiding principles, must implement them by working out a detailed insurance plan within the scope of his authority.

One of the most important decisions to be made is the selection of a competent insurance agent or broker who will act as insurance counselor. Considerable attention should be given to the latter's experience, educational qualifications, and reputation. He should be worthy of the greatest confidence and he should be assigned full responsibility to recommend appropriate insurance coverages. If the librarian specifies the perils and exposures to be covered without first obtaining the recommendations of the insurance counselor, he is not availing himself of a valuable service, a service to which he is properly entitled.

If the librarian negotiates all of the library's insurance through one insurance representative rather than through several, he will achieve better results. A fully effective insurance program cannot ordinarily be arranged unless the responsibility is centered in one person. This rule applies even in those situations in which the librarian, because of local conditions, is required, or finds it expedient, to place his insurance through several insurance organizations. He may still accomplish his basic purpose by fixing the responsibility in one agent who will make sure that coverage is properly arranged even though he may share the insurance with others.

The first step in preparing basic guiding principles is to have the man selected as the library's insurance counselor prepare a complete survey showing all exposures to loss that are insurable, with recommendations as to the best method of insuring them and an estimated cost for each type of coverage. This will enable the library board and the librarian to decide which perils may be left uninsured (as, for example, earthquakes) or which coverages may be omitted from the plan (such as extra expense or leasehold interest). The board should also decide upon the dollar amount that could be left uninsured under any one loss. It is more and more recognized that the use of reasonable deductibles in all types of losses produces long-range savings both to the insurance company and the insured. The adjustment expense for small losses is a major part of the company's outlay and is reflected in higher insurance premiums. In recognizing the ability of the library to stand losses up to a certain dollar value, another principle may be realized in the non-insurance of small items. If, for example, it is determined that the library can absorb $500 on any one loss, it would be reasonable to allow property away from the premises to go uninsured where it is known that in no case will any value in excess of $500 be exposed to a single loss.

After these general principles have been established by the board, it is the duty of the librarian to see that all necessary exposures are covered in the best possible way and at the lowest cost consistent with safety and good practice. There are certain facilities available to the librarian in carrying out this objective and the insurance counselor selected can be of value in recommending these facilities. The use of appraisal companies and insurance company or agency engineers, or independent consulting fire protection engineers, in establishing values or estimated values for insurance purposes is discussed in the section on valuation in Chapter 8.

The services of engineers affiliated with insurance companies should not be overlooked in the problems connected with safety and insurance rating. Fire rates are based on rather complicated rating schedules which take into consideration such factors as the level of public fire protection available in the community, building construction, area and fire cut-offs, and the effect of all occupancies on the risk. There are also credits for protective devices such as extinguishers or sprinklers. Under this system of rating, it is possible for an error to creep in. In addition, recommendations for protective measures can often be made which entail small outlays of money but which result in appreciable savings in premium costs. When changes or alterations in the building structure — both internal and external — are contemplated, it is important to consider the effect such alterations may have on fire insurance rates. The insurance counselor should be able to make available without charge the services of an agency or company engineer who will check the relevant fire rating schedule for accuracy and recommend any alterations or improvements which would result in premium savings. His services should also be obtained before any new construction is undertaken in order to make sure that the design will incorporate such features and materials as will result in the best possible rates.

In the same way, the services of *casualty* insurance engineers are available to make recommendations as to conditions and policies in the library related to personal safety and the prevention of accidents. Although casualty rates are not on such a complicated schedule rating form as are fire rates, adherence to good safety practices will have a bearing on direct insurance costs, and will, of course, also help to prevent accidents. (In this connection, the model accident prevention checklist included at the end of this chapter will assist the librarian in establishing and maintaining an environment in the library conducive to personal safety.)

Aside from the moral responsibility of the library to do everything possible to prevent accidents to the library staff and the general public, and the advantages of safe practices with respect to insurance, there are other considerations. When a personal injury accident occurs, there are hidden costs associated with the accidents which are often overlooked. These include such costs — which, incidentally, are uninsurable — as loss of executive time and staff time in providing assistance to the injured person, in discussing the accident, in paying visits to the hospital, and so forth. Time is lost in filling out forms and even, perhaps, in necessary court appearances on the part of library staff if liability claims arise out of the accident.

It is apparent from the foregoing that this discussion of the subject of insurance must proceed at a general level. First, the nature of risk and its relationship to the purpose and function of insurance will be discussed. Second, the subject of insurance itself will be taken up under the traditional divisions of coverage which have developed over the years.

Third, it is recognized that the librarian cannot deal intelligently with the particular insurance problems he is to face without some knowledge of the main categories of insurance and their policy coverage conditions — that is, what the insurance will provide for him and its limitations.

It is important for the reader to realize that, in this discussion, references to insurance forms and clauses are made for illustrative purposes only; they are not to be taken as representing exact insurance practice at any specific time or place. While there has been a great amount of standardization in insurance forms, there are still variations from state to state; moreover, in a particular state, some companies may use their own special forms which will vary from the standard.

Fourth, it must be noted that, since World War II, the insurance industry has been in a pronounced condition of flux: new policy forms are constantly being introduced into the market and this, combined with extensive revisions and modifications of older forms, has resulted in the vastly greater number of policies currently available.

Fifth, the most important recent developments and trends in the insurance field will be outlined. For example, only a few years ago, multiple-line legislation was passed in the various states which broke down the barriers which had previously restricted insurance companies to the writing of only one class of insurance. This legislation started a veritable revolution in the insurance business with a proliferation of concepts and practices that had been impossible before. A discussion of these new trends — which should be watched with interest by everyone concerned with insurance — leads logically into the final chapter of the book: "A Model Insurance Policy for Libraries."

## ACCIDENT PREVENTION CHECK LIST

Library furniture, equipment, fixtures — the building itself — deteriorate over time through the wear and tear of normal use. Conditions change; procedures may be modified or replaced by others. All of these can increase the probability of personal injury through accidents to staff personnel or the public. If accidents are to be avoided, the librarian must establish an effective system of safety inspections designed for the particular library. Elevators and escalators will generally be inspected for safety of operation by code-enforcing authorities or contractors engaged in elevator manufacturing and installation. Book lifts and conveyors may be inspected under contract or by the library's maintenance staff. In any case, the librarian should be alert to apparent deficiencies in operations and equipment which require attention.

The purpose of an inspection program is to protect the staff as well as the general public. Inspections may be conducted in a routine manner by one person. In larger libraries, they may be scheduled on a monthly basis and made by a safety committee composed of maintenance and staff personnel. In still larger institutions, the inspections may be conducted by safety engineers employed by the institutions or a representative of the casualty insurance underwriter.

The following form is so designed that a "No" answer indicates an unsatisfactory condition requiring corrective action. The questions included here do not constitute a complete list. Others may occur to the individual librarian as he observes conditions and situations peculiar to his equipment and operations.

|  | YES | NO |
|---|---|---|
| Has the library published a set of safety regulations? | ___ | ___ |
| Are the safety regulations periodically reviewed and updated to reflect current conditions in library procedures, building alterations, and new equipment? | ___ | ___ |
| Are the safety regulations posted throughout the library in conspicuous locations accessible to the staff? | ___ | ___ |
| Does the library have a safety committee? | ___ | ___ |
| Does the safety committee make regular inspections of the library facilities? | ___ | ___ |
| Are safety programs conducted to familiarize the library staff with good safety practices as well as hazards involved with specific pieces of equipment and procedures? | ___ | ___ |
| Is disciplinary action prescribed for repeated violations of the safety regulations? | ___ | ___ |
| Does the mechanical maintenance program provide for periodic inspection of furnaces, air conditioners, boilers, elevators, electrical services, and other items of equipment subject to wear and tear? | ___ | ___ |
| Are physical defects in furniture, fixtures, and equipment repaired promptly to eliminate potential hazards? | ___ | ___ |
| Are stairways, aisles, and corridors kept free of obstructions? | ___ | ___ |
| Are library personnel instructed in the procedure to be followed in the event of an accident requiring medical attention? | ___ | ___ |
| Are extension cords arranged so as not to trip personnel in the area? | ___ | ___ |
| Are safe ladders and/or stools provided to reach material stored above head height? Are they used properly? | ___ | ___ |

| | YES | NO |
|---|---|---|
| Are snow and ice removed from walks and outdoor stairs? | ___ | ___ |
| Are adequate warning signs posted around machinery? | ___ | ___ |
| Are safety guards provided on machines (table saws and grinders, for example) where required? | ___ | ___ |
| Is adequate lighting provided throughout the library to eliminate "dark corners" conducive to falls? | ___ | ___ |
| Is the library staff familiar with the location of *all* light switches? | ___ | ___ |
| If glass floor panels are used, have they been tested for ability to safely carry the appropriate static, live, and impact loads? | ___ | ___ |
| Is adequate venting provided for all heating appliances? (Do not overlook bookmobiles.) | ___ | ___ |
| Is adequate venting provided for areas used for the storage of paints, solvents, and waxes or other substances capable of producing toxic vapors? | ___ | ___ |
| Is a "non-skid" floor polish used? | ___ | ___ |
| Are the corners of shelves, stacks, counters, etc., free of sharp metal edges? | ___ | ___ |
| Are all pieces of electrical equipment (particularly portable units) properly installed and grounded to reduce the possibility of electrical shock? | ___ | ___ |
| Are hand trucks or carts provided to move heavy quantities of materials which might exceed the safe carrying capacity of staff members? | ___ | ___ |
| Are points of low head clearance adequately marked and lighted? | ___ | ___ |
| Are file cabinets and lockers properly installed so that they will not fall when opened? | ___ | ___ |
| Are clerical personnel instructed not to stand directly in front of file cabinets when opening them? | ___ | ___ |
| Are portable or pedestal-type fans located so that they do not create a personnel hazard? | ___ | ___ |
| If glass panels are used adjacent to exits or in corridors when they may be mistaken for doors, have they been made more visible by the application of decalcomanias or other designs? | ___ | ___ |

# CHAPTER 7

# The Nature of Risk

The mechanism of insurance was developed for the purpose of transferring risk of loss from one party to a professional risk carrier in order to minimize the impact of loss. In order to be susceptible to this treatment, a risk must be of such a nature that the law of large numbers will operate. For example, when a large number of individuals transfer the risk of loss by fire to an insurance company, the total cost of all losses each year can be distributed over one entire group. Thus the individual member of the group assumes an equal share of the loss through payment of his annual premium. The larger the group of homogenous risks, the more easily can the total number and extent of losses per year be predicted. In this way a risk of severe loss for the individual is eliminated and becomes a predictable loss for the insurance carrier.

Risks of loss from war, nuclear contamination, and similar perils are such that they do not adapt themselves to the operation of the law of large numbers and are therefore uninsurable. This may be because the loss experience of a particular group of risks is not sufficiently known to permit prediction of average losses over the group, or because certain losses are not of a regularly recurring nature and a catastrophe may wipe out large numbers of risks simultaneously and result in losses beyond the resources of any insurance company.

Other losses are not subject to insurance because they are of a normal recurring nature for the insured and do not represent the type of risks that should be (or can be) insured. They should be regarded as ordinary (predictable) operating expenses such as those for maintenance and upkeep of a building or wear and tear on the contents.

Another large category of risks not eligible for insurance may be called "business risks." For example, a person cannot be indemnified for failure of his business or because he hired a clerk and spent money training him only to find him incompetent. Similarly, a person cannot be indemnified because he lost money in the stock market.

Risks which are against public policy are not insurable; thus losses in the nature of fines or penalties for the infraction of laws cannot be insured.

An insurance policy does not purport to cover all risks, or even all risks of loss arising from a certain specified peril. There are several ways in which an insurance policy maps out the scope of its coverage.

First, there is the insuring agreement which immediately shows the general intent of the coverage and, by its designation of the risk covered, automatically excludes risks of loss which fall beyond that designation. Under the discussion of property owned by the insured, it will be seen that historically there have been two approaches to insurance on personal property: the "named-peril" approach and the "all-risk approach." Even if the insuring agreement states that it covers "all risks of physical loss," it must be remembered that the agreement restricts the coverage to the extent that losses other than those of a physical nature are not covered — for example, during a period in which a building is untenantable, a resulting contingent loss, such as loss of rental value.

There are definitions of terms in a policy and some of these definitions may have a bearing on the extent of coverage. Moreover, there are limitations of coverage which have a distinct effect on the amount of recovery.

Finally, and probably most important, there are the policy exclusions. These exclusions may be written for uninsurable perils already mentioned or they may apply to hazards requiring separate treatment such as boiler explosion and automobile accidents. Sometimes exclusions are made of property items where the intent is to cover them by separate specific insurance. In any event, it is important to keep all of these factors in mind.

If the insurable risks are classified into logical categories, they fall naturally into the following groups:

(1) Physical loss or damage to owned property or to the property of others in the possession of the insured.

(2) Contingent losses, such as losses of income or rental from property which is unusable due to an insured peril.

(3) Dishonesty losses, which, although entailing the loss of owned property, have been traditionally treated as a separate subject; they include employee dishonesty as well as theft by outsiders.

(4) Liability insurance covering legal liability of the insured for injury to another or for damage to his property.

After all of the risks that may not be insurable are eliminated, the insured librarian is left with a choice as to what part of the remaining risk he wishes to transfer to an insurance company. It might be well to explain the meaning of the terms "insurance," "self-insured," and "uninsured."

The term "insurance" implies that there are a large number of homogeneous risks which are numerous enough and well enough spread to give effect to the law of large numbers. This means that, although individual losses may not be predicted, the total losses of the group can be predicted within relatively small limits. These risks can ordinarily be transferred to an insurance company.

Sometimes a property owner feels that he owns enough property to be a "self-insurer." In order to fit this category, he must have a great amount of property. The property must be divided into units small enough and geographically spread enough to give effect to the law of large numbers; moreover, he must have a regular plan of setting aside funds (i.e., premiums) to meet losses when they occur. Anything less than such a program is equivalent to being uninsured, and this is quite different from self-insurance.

It is much wiser to insure risks which may produce a crippling loss — however remote — than it is to insure a risk which will produce a probable loss of a minor nature.

Thus the property owner has the problem of selecting perils which he may or may not insure; he also has the problem of choosing from among various coverages, as outlined in the following pages; finally he may choose to cover part of his own risk by agreeing to elect a *deductible amount* which he is willing to stand before making a claim against the insurance company.

# CHAPTER 8

## Insuring Physical Damage to Property

### Valuation

It is very important that the proper amount of insurance be written on the building and on its contents and that these valuations be kept up to date. When the value of a building is established for insurance purposes, the terms "replacement cost" and "actual cash" value are used. Insurance policies do not define these terms but over years of experience and through many court cases their meanings have become quite definite. By "replacement cost" is meant the cost of rebuilding the structure at the time of loss (i.e., the cost of labor and materials to replace the structure without any deduction for depreciation). By "actual cash value" is meant the replacement cost at the time of loss, less an allowance for depreciation or obsolescence, however caused. Obsolescence is not a factor to be considered in most risks, and normal physical depreciation on a building which has proper maintenance should be in the range of 1 percent to 1½ percent per year; it should not, in total, exceed 40 percent in most cases since maintenance will usually offset further depreciation at about that point. Until recent years, the only method of insuring buildings has been on the actual cash value. Today most buildings may be insured for their full replacement cost.

Personal property (see Glossary) values are based on the cost of buying the identical property new at the time of loss and applying a normal rate of depreciation based on the anticipated life of that type of property. If the personal property can be replaced by used property of equal age and utility, that valuation may be used.

Sometimes, articles of unusual value, or those such as books for which the value is difficult to determine, may be valued in advance and have specific amounts of insurance assigned to them. When articles are specifically listed with individual amounts of insurance assigned to them it is important to determine whether these are agreed valuations by the company or are merely limits of the company's liability. If they are agreed valuations, the company will be liable for the amount agreed upon for a particular item, if the item is lost. Unless the policy clearly shows that the insurance company has agreed that the stated amount is the value of the item, that amount is merely the limit of the company's liability and the *actual* value must be established *after* the loss occurs. This means that the company will not pay more for that item than it would cost to replace it at the time of loss.

We frequently find a coinsurance clause applying to either real or personal property. A credit, in the form of a rate reduction, is given for this clause because it is to the advantage of the insurance underwriters as well as the insuring public to have property insured in an amount approaching its full valuation. Although this clause is used in policies covering many different hazards, the application of its use to a fire policy covering a building will be used as an example.

Most fire policies covering buildings under city fire department protection are written with a coinsurance clause, usually 80 or 90 percent. To comply with this clause, the insured is required to maintain insurance equal to 80 or 90 percent of the value of the building insured. If the amount of insurance fulfills this requirement, the full amount of any loss is recovered (limited, of course, by the amount of the insurance policy). Many people seem to have the impression that an 80 percent coinsurance clause means that the insured will only collect 80 percent of his loss, but this is not true; it is only where the insurance falls below the percentage of value required that any penalty is involved. To see how this clause actually works in practice, consider a building, the value of which (at the time of loss) is $10,000, insured under an 80 percent coinsurance clause. Under the terms of the coinsurance clause, the insurance recovery would be reduced proportionately, *if the insurance is below $8,000* (80 percent of the valuation). In other words, if the insurance is $6,000, the recovery would be 6/8 times the loss. This would have an effect only on partial losses because, if the loss is total, the coinsurance clause would limit recovery to 6/8 times $10,000 or $7,500, which exceeds the policy amount of $6,000. Recovery in this case would be limited by the face amount of the policy, or $6,000.

We can appreciate what would happen if coinsurance clauses were not used. Many people, particularly where there is good public fire protection, would be willing to gamble that a fire in their building would be extinguished by the fire department before extensive damage resulted. They might feel that insurance at 25 percent or 50 percent of the value was adequate. If this were done generally, the premiums produced would be inadequate to cover losses and rates would have to be increased. Thus the prudent man who wished to be fully protected would pay more than his share of insurance costs.

This same principle is applied to insurance covering other perils. The percentage of coinsurance required will vary depending on experience in that line of insurance. For example, in sprinkler leakage insurance, damage is caused ordinarily by the malfunction of one sprinkler head and is confined to an area which is ordinarily a small percentage of the whole. The sprinkler leakage manual will quote a rate for use with no coinsurance and will give varying degrees of credit for coinsurance ranging from 5 percent to 80 percent. In arriving at building valuations for coinsurance purposes, it should be observed that the coinsurance clause in its application excludes certain values. These are such things as foundations below the lowest basement floor, cost of excavations, underground piping, etc.

In arriving at valuations, the librarian has available several different facilities. Every large city has many firms qualified to do excellent appraisal work, and the insurance agent may be called upon to recommend one or more. It must be kept in mind that no appraisal is binding on an insurance company, but a valuation made by a reputable company will be very persuasive in establishing a value at the time the appraisal was made, if not at the time of loss.

In establishing building values, there are alternative methods which should produce satisfactory results without incurring the expense of an actual appraisal. If the original cost of construction is known, it is quite simple for an engineer to apply trend factors of the interim changes in building costs and arrive at present-day replacement cost and actual cash value. It is worth a great deal to make sure that the library's insurance agent has available, either directly or through a company connection, the services of a good engineer. This engineer may also, ordinarily without charge, establish a satisfactory valuation by using average cost factors for the type of construction against the square footage of floor area. These methods produce only estimates, but a good engineer can arrive at a valuation with surprising accuracy.

If one considers the fact that contractors, in making bids for the construction of a new building, will vary thousands of dollars from the lowest bid to the highest, it can be seen that there is no such thing as a definite dollar figure for such valuations.

The problem of valuation is not limited to producing a proper valuation on a given date; a realistic valuation is necessary for the purpose of maintaining insurance at a proper level *between* the times of re-evaluation. Rapid changes in labor and material costs may change building and fixtures values significantly during a policy period, and the application of the coinsurance clause might result in a penalty. Some states make provisions in certain classes of risks for substituting an *agreed-amount clause* for the coinsurance provision. Under this plan, a periodic affidavit of values is made by the insured and the company will usually specify that 90 percent of that value will comply with the coinsurance provision. This agreement must ordinarily be extended each year by the filing of a new affidavit and the adjustment of the agreed-amount clause.

A problem of special concern to the librarian is the valuation and proper insurance of books, fine arts (including rare books, paintings, statuary, and other property of a similar nature), and such business records as card catalog systems and shelf lists. Several articles have been written in recent years which give a thorough discussion of the problems entailed and methods that have been used to solve them.[1]

Each library will have its own problem of placing a value on its card catalog depending upon factors affecting the methods of reproduction, such as the existence of duplicate records, by microfilm or otherwise. Books do not offer the same problem and, in the case of most library materials the recommended procedure is to arrive at an average value per book in each of a number of categories, such as adult fiction, adult non-fiction, juveniles, reference books, etc. This value may be arrived at by taking the average present-day replacement cost new and deducting an average amount for depreciation or adding an average amount for appreciation.

The discussion of contemporary insurance practice will show that property such as books or business records may be insured on an agreed-amount basis. In other words, the insurance company will agree on the value per book in each category and the value per card in catalog systems. This greatly reduces the difficulty of arriving at the amount of loss, and if proper valuations have been made in advance, a very satisfactory loss recovery should be made.

## Specific as opposed to blanket coverage

There are various ways in which items of property may be grouped in an insurance policy. *Specific insurance* refers to the situation in which a separate amount of insurance is applied to each item, either by writing separate policies or by enumerating each item with a separate amount of insurance on the policy form. *Blanket insurance* designates the case in which two or more items are combined under a single amount of insurance. Blanket coverage may combine items at more than one location (blanket as to location) as in the case where there are several buildings and the

[1] See: Charles W. Mixer, "Columbia Insures Its Main Card Catalog," *Library Journal*, LXXXII (October 1, 1957), 2304-11; Germaine Krettek, "What You Should Know About Library Insurance," *Library Journal*, LXXXII (October 1, 1957), 2301-3; H. Vail Deale, "Insurance Re-evaluation," *Library Journay*, LXXX (December 15, 1955), 2814-18; Mixer, "New Insurance for Library Collections," *Library Journal*, LXXIX (September 15, 1954), 1539-43; Mixer, "Insurance Evaluation of a University Library's Collections," *College and Research Libraries*, XIII (January, 1952), 18-23, 29; Donald K. Campbell and Seranush Jaffarian, "Insuring a Public Library's Books," *Wilson Library Bulletin*, XVIII (September, 1943), 44-47; W. G. Rich, "Insuring and Placing Insurable Values on Your Library Collection," *Special Libraries*, XXXIII (February, 1942), 49-57. See also, Appendix G and Appendix H in the present volume, and Dorothea M. Singer, *The Insurance of Libraries* (Chicago: American Library Association, 1946), 27-39.

buildings or contents are all insured in one blanket amount of insurance. On the other hand, blanket insurance may combine different types of property at a single location. When one item of insurance is written covering all contents, it is really blanket coverage combining furniture and fixtures with stock or merchandise. If the choice is made to write a specific policy covering certain items, such as books or fine arts, it is important that the policy providing insurance on the general contents be amended to exclude these items. Otherwise, what is called a "non-concurrency" will exist. Non-concurrency occurs when a certain property is insured differently under two different contracts. This makes a loss adjustment difficult and frequently results in an unfavorable recovery by the insured.

## Named-peril and all-risk policies

It is necessary to make reference to the historical development of insurance in order to understand the difference in treatment between named-peril policies and all-risk policies. Two important branches of property insurance have developed over the years. Until modern times these were entirely independent. One branch started about the time of the Great Fire of London, when it was brought forcibly to mind that fire could wipe out a person's financial resources and also that this risk could be shared by many through the use of insurance. As insurance companies developed they gradually added coverages, such as windstorm and explosion, and this process has continued to the present so that there are still long lists of perils, each with its definition and each with its exclusions.

The other great branch of property insurance was developed to provide protection for the property of merchants and received its greatest impetus at Lloyd's in London. Since ships at sea frequently never reached port and the cause of loss could not be surely determined, it was only natural to insure against all risks of physical loss or damage except those which might be specifically excluded. This procedure has continued through the years and, when commerce expanded into railroad and motor truck shipments, the marine companies continued to insure them under what came to be known as "inland marine" insurance. The aggressive marine underwriters still were not satisfied and gradually expanded to insure goods stored in warehouses and many other types of property which had always been in the private realm of the fire insurance companies.

Finally, in order to settle all of the bitter disputes arising between the fire and marine companies, an "inland marine definition" was promulgated, which spelled out in detail exactly how far the marine companies could go in writing their inland marine contracts.

In modern times, inland marine policies are sometimes written on an all-risk form and sometimes on a named-peril form.

There is an entirely different emphasis in the named-peril as opposed to the all-risk approach. In order to have coverage under a named-peril policy, it must be shown that the loss falls within the definition of coverage under the policy. On the other hand, the all-risk policy will cover any physical loss, unless it can be shown that there is an applicable exclusion. It will be seen how some of these inland marine policies may be useful in insuring movable property with respect to libraries.

## Insurance practices: direct damage to property

In this section, the traditional methods of insuring library property will be discussed without going into some of the recent developments which are even now making drastic changes in historical insurance methods. These recent developments, some of which cut across the traditional dividing lines between insurance categories, will be discussed in Chapter 13. Here the librarian will be given some acquaintance with older forms which are still in force. This will also provide an insurance foundation which will enable the librarian better to grasp the significance of the new forms. Again, this is not intended to be an exhaustive treatise on insurance; responsibility should be fixed squarely on the library's insurance agency to make sure that the librarian is kept informed of all insurance coverages applicable to his situation.

The information given here is presented at a general level, but it should serve to give the librarian a sufficient familiarity with general insurance practices so that he can more profitably discuss his insurance problems with his insurance representative.

## Fire, extended coverage, and vandalism insurance

For many years, fire insurance companies have issued policies with an extended coverage endorsement and perhaps a vandalism endorsement attached. In most cases, this gave all of the available insurance protection that most people felt was necessary. The basic fire policy, which for many years covered both fire and lightning, may be extended to cover also the following perils under an extended coverage endorsement:

Windstorm (subject to a deductible in some states)
Hail (subject to a deductible in some states)
Explosion
Riot (riot attending a strike, and civil commotion)
Aircraft damage
Vehicle damage
Smoke damage

Under windstorm coverage, there is an exclusion of damage by frost (or cold weather or ice), and snow or sleet, whether driven by wind or not. There is also an exclusion of damage done to the interior of a building caused by rain, snow, sand, or dust, unless the building first sustains actual damage to the roof or walls by direct force of wind or hail. This is principally to preclude claims for losses in which windows have been left open or where there is some defect in construction which allows rain or snow or other foreign material to enter. In some localities, dust driven by a dust storm will enter a building regardless of how tightly it is constructed.

There is also an exclusion of certain types of property, an exclusion which varies from state to state. Property excluded from coverage includes such things as windmills, wind pumps, and their towers, silos, signs, metal smokestacks, and buildings in process of construction. Outside radio and television antennae and towers are frequently excluded also. On some excluded items, specific insurance may be obtained at higher rates.

Under explosion insurance, the principal concern is with the provision commonly called the "boiler exclusion clause." This exclusion applies to the explosion, rupture, or bursting of steam boilers, steam pipes, steam turbines, or steam engines, or damage caused by the rotating parts of machinery through centrifugal force which sometimes causes the machines to fly apart. In most states, under the latest revised forms, this exclusion only applies if the object causing the damage is owned by, leased by, or actually operated under the control of the insured. Most states specify that damage from "concussion, unless caused by explosion" is not covered. This makes it clear that the so-called sonic boom shock waves set up by aircraft passing through the sound barrier are not considered explosions. There has long been a provision that electric arcing, water hammer, and bursting of water pipes are not covered as explosions.

Coverage for riot and civil commotion encompasses loss or damage from pillage and looting during and at the place of riot, including riot attending a strike. It also covers damage done by striking employees while the premises are occupied by the striking employees (sit-down strikes). Acts of destruction committed by others (i.e., persons other than sit-down strikers) are not covered unless they occur during an actual riot. There are a number of court cases that have dealt with the problem of "What constitutes a riot."

Most states have a requirement under aircraft and vehicle coverage that there be actual contact between the aircraft or vehicle and the insured property. This excludes such losses as damage caused by a truck hitting a power pole and knocking it against a building, or rocks flipped up by automobile tires, or "sonic boom."

Objects falling from aircraft, however, are usually included under the perils covered. There is also an exclusion of damage caused by any vehicle owned or operated by an insured or any tenant of the insured; however, an aircraft does not fall under the definition of vehicle so this exclusion does not apply to aircraft. In addition, there is a provision that excludes vehicle-caused damage to fences, driveways, walks, or lawns, regardless of who is driving the vehicle.

Smoke damage covers only smoke due to the sudden, unusual, and faulty operation of a heating or cooking unit which is attached to a chimney by means of a smoke pipe. Smoke from fireplaces or industrial apparatus is specifically excluded. The sudden and faulty operation of an oil-fired furnace will sometimes fill the building with an oily smoke which causes extensive damage, and this is the type of loss contemplated by the coverage. Smoke damage caused by "hostile fires" (see Glossary definition of "direct loss by fire") is covered under the basic fire policy.

In addition to the exclusions under each peril, there are three general exclusions:

(1) The nuclear exclusion, which excludes losses resulting from nuclear reaction, radiation, or radioactive contamination;

(2) War risk exclusion;

(3) Water damage exclusion, which includes damage caused by:

   (a) Flood, surface water, waves, tidal water or tidal waves, overflow of streams or other bodies of water, or spray from any of them, all whether driven by wind or not.

   (b) Water which backs up through sewers or drains.

   (c) Water below the surface of the ground including that which exerts pressures on or flows, seeps, or leaks through sidewalks, driveways, foundations, walls or floors.

Vandalism and malicious mischief coverage may be added to a fire policy to which an extended coverage endorsement is already attached. It covers willful and malicious damage or destruction of the described property.

The usual exclusions apply to glass breakage, pilferage, or theft, and the regular "boiler exclusion clause," as described under extended coverage. There is also a thirty-day vacancy limitation which means that the vandalism coverage is suspended after the building has been continuously vacant for a period longer than thirty days.

Thus far we have discussed the perils insured under a fire policy with an extended coverage endorsement and a vandalism and malicious mischief endorsement attached. To complete the picture, there must be a description of the property to be insured; thus a general discussion of the characteristics of typical insuring clauses for buildings and contents will be useful.

The building clause will insure the building and its foundations and will enumerate components such as machinery used for the service of the building, plumbing, electric wiring, and so forth, all while contained therein. The clause will also enumerate removable items such as screens, storm windows, and doors if these are the property of the owner of the building. Very often, items such as awnings, signs, and metal smokestacks will be listed to provide coverage where the windstorm and hail provision of the extended coverage endorsement excludes these items ". . . unless liability therefor is assumed under the form attached to this policy." Ordinarily no provision is made under the building item for covering outside improvements such as sidewalks and fences or signs not attached to the building. If these are to be insured, special care should be exercised to see that coverage is included. Signs may be quite valuable and, frequently, specific all-risk coverage may be desirable under a separate inland marine policy. In conjunction with the coinsurance clause usually appearing in these policies, a clause will be found (see the discussion of coinsurance in the section on valuation) which excludes foundations and other property not ordinarily subject to damage.

Normally, little difficulty is experienced in the adjustment of building losses where there are adequate amounts of insurance to cover the values.

Under an ordinary fire insurance policy, the contents of a library will be insured under a general contents item which will insure ". . . all contents and personal property" (except as otherwise excluded) of every description. It will specifically mention signs, awnings, and metal smokestacks when owned by the tenant or lessee and not otherwise specifically insured. It will cover personal property belonging to others (providing the insured is legally liable for it) which is held in trust or on consignment. It is extremely important in cases in which a library has possession of any extensive values of property belonging to others that the responsibility is fixed as to who will insure such property. If the library is to assume responsibility under the contents item, then this must be taken into consideration in arriving at the amount of insurance for coinsurance purposes. If the owner of property in the possession of the library agrees to insure it, the fact does not entirely relieve the library of liability for its damage or destruction. (See the discussion of fire legal liability in the section on liability.) The insurance company's liability for loss to books of account, drawings, card catalog, and other records will not exceed the cost of blank books, blank pages, or other material, plus the actual cost of labor in transcribing or copying such records. Because this provision makes the standard fire insurance policy a very unsatisfactory method of insuring such records, the standard Valuable Papers policy is much to be preferred.

There are usually a number of contents exclusions in standard fire policies, most of which have little real significance for the library. These exclusions have to do with personal property of others which is otherwise insured, or customers' goods in a laundry, or patterns, molds, and forms in a factory. One provision, however, which should be noted is the exclusion of accounts, bills, currency, deeds, evidence of debt, money, securities, aircraft, and motor vehicles and trailers licensed for use on public highways.

A contents policy will often have a small amount of off-premises coverage for property sent out for cleaning or repair. This does not cover property in transit or property on premises owned, leased, or controlled by the insured.

Over the years, fire policies with extended coverage and vandalism and malicious mischief endorsements attached have been very useful in insuring libraries and their contents. They have had to be supplemented, however, with Fine Arts and Valuable Papers policies in order to do the entire job effectively. Because of the failure of such policies to provide the broad coverage required to meet library needs, there have been in recent years some new developments. Even now, policies are being written that more closely tailor the forms to the needs of the library. These will be discussed in Chapters 13 and 14.

*Sprinkler leakage insurance.* The purpose of sprinklers, as was discussed earlier in the book, is to put out fires automatically by releasing water from the sprinkler system at the scene of the fire. The relative desirability of sprinkler systems in a library has been treated elsewhere, but the subject of sprinkler leakage insurance should be mentioned. This indemnifies for loss or damage when there is accidental leakage from the system. If, for example, a prankster set off sprinkler heads in the stacks by holding matches under them, this insurance would pay for any resulting damage. Of course, if the library carried Valuable Papers insurance or similar all-risk coverage on its books, that insurance would apply.

Water damage at the time of fire is covered by the fire policy. The sprinkler leakage policy covers leaking or discharge of water or any other substance from the system as well as damage due to collapse or falling of the sprinkler tank. (There are cases on record in which sprinkler tanks have collapsed and fallen through several floors of a building.)

Coverage is written under a separate sprinkler leakage policy or by attaching a separate sprinkler leakage supplemental contract to the fire policy. Coinsurance on sprinkler leakage, instead of being 80 percent or 90 percent, may be as low as 5 percent, as was pointed out in the discussion of coinsurance.

Substantial credits in premium rates are made for the attachment of the coinsurance provision and a 25 percent coinsurance provision represents a substantial amount of coverage. This is because the ordinary loss will be caused by the faulty operation of only one sprinkler head; this, in most cases, will result in a low percentage loss.

*Water damage insurance.* The librarian is interested in water damage protection chiefly with respect to books and perhaps fine arts, such as paintings, which are especially susceptible to water damage. Also, card catalogs and other records should be protected. A separate water damage policy is probably inapplicable to most libraries. This is because the protection available under the Fine Arts and Valuable Papers policies would include water damage and should be a better method of protecting books and similar property than the alternative of carrying this coverage under a separate water damage policy. While it is true that extensive damage might be done to buildings and equipment by water, it is unlikely that this damage would be of such a magnitude that clean-up and repairs could not be handled without resorting to water damage coverage. Water damage insurance is seldom carried by property owners unless they are particularly susceptible to water damage loss and because of this adverse selection, rates are quite high.

*Earthquake insurance.* Earthquake insurance is handled differently in the Pacific Coast area than in the balance of the country. On the West Coast, earthquake insurance is under the jurisdiction of the fire insurance rating bureaus and is handled through extending the fire policy by an endorsement called the *Earthquake Damage Assumption* endorsement. The endorsement covers the same property as the fire policy and is written for the same amount. There is a deductible of at least 5 percent of the value of the property (not the amount of the policy) and, on some classes of risk, this may be 10 percent or 15 percent. The earthquake coverage is subject to the same coinsurance as the fire policy, which must be at least 70 percent. However, even if the fire policy excludes foundations, they will be covered under the Earthquake Damage Assumption endorsement.

In the rest of the United States, earthquake insurance is written under a separate policy and rates and rules are set forth in a manual supervised by the Inter-Regional Insurance Conference. There is no mandatory deductible clause in the policy, but an optional 2 percent deductible may be added.

At least 50 percent coinsurance is required and there is no exclusion of foundations, which is understandable in view of this type of peril.

*Steam boiler and power plant insurance.* It has been pointed out that, under the explosion coverage of the extended coverage endorsement, there is an exclusion applying to steam boilers and rotating machinery owned or operated by the insured. This exclusion is introduced because such boiler and machinery coverage has always been handled by companies specializing in this field. The inspection work done by these boiler insurance companies is very valuable and its expense accounts for a good proportion of the premium paid. This is a field in which prevention of loss is emphasized far more than indemnity. For the library which owns its own power plant, this is an essential coverage. The form is designed to cover not only damage to the insured property but liability for damage to the property of others.

*Glass insurance.* Glass is covered under the fire and extended coverage endorsement for damage caused by the perils insured. It is, however, excluded under the vandalism endorsement. There are many things which can cause breakage of glass which would not be covered under a fire, extended coverage, and vandalism policy. These risks of damage to glass are often assumed by the insured on the basis that most glass damage from causes other than fire, windstorm, or explosion would result in only minor losses which could be assumed by the insured. However, where there are extensive glass areas or where there are expensive stained glass windows, they are frequently insured under a special glass policy which enumerates the insured windows and places a specific amount of insurance on each. When this is done, these windows should be excluded from the building policy and the building value adjusted accordingly.

*Fine arts insurance.* Fine arts, consisting of paintings, etchings, pictures, tapestries, art glass windows, and other bona fide works of art, may be specifically insured under a Fine Arts policy. Coverage is all risk and scheduled with a separate amount of insurance applying to each article and is written on a valued basis — that is, the amount designated for each article will be the measure of recovery for the loss of that article. Blanket insurance may be written on other property of this type not to exceed 10 percent of the insurance on scheduled items. Recovery on articles under the blanket item will be on an actual cash value basis and subject to a 100 percent coinsurance provision.

Fine arts are covered anywhere in the continental United States or in Canada except at fair grounds or at national or international expositions. Coverage is provided on newly acquired property up to a certain percentage of the policy amount (e.g., 25 percent). This must be reported to the company within ninety days and premiums paid from the date of acquisition.

Property under the Fine Arts policy is subject to the usual exclusions of war risks, nuclear energy, wear and tear, gradual deterioration, moths, vermin, inherent vice, and damage from any repairing, restoring, or retouching process.

There is also a clause excluding breakage of fragile articles. This exclusion may be removed by paying an additional premium.

*Valuable papers and records insurance.* The Valuable Papers policy may be written to cover written or printed records or books and insures on an all-risk basis. It will be seen that rare books may be insured under either a Fine Arts policy or under the Valuable Papers policy.

The property insured under a Valuable Papers policy may be either scheduled on an agreed-amount basis or may be covered in a blanket item on an actual cash-value basis. If property cannot be replaced, it must be scheduled on the agreed-amount basis and cannot be included in the blanket item.

The exclusions under this policy are wear and tear, gradual deterioration, vermin and inherent vice, war risks, nuclear damage, dishonesty of any insured partner, officer, director, or trustee, and (unless caused by lightning) electrical or magnetic injury or erasure of electronic recordings.

It will be noted that employee dishonesty is not excluded except as indicated above. In the case of libraries there is an exclusion of loss from failure of borrowers to return books or valuable papers.

This policy is very useful for insuring all books, papers, and records in a library, particularly the large values represented in card catalog systems.

It is important to be sure that property specifically insured under a Fine Arts policy or Valuable Papers policy is excluded from the general contents coverage.

This policy provides that 10 percent of the total amount of insurance is extended to cover property while being conveyed outside of the premises or while temporarily at other premises, except for storage.

*Transit insurance.* Some of the policies described above provide for coverage of personal property away from the premises. These valuable coverages are limited in amount and frequently have limitations as to where the coverage would apply. The limitations should be studied carefully and it should be determined whether the library is subject to exposures which are not covered and should be. If the library is the possessor of valuable paintings or other works of art which might be exhibited at a fair or exposition, it would be desirable to take special care to see that such materials are insured. If the library has substantial values in books which are at a bindery or other outside location, it should be determined if the bindery is assuming liability for any damage while books are in their possession and if not, whether special insurance arrangements are needed.

*Insurance for cameras and projection machines.* If cameras or projection machines are owned by the library, they may be insured under a camera floater policy. The standard camera floater policy covers all risks, anywhere in the world. The exclusions are few and pertain to war risk, nuclear radiation, or wear and tear, gradual deterioration, moths, vermin, or inherent vice. The property is scheduled with an amount listed for each separate item. The company's liability, however, is limited to the actual cash value at the time of loss.

*Automobile physical damage insurance.* The operation of automobiles is inherently hazardous and for this reason automobile insurance has been treated as a specialty. Automobile insurance policies have their own particular forms and automobiles are excluded from other insurance policies covering property or liability of a general nature.

Ordinarily, when one or more automobiles are owned by a husband and wife, the cars are insured in the same company and usually both the physical damage and liability insurance are combined in a single combination policy. Where a partnership or corporation (or a library owning automobiles) is concerned, it is much better practice to write a comprehensive automobile liability policy which automatically picks up all of the liability exposures; this will be discussed under the section on liability insurance. The physical damage coverage is then provided under a separate policy which schedules each vehicle owned or leased which is to be covered.

It is important, in scheduling vehicles under an automobile policy, to make sure that nothing is left out. Some types of motorized equipment are included under other policies, such as the contents policy, and would not have to be scheduled under the automobile policy. The typical contents policy excludes "motor vehicles and trailers *licensed for use on public highways*" which means that any motor vehicle or trailer not so licensed would be covered. This coverage, however, is limited to the perils insured and if the contents coverage is for fire, extended coverage, and vandalism, there would not be coverage, of course, for other losses, such as theft or collision. Also, there may be yard maintenance equipment stored on the premises or in another building. If the intent is to cover these under the contents form, limited to the perils under that policy, care should be taken to make sure that the location description under that policy is adequate to cover them.

After consideration has been given to proper protection of motor vehicles and equipment which are to be insured otherwise, the remaining vehicles should be scheduled under the automobile policy in which physical damage is insured under two optional sections.

Comprehensive coverage insures virtually all risks of damage to the insured automobile except collision. The latter was originally available only to private passenger automobiles but is now available to commercial vehicles. It replaces the more limited coverages previously insured separately under fire and theft and certain additional specified perils. These are still available on most automobile policies as separate items but they are rarely used. In some states, comprehensive coverage may be written with a $50 deductible clause applying to some perils.

The collision insuring agreement covers "all direct and accidental loss of or damage to the automobile caused by collision of the automobile with another object or by upset of the automobile. . . ."

Collision insurance is ordinarily subject to a $50 or $100 deductible for each loss. Since collision losses are relatively frequent, this elimination of small claims substantially reduces insurance costs from what they would otherwise be. Comprehensive insurance is rarely made subject to a deductible since the frequency of these claims is much less. In order to clarify coverage and the application of the deductible in borderline cases, there are certain losses deductible such as glass breakage, missile damage, falling objects, fire, and theft — which are brought within the comprehensive coverage by definition. This eliminates any application of the collision deductible in these claims.

The ordinary automobile policy provides automatic protection on substitute or newly acquired automobiles providing they are reported to the company within 30 days after date of delivery. It is important that the schedule of insured automobiles be kept up to date. Any trailers should be listed in the schedule as these would fall under the automobile coverage.

A careful check on *exclusions* should be made. The standard automobile policy excludes coverage while the automobile is used as a public or livery conveyance. It also excludes coverage on vehicles where there is an encumbrance not shown by the policy. Wear and tear, freezing, and mechanical or electrical failure are excluded. Damage to tires except by theft is excluded.

## Insurance practices: contingent coverages

A general discussion of contingent insurance coverages will enable the librarian to see where these may be used advantageously in the library insurance program. The use of some of these will depend on whether or not the building is owned by the library. Others are of doubtful use because, for example, earning a profit is not a factor in operating a library.

When an insured peril results in damage to a building and its contents, a certain length of time is required to restore the building and contents to the same condition as before the loss. For this reason, there is not only direct loss due to physical destruction of property but also an indirect loss resulting from the loss of use during the period of restoration. The value of this *loss of use* may be insured in several different ways.

*Rents and rental value insurance.* A building owner may insure either rents or rental value. If he owns a building and leases it to someone else, he will suffer an actual loss of rental income if the building is rendered untenantable by fire or other peril. If he occupies the building himself, he will not have a rental income to insure, but he does have an insurable interest in the rental value of the building since he would have to pay rent for suitable space if he did not own his own building.

Rents or rental value usually are insured for six-, nine-, or twelve-month rental values. This does not mean that the policy itself is written for that period; the policy may be written for one, three, or five years. The policy written for a six-month rental value would provide that not more than one-sixth of the policy amount would be collectible in any one-month period, and, similarly, the others would provide for either a one-ninth or one-twelfth limitation on the monthly recovery.

*Extra expense insurance.* The usual commercial or manufacturing operation will carry business interruption insurance, which will compensate for loss of profits and continuing expenses during a period of restoration following damage caused by an insured peril. This has little application to the library operation where there ordinarily is little or no revenue. Another coverage which is complementary to business interruption insurance is extra expense insurance, which may have an important application in some library situations.

The usual commercial application of extra expense insurance is in those types of operations, such as newspaper publication or milk distribution, where uninterrupted operation is very important. The policy will pay any necessary extra expense incurred by the insured in order to carry on his normal operations. Any extra expense incurred to expedite the restoration of property in order to reduce the amount of loss under the policy would also be covered. In those cases where the use of library facilities would justify the expenditure of large sums to expedite the restoration of operations, this type of insurance should have a worthwhile application.

*Improvements and betterments insurance.* An insurable interest in improvements and betterments arises when a building is owned by one party and leased by a second party. Any improvements which become a part of the building immediately become the property of the building owner, and, as such, should be covered by him as part of the building value. In addition to this, the tenant who installs such building improvements has an insurable interest arising from his right to enjoy the use of these improvements during the term of his lease. If substantial improvements have been made by a tenant under a long-term lease and a fire results in the destruction of the improvements, or in a cancellation of the lease, the tenant will suffer monetary loss.

There is not entire agreement on the amount of loss sustained by the tenant. It is generally agreed that, in the event a fire or other peril damages the property to the extent that the lease is cancelled, then the loss is measured by amortizing the cost of the improvement from the date it was made to the expiration of the lease and taking the unamortized portion at the date of loss as the measure of loss.

If, on the other hand, the lease is not cancelled by the loss in question but the improvements are physically destroyed, another situation arises. If the terms of the lease do not require the building owner to restore the improvements, it would seem that the tenant must restore them in order to properly enjoy his tenancy for the balance of the term. Where substantial values are involved in building improvements, this subject should be explored very carefully with the insurance company.

In the case of fixtures attached to the building, which fall under the classification of "trade fixtures" and are removable at the termination of lease, no problem should arise; such fixtures may be covered with the contents. Where the building is not owned by the library but is owned by a closely affiliated organization, many of the difficulties of properly insuring tenant's improvements may be eliminated by proper drawing of leases or by collateral agreements on the part of the building owner to restore the improvements.

*Leasehold interest insurance.* Leasehold interest sometimes arises in connection with a long-term lease that has been in force for a number of years. If, because of the increased valuation of the leased property since the term of the lease began, the monthly rental under the lease is substantially lower than it would be under a new lease for the same or similar property, there will be a leasehold interest value. The measure of this leasehold interest is the difference between the actual rent paid under the lease and the rent that would have to be paid under a new lease for the same or similar property. This differential in monthly rental is multiplied by the number of unexpired months of the lease and is discounted for an interest factor (usually 4 percent) so that a lump sum payment under the policy terms would be the equivalent of the monthly leasehold interest spread over the remaining term of the lease.

*Insurance for contingent liability from building laws.* A special problem arises when a building does not comply with the existing building code. In the case of old buildings, a revision of the building code since they were built results in this type of noncompliance, and the law usually provides that buildings which are destroyed beyond a certain point (e.g., 50 percent) must be torn down and rebuilt according to the current building code. The standard fire policy provides only for paying an amount equal to the value of the destroyed portion and leaves several areas uncovered. First, there is the loss of the value of the undamaged portion of the building. Second, there is the actual expense of tearing down that portion of the building, less any salvage; and, third, there is the increased cost of putting up a building that will meet the requirements of the present building code.

Several special endorsements are in use which take care of these losses in whole or in part. In some states, these endorsements are called "demolition endorsements," or "demolition and increased cost of construction endorsements." In other states, they are called "contingent liability from operation of building laws." Some of these cover one of the problem areas and not others and there is sometimes a variation in effect when the building is insured on a replacement cost basis. All of these things should be carefully considered in setting up a library's insurance program.

# CHAPTER 9

# Protection Against Dishonesty

The subject of protection against dishonesty cuts across both insurance and bonding. Policies cover losses resulting from the dishonesty of individuals who may be outsiders (insured under burglary, robbery, theft, or larceny policies), or employees entrusted with the property which they embezzle (covered under fidelity bonds). These types of protection will be discussed in separate paragraphs. Prior to this, however, some general comments on the over-all subject of dishonesty insurance are in order.

First of all, the dishonesty loss problem is not a serious one in libraries. Ordinarily books are not as attractive to thieves as are furs, jewelry, and other valuable merchandise. To be attractive to a thief, property must be valuable, easily transportable, and readily convertible into money. Books may be subject to pilferage or non-return by borrowers but, although this is a subject of concern to librarians, it is not considered a subject for insurance by underwriters and this type of loss is therefore excluded from insurance policies.

Libraries ordinarily do not handle large sums of money or securities which would give rise to theft or defalcation by employees.

Rare books or fine arts might be the subject of theft, but we have seen that under the Fine Arts and Valuable Papers policies, the broad protection available for these properties includes theft and is a much better method of insuring them.

Although dishonesty insurance is not of major concern to the librarian, a knowledge of some of the terms used and basic coverages available will be discussed. Many dishonesty or crime policies today are packaged contracts combining several basic coverages to fit a particular type of risk. It would be of no use to a librarian to have an analysis of all of these various combinations; thus the discussion will be limited to the general characteristics of the basic elements.

## The difference between insurance and bonding

The question often arises as to the distinction between *insurance* and *bonding*. An insurance policy is a two-party contract by which the insurance company agrees to indemnify the insured for financial loss arising out of a certain event. While it is true that a third party may be involved (as in liability insurance), that third party is not a party to the contract.

Bonding is fundamentally different in that it involves three parties. By definition, a bond is a guaranty by the surety that he will meet an obligation due the obligee by the principal if the principal fails in his duty. To explain this: The concept of bonding arises out of the situation in which Person A (the principal) owes a duty to Person B (the obligee). The performance of this duty is guaranteed by an individual or company (the surety), by issuing a bond which states that if Person A fails in his duty, the surety will perform the duty or compensate Person B for his resulting loss. Bonding arose in antiquity and is mentioned in the Bible. Originally it was a personal contract of guaranty and the surety may have pledged something other than money — even to his life (as in the legend of Damon and Pythias). Today bonding has been taken over largely by corporations and the pledges are always on a monetary basis.

In present day insurance and bonding practices, several major divisions have developed:

(1) Financial guaranty bonds are commonly referred to as "surety bonds" while coverages against employee dishonesty are commonly referred to as "fidelity bonds" although technically all bonds are surety bonds. These so-called surety bonds cover a wide variety of financial obligations such as: performance bonds for contractors, court bonds required in legal proceedings, public official bonds required by statute or municipal ordinance, and many others.

(2) Fidelity bonds, which guarantee an employer against dishonesty of his employees.

(3) Forgery bonds, which are more in the nature of insurance policies than bonds, although written by surety companies.

(4) Blanket bonds, which cover a wide variety of hazards including burglary, robbery, or theft but always include fidelity of employees.

## Burglary, robbery, theft

Burglary is defined as breaking and entering for the purpose of stealing property when the premises are not open for business. One policy in general use for merchants, but of little use to the librarian, is the open-stock burglary policy which covers merchandise, furniture, and fixtures against burglary. There is also a safe burglary policy which covers insured property while it is within a described safe and the safe is closed and locked by all combination and time locks. With respect to payment of claims, all burglary policies require visible signs of forcible entry.

Robbery has a very technical meaning and the policies give their own definitions rather than leaving this kind of loss to the general interpretations of common law. A typical policy would define robbery as "the taking of the insured property . . .

"(1) by violence inflicted on a messenger or custodian;

"(2) by putting a messenger or custodian in fear of violence;

"(3) by any other overt, felonious act committed in the presence of a messenger or custodian and of which he was actually cognizant (e.g., snatching a satchel or other container);

"(4) from the person or direct care and custody of a messenger or custodian who has been killed or rendered unconscious."

Money and securities destruction coverage covers such destruction from any cause. It insures the money and securities within the premises during business hours and while located within a locked safe or vault outside of business hours. Wrongful abstraction or disappearance is not covered and there must be evidence of actual physical destruction.

The broad-form money and securities policy covers not only actual destruction but also disappearance or wrongful abstractions of money and securities. It also insures other property against loss caused by safe burglary or robbery within the premises.

The "office burglary and robbery policy" is a package policy which provides a variety of burglary and robbery coverages in small amounts. The latest standard policy covers losses up to $250 on each of six different divisions, none of which may be omitted:

(1) Robbery of money and securities from within premises;

(2) Theft inside the premises. Covers loss of office equipment by theft within the premises. Theft is any act of stealing and includes burglary, robbery, and any other felonious taking of property;

(3) Safe burglary, which covers money and securities against burglary from a locked safe within the premises or up to $100 for burglary from within the premises but outside of the safe or vault;

(4) Robbery outside the premises which covers money securities and office equipment against robbery from a messenger outside of the premises;

(5) Theft of money and securities from a night depository or from the living quarters of a messenger;

(6) Damage to the premises and to money securities and office equipment by an insured crime.

## Forgery bonds

Forgery bonds are of little interest to the librarian but two of them which may have possible application are listed for reference:

Depositors forgery bond — This covers checks, drafts, and other outgoing instruments issued by or purported to have been issued by the insured. The bond may be endorsed to cover checks and other instruments received by the insured.

Securities bonds — These cover securities which have been forged, counterfeited, raised or otherwise altered, or lost or stolen.

## Fidelity bonds

Fidelity bonds guarantee an employer against loss through dishonesty on the part of his employees. Originally, bonds were issued individually on each employee to be bonded. The name-schedule bond was developed next by which one bond was issued covering a schedule of named employees. Later a position-scheduled bond was brought out whereby employees were not named but the policy covered any occupant of a scheduled position. Finally, bonds were issued on a blanket basis whereby all employees were covered. Two forms of blanket bond are in common use (not counting specialized bonds for financial institutions); these are the blanket position and the commercial blanket bonds. Either of these may be used where a blanket bond is desired although there are certain technical differences which may make one or the other more desirable in any particular case.

## Comprehensive DDD policy

The comprehensive DDD policy is an example of the packaging of individual coverages in the insurance and fidelity bond field. This is a policy with sixteen different optional insuring agreements each with its separate limits. These are fidelity coverage, premises coverage, outside coverage (both inside and outside protection are under the terms of the money and securities broad form), robbery from armored cars and theft from the home of a messenger, money orders and counterfeit papers coverage, depositors forgery, forgery on incoming instruments, burglary on merchandise, paymaster robbery, paymaster broad form (inside and outside, or inside only), burglary and theft on merchandise, warehouse receipts forgery, securities safe deposit box coverage, burglary on office equipment, theft on office equipment, and paymaster robbery — premises only.

# CHAPTER 10

## Liability Insurance

There is one great category of potential financial loss in addition to loss of owned property; that is the possibility that a person may become obligated to pay money as damages for injury to another person or his property.

Liability to another may be created in several different ways and these are customarily divided into "contracts" and "torts." With respect to contracts, if Party A makes an agreement with Party B, either express or implied, Party B may have a legal claim against A either by virtue of damages sustained from the breach of the contract or through some agreement A had made to indemnify B under certain circumstances.

The subject of "torts" has to do with non-contractual liability and, by definition, a "tort" is a legal wrong. It is a violation of the inherent rights that another person has by virtue of being a member of an organized society. Torts may be intentional or unintentional. If one willfully violates another person's rights by shooting him or by stealing his property, it is easy to see how the former will be held liable to the other person for his resulting damages. In addition to this civil liability, a person may be guilty of violating a criminal code, but this would be liability to the state and would be in addition to one's civil liability to the injured party.

A great part of tort liability arises out of unintentional acts rather than willful acts, and this part is treated under the laws of negligence. The law requires that everyone act as a reasonably prudent person would act under the existing conditions. If a man's failure to exercise this required degree of care results in injury to another person or damage to his property, the former will be responsible to the injured person.

The law not only holds a person responsible for his own acts, but, if he has another person acting as his agent or employee, he will also be held responsible for acts committed by those agents during the course of their employment. This is a brief and simple statement of the legal doctrine of "Respondeat Superior."

There also may be personal liability of the trustees of a trust when they are responsible for its control. Many court cases have held that it was not the intent of the trust that the trust property should be used to pay damages incurred by the negligence of the trustees. It is good practice to make sure that trustees are named as additional insureds under the terms of a liability contract.

## Liability of charitable organizations

The state of the law as to the liability of charitable, nonprofit organizations, in which category most libraries would be included, is in such a state of confusion and flux that any institution which takes the stand that it does not need liability insurance is courting trouble.

The states are not in agreement on their decisions. Some hold that charitable non-profit organizations are on the same footing and have the same liabilities as other organizations. Other states hold that such charitable organizations are liable to those who pay for services and to members of the general public, but not to beneficiaries who pay less than full value for their services. Some states have their own specific statutes and there have been cases where statutes, limiting the liability of charitable non-profit organizations, have been held unconstitutional. Some states have held that the carrying of liability insurance waives the immunity to liability that such organizations otherwise would have. In these states, many charitable non-profit organizations have taken the attitude that they have a moral obligation to bear the cost of injuries resulting from the negligence of their employees and have voluntarily carried liability insurance. In these cases, most insurance companies will, on request, issue an endorsement to the effect that they will not avail themselves of the defense of the legal immunity of the insured.

Sometimes slight variations in the facts have resulted in the same state ruling differently in two different cases. In several states, old decisions exempting charitable non-profit organizations from liability have been overthrown by more recent cases.

The tendency seems to be toward expanding the liability of such organizations. Many attorneys are aware of this trend and it seems reasonable to assume that there will be more attempts to over-rule previous decisions in other states which have restricted the liability of these organizations in the past. Even if these attempts should be unsuccessful, the defense provision of a liability policy could be an important benefit.

## Care, custody, and control clause

The usual liability policy will contain among its exclusions a statement to the effect that the policy does not apply to the injury to or destruction of property in the care, custody, or control of the insured. It will also exclude property occupied by or rented to the insured.

There has always been the feeling that, in many cases where one person has possession or control over property belonging to another, he should exercise a higher degree of care than ordinary, and this has been coupled with the feeling that in most instances it would be against public policy and would encourage carelessness to transfer the liability to an insurance carrier.

Under the law of bailments, a bailment is created when possession of personal property owned by one party (bailor) is transferred to another party (bailee) for some particular purpose under an agreement (contract), express or implied. An example is a library sending a consignment of books to a bindery. Much has been said about the different degrees of care required of the bailee depending on whether the bailment is for the benefit of the bailor, for the bailee, or for their mutual benefit. More important, however, is the rule that in a suit for damages the bailor need only show that the property was delivered to the bailee in good condition and that it was not returned in that condition. It is then necessary for the bailee to prove that he was not negligent. This reversal of the usual burden of proof is also applied to a great extent to real property under the control of the insured. The general rule arises from the fact that the bailee should be in a position to know all of the facts surrounding the treatment and care taken of property entrusted to him, while it is very difficult for the owner to prove negligence in the case of an unexplained loss when his property is in the possession of another.

All of these considerations have led insurance companies to employ this exclusion except as to certain specified conditions. Examples are side-track agreements or the use of elevators. There are also certain specified perils to which the insurance companies have made an exception. It will be recalled that, in the discussion of property insurance, the contents form may include property on the premises, property belonging to another party, for which the insured is legally liable. When the property is insured in this manner, the insured has usually agreed to be responsible for damage from the insured perils and the question of negligence does not even arise. The insurance company settles the loss on the property belonging to others on the same basis as on the insured's own property.

Later on — in the discussion of fire legal liability and sprinkler leakage and water damage legal liability — it will be shown how these specific perils may be insured to cover property in the care, custody, and control of the insured.

## "Caused by accident"

Most public liability policies restrict their coverage to liability of the insured for bodily injury or property damage "caused by accident." This language will cover most cases that may arise but there is always a possibility that an insured may be held liable in a situation which may not have been caused by accident. Not all courts are in agreement in their definition of "accident." Most of them agree that an accident is an undesigned, sudden, and unexpected event, but they do not seem to agree as to whether the event must be traceable to a definite time, place, and cause.

Several controversial cases have hinged on whether a *repeated* exposure to a certain condition is an accident. Other cases have been argued on the basis that the result was the natural consequence of a certain act and therefore not an accident. Others have turned on the question as to whether the liability arose from a failure to perform a contractual obligation (i.e., to perform a satisfactory job) rather than from accident.

Sometimes insurance companies are requested to remove the "caused by accident" clause, and the National Bureau of Casualty Underwriters has published an advisory clause. The latter clause has been used in some cases on a specially rated basis. Specific provisions are made not to cover injuries intentionally inflicted by the insured or at his direction.

## Insuring the liability exposure

It is apparent from the discussion of liability that not all of one's liability can be transferred to an insurance carrier. The exposures to liability that can be transferred to an insurance company have been divided into different classifications for easier handling.

There are two general liability forms in use, one of which is called the "Manufacturers and Contractors Liability Form." This division is made mainly because of differences in rating procedures and minor differences in coverage. As the names imply, the Manufacturers and Contractors form deals with manufacturing and contracting risks, whereas the large bulk of mercantile and office risks fall under the Owners, Landlords, and Tenants form. Both of these forms are on a scheduled basis to provide coverage for *premises and operations, elevator, products, and limited contractual liability.* Our discussion will be confined to the Owners, Landlords, and Tenants form with which libraries would be principally concerned.

The basic liability policy excludes automobiles, watercraft, and aircraft since these are separate liability areas, each with its own problems and rating procedures. The standard policy used by most companies defines "automobile" as a land motor vehicle, trailer, or semi-trailer. There are certain types of motor vehicles which are excluded from this definition and therefore brought within the scope of the basic policy. The one of most interest to libraries is "other equipment not subject to motor vehicle registration and designed for use principally off roads." This would bring within the scope of the basic liability policy motorized equipment used within a library for moving books or motorized yard equipment used for the upkeep of the grounds.

The standard Owners, Landlords, and Tenants Policy used by most companies will have bodily injury liability and property damage liability separately rated under each division. The first division — premises-operations — covers liability for the ownership, maintenance, and use of the premises and all operations necessary or incidental thereto. It does not cover hazards classified under the other rating divisions.

Division 2 covers elevator liability which, under the standard definition of "elevator," includes any hoisting or lowering device to connect floors or landings at the premises unless the insured owns, rents, or controls only a part of the premises and does not operate, maintain, or control the elevator. The definition does not include hoists outside of the building without mechanical power and not attached to the building walls. It does not include inclined conveyors used exclusively for carrying property or a dumbwaiter used exclusively for carrying property with a compartment height not exceeding four feet. The elevator coverage insures liability for the ownership, maintenance, or use of any designated elevator and the "care, custody, and control" exclusion does not apply to elevator liability.

Elevator collision coverage is available by endorsement. This is not a liability coverage but the hazard is insured in connection with the liability policy. It covers direct damage to the elevator or to any property owned, occupied, or used by, rented to or in the care, custody, or control of the insured caused by collision of the elevator or anything carried thereon with another object.

Division 3 covers "structural alterations, new construction, demolition." Ordinary maintenance and repairs done either by the insured's employees or by an independent contractor will come under premises-operations, but work beyond that point requires specific insurance.

Division 4 is "products-completed operations." This coverage, which would have no relevance to library operations, principally applies to manufacturers or distributors of commercial goods and products. It covers for accidents resulting from negligence on the part of the manufacturer or distributor, accidents which occur after possession of the property has been relinquished to others. It also covers accidents occurring away from the premises caused by completed installations which have been made by the insured.

In the general discussion of liability insurance, the question of how liability might arise out of contract was briefly mentioned. Most liability insurance protects against liability which the insured incurs by operations of the "law of negligence." To a limited extent, contractual liability may be insured but this is an area in which extreme care must be taken. Every day, businessmen — and to a limited extent, librarians — enter into contracts, many of which contain broad assumptions of liability of which they are not even aware. To mention only a few of the agreements frequently in force: there are leases, contracts for goods or services, and permits from municipal authorities. Many of these contain "hold harmless" agreements, some of which carry amazing assumptions of liability. The basic liability coverages will exclude contractual liability (except under the *premises-operations* division, in a very limited way — perhaps under an easement agreement or an agreement required by municipal ordinance or under the *elevator* division as to elevator maintenance provisions in a lease of premises agreement). It should be noted also that, when contractual liability is specifically insured, it is ordinarily defined and restricted to contracts of a very limited type dealing with lease of premises and elevator maintenance agreements, etc. Each agreement should be specified in declarations and a premium charged unless it is automatically covered under a comprehensive policy provision.

Liability assumed under other agreements may be covered by endorsement provided they are specified and a premium paid.

In any discussion of contractual liability assumed by an insurance company, it must always be kept in mind that the risk assumed is only for bodily injury and property damage as defined in the contract. Also, the exclusions applying to contractual liability, such as the "care, custody, and control" exclusion, should be taken into consideration.

*Medical payments insurance* is an optional coverage which may be added to a liability policy and may cover the premises-operations and the elevator hazard providing it is so indicated and a premium paid, but it cannot cover the products liability hazard. The standard form covers necessary medical, surgical, and dental services including prosthetic devices and necessary ambulance, hospital, nursing, and funeral expenses incurred within one year of the date of an accident covered by the liability policy. This coverage applies regardless of the legal liability of the insured. The medical limit of liability is separate from the liability limit and the payment of medical expenses does not preclude the injured party from making a further claim under the liability section. Medical coverage does not apply to the owner, to a partner, or to an employee in an accident arising out of and in the course of his employment.

Many organizations providing services to members of the public in large numbers furnish their own nursing or first-aid service, or contract for this service. This usually results in a reduction in the medical payments premium, but the medical payments provision does not pay for salaries, fees, or other expenses of such service.

Medical payments insurance excludes anyone engaged in maintenance, alterations, demolition, or new construction. There is also an exclusion applying to motor vehicles, aircraft, and watercraft. The form should be carefully checked as to the provisions of any other exclusions that may apply.

## Limits and rating

Theoretically, there is no limit to the liability that a person might incur as a result of accident. Under the bodily injury section for example, one can imagine an accident where many people are seriously injured for life. A sympathetic jury might award each one of these people $50,000, $75,000, or even more. Although the insured cannot limit his legal liability, the insurance company can and does limit its liability by providing a limit per person and a limit per accident under the bodily injury liability provision and a limit per accident under property damage liability. Basic limits, on which published rates are based for bodily injury, are $5,000 per person and $10,000 per accident. This means that the insurance company would not be liable for more than $5,000 to any one person injured nor for a total of more than $10,000 if more than one person were injured in a single accident. These basic limits, of course, are far too low for practical purposes, so provisions are made for substantial increases in the limits of liability by making certain percentage increases in the basic premium. These increases in rates are on a sliding scale so that a relatively small increase in rate will provide for a substantial increase in limits. The size of liability limits is an important decision on the part of the library and high limits should be carefully considered — possibly $100,000 per person with $300,000 per accident or even as much as $500,000 per person and $1,000,000 for each accident.

Property damage limits are ordinarily held to a much lower level since the ordinary accident results in much lower property damage losses than bodily injury losses. (See, however, the discussions on fire legal liability, sprinkler leakage liability, and water damage legal liability.) The basic limit of liability for property damage is $5,000 and this quite often is increased to $25,000 or more, but does not approach the levels advisable for bodily injury.

To determine the total premium which is to be charged for a liability policy, the company will determine a separate premium for each section insured under the policy. Each section will have its own rate and its own premium base. For example, the section applying to premises-operations in the case of a library would usually be based on area, so the liability rate book would produce a certain rate per 100 square feet of floor space for the library classification. The area multiplied by the rate would produce the premium for that section of the policy. The rate for elevators would be a unit charge, so the number of elevators multiplied by the rate would produce the proper premium. For structural alterations, the cost of alterations would be the basis for the premium charge and the proper rate would be multiplied by this cost. Contractual liability would be specially rated and added to the premium. Each of these categories would be subject to a minimum premium charge. In this way, the liability premium is built up on the sum of these component parts.

## Comprehensive general liability insurance

The previous discussion referred to the different coverages available under a scheduled liability policy. All of the coverages are optional and, unless a coverage is specified and the premium charged, the insurance company will not be liable for any loss under that section. The insured, for example, may decide to cover only bodily injury liability and not property damage liability and, in that case, any claim based on damage to property of others would not be covered by the policy. If a library had no elevators and therefore no elevator liability listed on their scheduled policy, the construction of an elevator or escalator would require amendment of the insurance policy to provide this protection. In the same way, the insured may elect whether or not he may wish to insure liability for products or contractual liability. If new construction or alteration were started, it would be necessary to endorse the policy if owners protective coverage was desired.

By writing a comprehensive liability policy, it is possible to have automatic protection in some of those areas and yet allow a certain degree of flexibility in selecting coverages. The comprehensive general liability policy has a broad insuring agreement, the standard form for bodily injury liability reading ". . . to pay on behalf of the insured all sums which the insured shall become legally obligated to pay as damages because of bodily injury, sickness, or disease, including death at any time resulting therefrom, sustained by any person and caused by accident." This covers all business operations of the insured, although arrangements may be made, if desired, to exclude different locations or operations provided they are clearly separable and definable. Property damage liability insurance is optional but, if elected, it must apply to the entire risk except products or contractual hazards.

Contractual liability under the comprehensive policy provides automatic coverage only on contracts as defined in the policy. These are restricted to lease of premises, easement agreements, agreements required by municipal ordinances, side-track agreements, and elevator maintenance agreements. Any other contracts which are to be covered must be specified by the policy. Complete automatic contractual liability insurance is not prohibited but, in practice, companies are unwilling to grant this broad coverage since it is difficult to uncover all contracts and charge a proper premium. Contractual liability is optional and may be removed by endorsement.

Product liability is also optional in the comprehensive form, although in the case of libraries it is difficult to imagine a case where this coverage would be needed.

The comprehensive liability policy will automatically pick up new exposures to risk that occur during the policy term (such as construction of elevators) unless the new exposure is in an area that has been excluded from coverage. For rating purposes, a comprehensive general policy is divided into sections the same as a scheduled liability policy. When a policy is written, the original premium is based on all of the exposures in evidence at that time, the same as on a scheduled liability policy, and a small additional premium is charged for the automatic coverage feature. On each anniversary date, an audit is made of actual premiums earned during the previous year based on actual exposure to risk under each section and an adjustment of premium is made.

## Special categories of liability insurance

*Fire legal liability.* It is interesting to note that in carrying direct fire insurance on a person's property, the question of his negligence in starting a fire does not arise. Even gross negligence (where there is no question of arson) does not give the fire insurance company grounds for denying liability. This is also true when one insures property belonging to others, which is held in his possession, under the fire insurance policy, because he is placing himself in the same position and is acting for the actual owners.

The case is entirely different with respect to buildings or personal property of others where there is no insurance. If a fire is caused by Party A's negligence and causes damage to buildings or personal property belonging to someone else, Party B, the former may be held liable. Not only may the owner of the damaged property make a claim against Party A, but if the owner is insured and collects from his insurance company, that company may take an assignment of rights (called a "subrogation assignment") from the insured owner and take legal action against Party A to recover the amount they have paid Party B for a loss caused by A's negligence.

This is an area of liability which is often overlooked, and the presence of the "care, custody, and control" exclusion, as well as the low limits of liability ordinarily carried on property damage liability, can create an embarrassing situation. In this connection, the librarian should consider the personal property of others in his possession or control as well as the building which he occupies in the light of their values, possible contractual liabilities he has assumed, and the wording of his insurance policies. He should also consider possible liability from the spread of fire to neighboring premises.

As to the liability of a tenant for fire damage to the building occupied, several solutions have been proposed but there is not entire agreement as to the efficacy of these methods.

Some people have advocated the adding of the tenant's name as an additional insured on the fire policies insuring the building. There is some disagreement as to whether the tenant has the necessary "insurable interest" as required by the standard fire policy. There are also practical drawbacks since, frequently, the building owner, mortgagee, or other interested party objects to the appearance of the tenant's name on the building policies.

Sometimes one or more insurance companies, sharing the insurance on the building, will agree to waive their subrogation rights against the library occupying the building. In those cases in which the insurance companies do agree to endorse the building's fire policies with a waiver of their subrogation rights against the library, at least part of the problem is solved. The librarian may then feel reasonably sure that if the building insurance is adequate and the building owner makes a satisfactory recovery from the insurance companies, the library will be free of a suit for damages.

In some cases the leases have been drawn to show that the landlord waives his rights to proceed against the tenant for damage to the premises by fire which would deprive the insurance company of its subrogation rights (the insurance company cannot be assigned any greater rights than its insured possesses). It is quite universally agreed that this is satisfactory where the policies take effect after the agreement since, in that case, the insurance company accepts the risk as it exists when the policy is written.

In the case where the agreement is made after the effective date of the lease, there is some contention that this relinquishes a right of the insurance company which would give the company grounds for denying liability. Although this is a minority viewpoint, it would be better practice to have the companies acknowledge this condition where leases are drawn or amended during the term of the fire insurance policy.

There had not been much importance attached to fire legal liability until the landmark case of *Goldman vs. General Mills* in which the landlord Goldman was awarded over $100,000 by a lower court following fire damage to a building occupied by General Mills. This was reversed in 1950 by the U. S. Court of Appeals but only on the grounds that the terms of the lease absolved General Mills of liability. The principle that a person or corporation may be held liable for fire damage resulting from his or its negligence was not upset.

Following the General Mills case there was a great deal of agitation with regard to fire legal liability and disagreement as to whether it should be handled by fire companies or casualty companies. Some standard forms have been approved in several eastern states for this coverage and in other states it is written independently by some insurance companies.

There are such varieties of forms and conditions, both under fire policies and as endorsements amending liability policy conditions, that it would be of little benefit to discuss the details here. The library should recognize this exposure to loss and should study the possible ways to eliminate the exposure or insure it.

Although the preceding discussion has been restricted to fire, the same reasoning may be applied to explosion or other insurable perils where negligence by the tenant may be a factor. These other possibilities should be taken into consideration. Water damage legal liability and sprinkler leakage legal liability follow the same principles but, since there are several special considerations, they have been treated under separate paragraphs.

*Water damage legal liability.* Water damage legal liability insurance is available under standard forms under the jurisdiction of the Allied Lines Association. The standard policy covers leakage of water or steam from plumbing and heating systems or damage from rain or snow which enters the building through defective roofs or through defective or open windows, etc. It does not cover leakage of sprinkler equipment which is a separate subject of insurance. It does not cover flood or seepage through basement walls or backing up of sewers. It covers only liability imposed by law and not liability assumed by contract. Neither does it cover liability for damage to personal property in the portion of the building occupied by the insured.

The principal concern of the librarian in regard to water damage would be with books, manuscripts, paintings, or other similar property, either owned by the library or property which is in its possession but owned by someone else. The legal liability water damage form is of little benefit in either situation and in view of the broad coverages available under direct damage insurance policies (see the discussion on Fine Arts and Valuable Papers), it would be preferable to come to an agreement with the owner of this type of personal property presently in the possession of the library and cover it directly. If the library agrees to be responsible for the property and insures it, this would prevent the possibility of the owner's insurance company making a claim against the library under its subrogation rights.

*Sprinkler leakage legal liability.* There are two standard forms in current use; they are called the "property damage" form and the "liability imposed by law" form. The former covers the legal liability of the insured for property *similar to his own insured contents* held by him in the building. This wording is broad enough to include liability assumed by contract. The "liability imposed by law" form covers the liability for sprinkler leakage damage to property of others *away from the portion of the building occupied by the insured* but it excludes liability assumed under contract by the insured. This policy will cover liability for damage to property of other tenants or damage to the building providing the liability does not arise out of any contract. The policy may be extended to cover property of others in the care, custody, and control of the insured.

In the ordinary library situation, as mentioned in the paragraph on water damage liability, better results will probably be obtained under Fine Arts or Valuable Papers policies for property of others in the library's possession. Possible liability for damage to the building or contents of other tenants in a multiple-occupancy building would have to be considered but this is not a problem ordinarily pertinent to library occupancies.

*Steam boiler and machinery.* It was briefly mentioned under the property insurance section that explosion coverage under an extended coverage endorsement excluded damage caused by explosion, rupture, or bursting of steam boilers, machinery, and similar equipment. It was noted also that accidents caused by this type of property were excluded under general liability policies. The reason stated for these exclusions was the specialized treatment given by boiler insurance companies and a brief comment is in order as to the manner in which these policies are written.

Unlike any other form of insurance, boiler and machinery policies are written for a single maximum limit covering six basic coverages. The amount of the policy is not allocated in any way among these six coverages, but there is a certain sequence of payments each of which is made in turn until the policy limit is exhausted. These coverages in the order of their payment are as follows:

Coverage A. Loss on property of the insured. This covers loss or damage to all property, real or personal, owned by the insured.

Coverage B. Expediting expense, which covers the reasonable cost of temporary repairs and expediting of permanent repairs limited to $1,000 or the amount payable under Coverage A, whichever is less.

Coverage C. Property damage liability.

Coverage D. Bodily injury liability.

Coverage E. Defense costs (paid regardless of limit per accident).

Coverage F. Automatic coverage: new installations on property acquired during the policy term.

Most of the exclusions under the contract apply to Coverage A and the principal one excludes fire damage following a boiler explosion and boiler explosions caused by a hostile fire originating outside of the vessel. Both of these situations are covered under the fire policy. Other exclusions under Coverage A are flood; interruption of business; lack of power, light, heat, or refrigeration; and any indirect result of the explosion.

*Dram shop laws.* The library is unlikely to be concerned with this type of insurance. However, in general, the scope of liability is gradually increasing so that a brief discussion is in order. In some states at the present time, the owner of premises where liquor is sold may be held liable even though he is a non-resident and has no knowledge of his tenant's business.

Dram shop laws, sometimes designated as liquor control laws, are in force in many states and impose special liability on operators of businesses in which liquor is sold or distributed. The liability is for damage to other people arising out of the sale of liquor and these laws provide not only for liability to the intoxicated person, but also to others injured by him and to his family's loss of support.

Some states recently have imposed liability on tavern operators at common law where no dram shop law existed.

General liability policies exclude liability arising out of the application of any dram shop law and where needed, special dram shop liability must be purchased.

This is an interesting and unusual situation of liability arising out of statute and, while its present application to libraries is exceedingly remote, it is the type of thing that an alert insurance counselor would be aware of. If there were any change of the law or insurance liability policies in relation to other activities, such as the serving of liquor in entertainment or Christmas parties, he would be ready to make the proper provisions for coverage.

*Personal injury liability.* The general liability policy refers to "bodily injury liability" which is liability arising out of actual physical injury to a person. There are other injuries which a person may suffer such as libel or slander which are included in the term "personal injuries." Liability for certain designated personal injuries may be covered by attaching a "personal injury liability coverage" extension endorsement to the general liability policy. This endorsement in its standard form may be written to cover personal injuries under the following divisions:

A. False arrest, detention or imprisonment, or malicious prosecution;

B. Libel, slander, or defamation of character;

C. Invasion of privacy, wrongful eviction, or wrongful entry.

Liability for copyright infringement is a form of personal injury liability which is not commonly insured by casualty companies; however, there are specialty companies who write this form of coverage. This insurance is of special interest to librarians who more and more are offering photocopying services to the public. The applications of copyright infringement to photocopying or other forms of reproduction of library materials are discussed in detail in Appendix I.

## Automobile liability insurance

Because the operation of automobiles is the source of many accidents, automobile liability insurance is a specialized field and it is very important that no exposure to automobile liability be overlooked. Liability for the library may arise through the ownership of automobiles or through the use of either owned or unowned automobiles in the regular course of operation of the library. (The term "automobile" in insurance language may include ordinary passenger cars, trucks, bookmobiles, semi-trailers, and other motor vehicles licensed for use on the public highways.) Unowned automobiles may be vehicles which are leased on an annual basis, hired for a temporary period as through a "rent-a-car" agency, or the term may be applied to the use by an officer or employee of their own automobile on library business. The use of a comprehensive automobile policy is the best way to make sure that all automobile liability exposures are covered. It is very important that the comprehensive general liability insurance and the automobile liability insurance be written through the same insurance company.

The definition of "automobile" in the exclusion clause of the standard comprehensive general liability policy is identical with the definition of "automobile" in the standard comprehensive *automobile* liability policy. It is the intent that all motor vehicles not covered by the comprehensive automobile policy be covered under the general liability policy, but there is always the possibility of disagreement in a borderline case. It is not beneficial to the insured to have two different insurance companies in a long drawn-out battle over which of them is responsible in a particular case.

It is clear that if a library has motorized equipment for upkeep of grounds, the liability for operation of such equipment would be covered under the comprehensive *general* liability policy; other motor vehicles or trailers used on the highways would come under the comprehensive *automobile* policy.

The comprehensive automobile liability policy automatically covers all liability of the insured arising out of the ownership, maintenance, or use of any automobile. On the effective date, an initial premium is charged which is based on the exposures existing at that time. At each anniversary of the policy, an audit is made to determine the earned premium based on the actual risk covered during the previous year, and an adjustment of premium is then made. Thus the insured gets complete protection but pays only the premium required by the actual risks incurred.

The insuring agreements are for bodily injury liability, property damage liability, and medical payments coverage. The bodily injury liability insuring clause covers the insured against ". . . all sums which the insured shall become legally obligated to pay as damages because of bodily injury, sickness, or disease, including death at any time resulting therefrom, sustained by any person, caused by accident and arising out of the ownership, maintenance, or use of any automobile."

The property damage liability insuring clause is similar and reads ". . . because of injury to or destruction of property, including the loss of use thereof. . . ."

Medical payments coverage is not liability insurance at all but is really accident insurance which pays defined medical expenses for persons who are injured in an accident in connection with an insured automobile. Property damage liability and medical payments coverage are optional. The insured may also select the limits of liability which he wishes to apply to each of these coverages.

For the purpose of arriving at a premium, the comprehensive automobile policy divides automobiles into these groups: (1) owned automobiles; (2) hired automobiles; and (3) non-owned automobiles. This is substantially the same as coverage under a scheduled automobile liability policy except for the provisions for automatic coverage of all automobile exposures.

Owned automobiles are all automobiles owned by the named insured. They are listed in a schedule and the required premium is charged for each automobile.

Hired automobiles are those ". . . used under contract in behalf of or loaned to the named insured," but the term does not include an automobile owned by the named insured, an executive officer, employee, or agent who has an operating allowance of any kind for its use. The last exclusion is made because such cars fall within the third category of "non-owned automobiles." This category may be rated either under a specified-car basis or a cost-of-hire basis depending on whether the use is fairly steady or intermittent.

Non-ownership liability is incurred by employers when employees use an automobile in the course of their employment. Under the law of agency, employers can be held liable for the negligence of employees who use an automobile for business purposes, regardless of the ownership of the automobile. Frequently, employees use their own automobiles in business and no doubt have liability insurance of their own under a family automobile policy which would protect the employer under its definition of "insured" which includes ". . . any other person or organization legally responsible for the use of the insured automobile." This, however, does not give the employer any real guarantee of protection since the employee's policy might lapse through some oversight or inadvertently cover the wrong car. The policy also might be voided by some act of the insured.

The non-ownership liability coverage insures the use of any private passenger automobile (or the occasional and infrequent use of any commercial-type automobile) not owned, hired, or leased by, lent to, or registered in the name of the insured, by anyone engaged in the business of the insured. For example, the personal automobile of a library staff member used in a library errand would be insured under this division of coverage.

This insures only the liability of the employer (and not the liability of the employee) and is excess insurance over the personal insurance carried by the owner on the automobile in question. It is clear that this leaves no loophole for an employee to feel free to drive without liability coverage.

Since this coverage, in almost every case, is excess over other existing insurance, the premium charges are low and a specific premium charge is made for each employee who falls into either one of two classes:

Class 1 employees are—

(a) All outside employees including officers whose usual duties involve the use in the insured's business of automobiles not owned, hired, leased by, lent to, or registered in the name of the insured;

(b) All other officers and employees whose usual duties in the business include the use of automobiles not owned . . . etc., and who are compensated for the use of these automobiles;

(c) All exclusive agents and representatives of the insured whose usual duties include the use of automobiles not owned . . . etc. Class 2 employees are all other employees.

The premium for the comprehensive automobile policy is the sum of the premiums for each of the divisions of exposure. To this is added a small charge for the automatic coverage feature. Each of the divisions is rated the same as in a scheduled automobile liability policy, but in the latter case, the divisions are elective by the insured. If either hired-car coverage or the non-ownership liability coverage is omitted on a scheduled liability policy, there is no coverage for an accident falling under the definition of the omitted coverage. Under the scheduled liability policy, there is some provision for automatic coverage of newly acquired, owned vehicles, but they must be reported within thirty days.

# CHAPTER 11

# Workmen's Compensation and Employers' Liability

Before the advent of workmen's compensation laws, the financial recovery by an employee for injuries sustained through his employment had to be based entirely on negligence under the common law. There were three common law defenses available to the employer, which made recovery by the employee extremely difficult. These are known as the fellow-servant rule, the doctrine of assumed risk, and contributory negligence. Under the fellow-servant rule, the master is not held responsible for the negligence of one servant to another. According to the doctrine of assumed risk, the servant is deemed to have voluntarily accepted the risks usual to that type of employment when he accepted his job. The doctrine of contributory negligence is that the master can not be held responsible if the injury to the servant is due in any way to his own negligence.

In the past the situation was such that the vast majority of injured workmen were going without any compensation for lost time or medical expenses; this was because the workmen were reluctant to institute a suit against their employer and few were financially able to do so. Moreover, the few suits that were instituted were in most cases doomed to failure.

Early in the twentieth century, workmen's compensation laws were enacted in some of the states. These were based on the philosophy that injury to workmen was one of the consequences of doing business and the reasonable cost of these injuries should be regarded as part of the cost of doing business, regardless of negligence or fault. This concept was quickly adopted and now all states have workmen's compensation laws, which set up in detail the recoveries that may be made by the injured workmen. Recoveries are based on loss of time, medical expense (with allowance for death benefits), and loss of members (e.g., limbs or sight).

All state compensation laws cover injuries sustained in the course of employment and some are extended to cover occupational disease. There are wide variations from state to state in the provisions of the laws as to which types of employment must come under workmen's compensation and which are optional. There are also provisions made for employees to elect to preserve their common law right to sue.

Workmen's compensation policies are divided into two sections, Coverage A covering workmen's compensation and Coverage B covering employers' liability. Under Coverage A, there is no amount of insurance or limit of liability shown. Reference is made to the workmen's compensation law and the insurance company agrees to do everything and pay everything required by law.

A limit of liability is provided under Coverage B. This is a basic limit of $25,000 with provisions for increasing the amount. Employers' liability provides protection in any case in which an employee brings suit at common law.

There is some variation from state to state in the methods of providing insurance. Some states provide for monopolistic state funds, and, in those states, insurance by private carriers is illegal. Other states provide for competitive state funds and private carriers may provide workmen's compensation insurance in competition with the state funds. The majority of the states are served entirely by private insurance carriers.

The workmen's compensation policy restricts protection to the law of the state or states listed in the declaration. Most state compensation laws have extra-territorial provisions covering injuries which occur in other states and the workmen's compensation policy is as broad in coverage as the state law. If, however, an employee injured in another state files a claim under the workmen's compensation law of that state (not listed in the policy declaration), the insurance company would not have to pay the claim. Where operations may extend to more than one state, it is important to make sure that proper coverage is provided.

Provisions are made in both workmen's compensation section and the employers' liability section to relieve the insurance company of liability where employees are illegally employed with the knowledge of the insured or any executive officer. This occurs often in the case of illegally employed minors, but it could arise out of the violation of any laws regarding employment. Every employer should realize that if he knowingly employes anyone illegally, he is assuming a serious risk.

# CHAPTER 12

## Construction Work

When new building construction or alterations of present structures are undertaken, several things should be taken into consideraton, namely (1) insuring the building against physical damage while under construction; (2) properly covering the liability exposure; and (3) making sure that proper performance bonds are issued.

The insurance against physical damage to a building undergoing alterations or where an addition is being constructed is handled ordinarily under the policies in existence which insure the building. It is almost universal practice for the forms used to insure buildings to contain an "alterations and repairs permit," which automatically extends the policy to cover additions or extensions to the building. Care must be taken to increase the insurance to cover the increased values so that coinsurance provisions will not apply. It is also important to make sure that no warranty provisions of the policy are violated, such as a sprinkler protection warranty which might be violated by shutting down the sprinkler system during construction.

New buildings under construction are covered under builder's risk policies. These are set up in a manner similar to that of permanent fire insurance policies except that the form provides for charging a premium approximating the actual amount at risk. In order to accomplish this, two forms are provided called the "completed value form" and the "reporting form." The completed value form adequately serves the purpose except on very large risks and it is much easier to administer. The policy is written for the completed value and premiums are based on 55 percent of the builder's risk rates, and, when construction is completed, the policies are cancelled and replaced by permanent building policies. Under this plan, the insurance company gets a little more premium than actual values would produce if the values increased evenly throughout the construction period. Actual values are reported monthly under the reporting form and an earned premium is calculated on the basis of actual values at risk. This is used where substantial premiums are involved. The builder's risk policies are ordinarily issued to cover the perils of fire and extended coverage. The vandalism rate is usually considered prohibitive on this class, and theft insurance is not usually undertaken by the insurance companies due to the pilferage hazard. The contracts are normally drawn so that the contractor is responsible for safety to building materials and fixtures until they are actually incorporated in the building.

The problem in connection with construction work has been discussed under the liability section. This is generally handled under an owner's protective endorsement and, if the comprehensive general liability policy is carried, this exposure would be automatically picked up.

The three basic types of bonds involved in construction work are contract bonds, bid bonds, and completion bonds, each of which guarantees performance in a different way.

A bid bond guarantees the property owner that the party bidding for a contract will actually enter into a contract and will provide a contract bond if his bid is accepted or he will pay any financial loss due to the acceptance of a higher bid.

A contract bond guarantees the property owner that the contractor will perform his contract in full and deliver the work free and clear of any liens.

A completion bond guarantees a mortgagee or money lender that the borrower of money for construction purposes will apply the money to the job in question and will complete the construction free of liens.

Completion bonds are never required except in the case of private financing, while bid bonds ordinarily are required only on public contracts. Therefore, it is seldom that all three are used on the same building.

There is an owner's protective bond which may be used for private construction work. It is a special form of contract bond and may be used on almost any type of private construction work which is under the supervision of an architect. This differs from the usual contract bond in that the surety company must either complete the contract when the contractor defaults or pay the loss in cash. Under the usual contract bond, the owner must complete the work himself and prove his loss. Also, under the owner's protective bond, subcontractors and suppliers of materials may file claims directly against the surety company rather than filing liens against the property to enforce their claims.

# CHAPTER 13

# Recent Developments in Insurance

To provide background for an understanding of what is happening in the insurance industry today, it is necessary to take a brief look at certain changes that have taken place in residential dwelling coverages. Since dwellings are numerous and of low average unit value compared with other buildings, and because they have a more homogeneous exposure to loss, they have been used by the insurance industry as a subject for experimentation with new forms.

In the early 1950's, a revolution in insurance methods began and has been continuing without abatement ever since. Some of the changes that were made in dwelling coverages a decade ago are now being introduced into other classes of risk and it is reasonable to expect that more recent trends in dwelling coverages will be carried over into other categories wherever they are practical.

Until 1950 there had been no significant changes in fire insurance practices for nearly twenty years. After the extended coverage endorsement was introduced about 1930, most dwellings were insured for fire and extended coverage. Separate insurance on contents was usually carried in inadequate amounts and frequently without extended coverage. Theft insurance was not usually included in the insurance program.

Since 1950, radical changes have taken place in several directions. First, the number of perils insured against were increased by the introduction of an *additional extended coverage endorsement,* which included a few specifically named perils. Later a *dwelling and contents broad form,* which named a large number of additional perils was added, and finally an *all-risk form.* The inclusion of a large number of perils in a single form prevented the insurance buyer from selecting only those hazards to which he felt vulnerable; in this way the industry prevented what is known as "adverse selection" against the insurance company.

Another feature, introduced at the same time, was the use of deductibles. The deductible provision enables the company to reduce the insured's premium by a considerable amount. This is because of the elimination of small claims which produce disproportionately high administrative costs for the amount of loss entailed.

Another radical change which has occurred recently is the insuring of buildings for *replacement* cost instead of *actual cash value.* Insurance for replacement cost pays for the cost of rebuilding the structure without any deduction for depreciation. This feature was incorporated in the *dwelling and contents broad form,* and in other forms introduced subsequently in the dwelling insurance field.

Up to this point, fire insurance coverage had been held within the traditional insurance framework by adding new perils to the fire policy through endorsement. The next step was to move into the casualty field and bring liability coverage into the scheme. This was done under an insurance industry program which created a series of multi-coverage forms called "homeowners' policies." Today, under these new forms, a homeowner may obtain practically every coverage he needs (except automobile insurance, which is still handled separately) and his insurance premium is considerably less than it would be for the same insurance under separate policies.

Many of the features that have been tested in the dwelling insurance classifications are now being introduced into other classes of risks. It is only natural that the less hazardous risks are selected first for this treatment. Thus, public buildings, libraries, and other educational institutions, and to some extent mercantile risks, have broader coverages available than manufacturing risks.

The most recent development under a standard form is the *Public and Institutional Property form* recommended by the Inter-Regional Insurance Conference. The main features of this form are described here. This discussion is followed by a detailed comparison of the key elements of the model insurance policy for libraries (Chapter 14) with similar elements of the Public and Institutional form plus the standard Valuable Papers policy and Fine Arts policy. It cannot be emphasized too often, however, that various companies have their own special forms and that the chances are remote that even the forms described here will remain unchanged.

The Public and Institutional Property form covers fire and extended coverage with vandalism and malicious mischief available by endorsement. A special extended coverage endorsement may be attached which provides "all-risk" coverage. This all-risk form has all of the usual exclusions found in standard all-risk forms and a number of others in addition. If the Public and Institutional Property form is used, the exclusions should be carefully checked and consideration should be given to coverage under separate policies covering boiler and machinery, glass, demolition, or contingent liability from building laws, theft, fidelity, and earthquakes. This is not an exhaustive list of coverages to take care of all exclusions, but it does indicate the coverages available under standard forms, which may be used to protect against those exclusions which seem to be most important.

The basic form provides blanket coverage on all property subject to certain exclusions. However, an endorsement is available to convert it to a scheduled policy if this is preferred by the insured. A mandatory deductible of $100 applies to all perils except fire and lightning.

There is no coinsurance clause in the Public and Institutional Property form. Instead, the form employs an *amount-of-insurance* clause. A sworn statement of values is required initially and a new one must be filed each year. The amount of insurance stipulated in the endorsement must be at least 90 percent of this total valuation and a penalty will apply if insurance is allowed to fall below that level. The amount-of-insurance clause has its own expiration date each year and failure to file a new sworn statement will cause a 90 percent coinsurance clause to replace it.

The risk (the property insured) is inspected annually by the insurance company and quarterly self-inspection reports must be completed by the insured.

The policy provides that 1 percent of its amount (not exceeding $5,000) will cover personal property at temporary locations within the same state and that 5 percent of the amount (not exceeding $100,000) will cover newly acquired property (real or personal) within the state automatically for a period of 180 days. There is also a provision that 1 percent of the amount (not exceeding $5,000) will cover personal property of employees, not otherwise insured, to the extent of $500 per person. All of these extensions are additional amounts of insurance above the policy amount.

Additional insurance is also provided to the extent of 1 percent (not exceeding $5,000) for cost of research or other expenses necessary to replace or restore books of account, card catalog systems, and other records.

There is a replacement cost endorsement available for optional use which applies to both real and personal property.

In using this policy in a library insurance program, the Public and Institutional Property form should be written with an exclusion applying to books, card catalogs, and fine arts, and these should be written under separate Fine Arts and Valuable Papers policies. Under the Valuable Papers policy, the average value per book in each category may be set at a figure which will allow for replacement cost plus any indexing or other processing costs. In the same way, the value per card in the card catalog will be based on the full cost of reproducing the cards including any necessary research or other expenses. The additional coverage for research and other expenses granted by the Public and Institutional Property form may then be reserved for books of account and records used for other purposes. To carry out this method, the premium on property insured under the Public and Institutional Property form must be at least $500 per year in order to meet the minimum premium requirement.

# A COMPARISON OF THE MODEL POLICY WITH STANDARD POLICIES

The main features of the model policy have been compared with three current standard policies which have been combined to afford over-all coverage somewhat comparable to that provided under the model policy. The hypothetical package consists of a Public and Institutional Property form written to cover all personal property excluding books, administrative and holding records, manuscripts, rare books, and fine arts. These excluded properties are to be insured under the Valuable Papers and Fine Arts policies.

Although building insurance is optional under the Public and Institutional Property form, to make the comparison meaningful, any clauses or exclusions applying strictly to building coverage have been omitted. Also, liberties have been taken in condensing the listing of exclusions by omitting words of similar import. For example, under the Public and Institutional Property form, the exclusion of "flood" replaces the actual words in the policy form, "flood, surface water, waves, tidal water or tidal wave, overflow of streams or other bodies of water, or spray from any of the foregoing, whether driven by wind or not."

In addition to the condensation of exclusions, clauses which are believed to be of little interest to the reader have been omitted from the comparison. Following the pages showing the comparison, there is a discussion of three interesting features of coverage which could not be efficiently treated in a tabulated form.

In evaluating the applicability of either of these systems of insurance to the needs of a particular library, several factors should be constantly in mind. The size of the deductible elected will affect the importance of some of the exclusions. For example, water damage from rain or seepage, when furniture, fixtures, and equipment alone are considered, might not be able to produce damage exceeding the deductible which the library has assumed. On the other hand, if valuable office equipment is owned, which would be unusually susceptible to water damage, the damage might exceed the deductible. Books, card catalog systems, and fine arts insured under the Valuable Papers and Fine Arts policies would be covered for water damage.

## COMPARISON

|  | THE MODEL POLICY | COMBINATION OF THREE STANDARD POLICIES | | |
|---|---|---|---|---|
|  |  | Public and Institutional Property Form | Valuable Papers | Fine Arts |
| **Property Insured** |  |  |  |  |
| Buildings | No | Optional | No | No |
| Personal property of insured | Yes, unless excluded | Yes, unless excluded | Valuable papers | Fine arts |
| Personal property of employees | Yes, up to $250 per person | Up to 1 percent of policy amount or $5,000 if less. Limited to $500 per person | No | No |
| Personal property of others in care, custody, or control | Up to 10 percent of policy amount for not more than $250 on any one item | Yes, without limit if insured assumes liability prior to loss | Yes, if insured assumes liability | Yes, if scheduled under special endorsement |
| Newly acquired property | Yes, but a limit of $250 per item if not of a class specifically scheduled | Yes, no limitation except on newly acquired property away from premises |  | Automatic coverage for 90 days, limited to a certain percentage of policy amount —not over 25 percent |
| Property away from premises | Anywhere in U. S. and Canada. Limit of 10 percent of policy amount on property in transit or outside U. S. or Canada. No coverage in Iron Curtain Countries. Limit of 60 days outside U. S. and Canada | 1 percent of policy or $5,000 if less, on personal property temporarily located elsewhere in same state. 5 percent or $100,000 if less, on newly acquired property elsewhere in state for 180 days | 10 percent may cover in transit or at temporary locations (not in storage) | Anywhere in continental U. S. and Canada except at fair grounds and expositions |

## COMPARISON

| | THE MODEL POLICY | COMBINATION OF THREE STANDARD POLICIES | | |
| --- | --- | --- | --- | --- |
| | | Public and Institutional Property Form | Valuable Papers | Fine Arts |
| Improvements and betterments | Yes | Yes | | |
| Extra expense | Yes, if an amount of insurance is designated | No; must be covered under separate policy | | |
| Specific or Blanket | Blanket | Blanket; can be specific by items if desired | Specific amounts on each item, or blanket, or both | Specific amounts on each item. A blanket item (not exceeding 10 percent of policy amount) is permitted |
| Method of Valuation | | | | |
| 1. Books, administrative and holding records | Agreed valuation | See Valuable Papers | Agreed valuation on specified items. Sound value on blanket | |
| 2. Special collections and fine arts | Agreed valuation | See Fine Arts | | Agreed valuation except on newly acquired property or blanket item |
| 3. Similar property not scheduled and other contents | Replacement cost | Sound value or replacement cost as selected by insured | | |
| 4. Personal property of officers, employees, or others | Replacement cost | Sound value or replacement cost as selected by insured | | |
| 5. Buildings | Not insured | If insured, sound value or replacement cost as selected by insured | | |

## COMPARISON

### COMBINATION OF THREE STANDARD POLICIES

| | THE MODEL POLICY | Public and Institutional Property Form | Valuable Papers | Fine Arts |
|---|---|---|---|---|
| 6. Improvements and betterments to buildings | Sound value | Sound value if repaired or replaced at expense of insured. If not repaired or replaced, the original cost pro-rated to the expiration of the lease | | |
| Deductible | $250, $500, $1,000, $5,000 or $10,000 | $100. Some companies have special filings for increasing this if desired | None | None |
| Coinsurance | Full reporting clause replaces coinsurance | Agreed-amount clause with annual expiration subject to 90 percent if not renewed | None | None |
| Reporting of Values | Annual report of values and adjustment of premium at expiration of policy term | Annual affidavit of values to establish agreed amount of insurance | None | None |
| Perils Covered | All risks of physical loss except as excluded | May be issued for named perils of fire, extended coverage, vandalism, and sprinkler leakage. It may also be made subject to a special extended coverage endorsement providing all-risk coverage with numerous exclusions as listed below | All risks of physical loss except as excluded | All risks of physical loss except as excluded |

## COMPARISON

| | COMBINATION OF THREE STANDARD POLICIES | | |
| THE MODEL POLICY | Public and Institutional Property Form | Valuable Papers | Fine Arts |
| --- | --- | --- | --- |
| **Exclusions** | | | |
| Accounts, bills, currency, deeds, money, notes, securities, evidences of debt, aircraft, motor vehicles, and trailers | Accounts, bills, currency, deeds, money, notes, securities, evidences of debt, boats, aircraft, and motor vehicles (except motorized equipment not licensed for highway use) | | |
| Electrical injury from artificial causes | Electrical injury caused by currents artificially generated | Electrical or magnetic injury or erasure of electronic recordings | |
| Nuclear energy | Nuclear energy | Nuclear energy | |
| War risk | War risk | War risk | |
| | Earthquake or land movements | | |
| | Flood, backing up of sewers, seepage | | |
| | Theft and mysterious disappearance | | |
| Infidelity or any dishonest act committed by any employee or by persons to whom the property has been entrusted | Dishonesty of the insured or any associate, employee, or agent | Dishonest act of any insured, partner, officer, director, or trustee | |

## COMPARISON

### COMBINATION OF THREE STANDARD POLICIES

| THE MODEL POLICY | Public and Institutional Property Form | Valuable Papers | Fine Arts |
|---|---|---|---|
| Exclusions (cont'd) | | | |
| | Explosion of steam boilers or machinery owned, leased by, or under control of the insured | | |
| | Glass breakage (except by fire or other specified perils) | | Breakage of glass or similar fragile articles (may be removed) |
| | Cloth awnings, signs, radio or T.V. antennas caused by ice, snow, or sleet | | |
| | Caused by rain, snow, sand, or dust unless it enters through openings in the walls or roof caused by the direct force of the wind or hail | | |
| Due to any process, or while actually being worked upon and resulting therefrom | Any property undergoing alterations or repairs where the loss is caused by the work being performed | | Damage from any repairing, restoring, or retouching process |
| | Property involved in any test or research project | | |

## COMPARISON

### COMBINATION OF THREE STANDARD POLICIES

| THE MODEL POLICY | Public and Institutional Property Form | Valuable Papers | Fine Arts |
|---|---|---|---|
| **Exclusions (cont'd)** | Caused by discharge of any chemical refrigerant or lubricant | | |
| | Loss to property outside of buildings caused by rain, snow, sleet, frost, or cold weather | | |
| Smog, smoke from agricultural smudging or industrial operations, rust, wet or dry rot, mold, inherent vice, latent defect, wear and tear, gradual deterioration, vermin, moths, atmospheric conditions, changes in temperature, delay, loss of use or markets, mechanical breakdown, sudden and faulty operation of heating or cooling equipment | Wear and tear, deterioration, rust or corrosion, mold, wet or dry rot, inherent vice, inherent or latent defect, smog, smoke from agricultural or industrial operations, mechanical breakdown, animals, birds, vermin, termites, or other insects | Wear and tear, gradual deterioration, inherent vice, vermin | Wear and tear, gradual deterioration, moths, vermin, and inherent vice |
| Insured voluntarily parting with property due to fraud or false pretenses | | No coverage under blanket item of property that cannot be replaced by other of like kind and quality | |

## Personal property of others

Automatic coverage for the property of others is provided under the model policy subject to a limit of $250 per item. If, for example, a set of four items valued at $400 each was borrowed by the library, there would be automatic coverage to the extent of $1,000 ($250 on each item) less a deductible of $250. Total loss of the collection, valued at $1,600, would result in an insurance recovery of $750. If the loss were due to mysterious disappearance or theft where burglary was not involved (burglary consists of breaking and entering), the deductible would apply to each item. This would result in a recovery of $150 per item, or a total of $600. If each of the borrowed items was valued at not more than $250, no recovery for theft could be made. Where library contents are insured under the model policy, it is important to evaluate immediately the need for making special insurance arrangements when property of others is held by the library.

If insurance were carried under the combination of standard policies contemplated in this comparison, there would be immediate automatic coverage for property of others, where liability has been assumed, without limitation per item under the Public and Institutional Property policy. This would cover fire, extended coverage, and many other hazards but would not cover burglary, theft, water damage, or other excluded perils (see list of exclusions). This coverage would probably be adequate except where fine arts or valuable books are concerned, in which case immediate coverage should be arranged under the Fine Arts or Valuable Papers policy.

## Exclusions which may be insured under separate policies

Where steam boilers or rotating machinery are owned or controlled by the library, boiler insurance should be carried. This would usually occur when the building itself was owned by the library, and although the model policy does not exclude damage to contents from this peril it would still be necessary to insure the building as well as the liability exposure. If the combination of standard policies is used, furniture, fixtures, and equipment would have to be insured under the boiler insurance policy also, but not the property insured under the Valuable Papers or Fine Arts policies.

The glass exclusion is not of great importance, in view of the deductible feature, unless the building is owned and has substantial glass areas. Here again the model policy has no exclusion but, since it does not cover the building, the desirability of a special glass policy should be considered under these circumstances, whichever system of insurance is employed.

Earthquake coverage is included under the model policy and also under the Valuable Papers and Fine Arts policy. Separate insurance against this hazard should be considered where the building is owned, or on furniture, fixtures, and equipment where the Public and Institutional Property policy is used.

Fidelity insurance is not provided by the model policy or the Public and Institutional Property form, and the advisability of a separate policy should be seriously considered. It is interesting to note that the Fine Arts policy has no exclusion of dishonest acts of officers, directors, trustees, or employees, and the Valuable Papers policy does not exclude dishonest acts of employees.

## Reporting provisions and excess valuations

The two insurance systems compared here have altogether different approaches to the problem of maintaining adequate insurance. Under the model policy, annual reports of values are made and the final premium is determined after the expiration of the policy term by averaging these reported values. The initial premium is based on the total amount of coverage, which may be somewhat in excess of the total values at risk when the policy is written. This provides for new acquisitions during the policy term, and since no coinsurance applies, the only possibility of suffering from inadequate insurance would be where a loss exceeded the amount of the policy.

Under the Public and Institutional Property form, an affidavit of values insured under the policy is filed at the time the policy is written. An agreed-amount clause, in lieu of coinsurance, is based on an amount equal to at least 90 percent of the value declared in the affidavit. This agreed-amount clause is in force for one year and stipulates that as long as the agreed amount of insurance is in force, there will be no coinsurance penalty. If a new affidavit is not filed at the end of the year, the agreed amount clause is not renewed and 90 percent coinsurance applies.

Although the latter method produces a lower amount of insurance, this should be of little concern in most cases where the probability of a total loss is remote. Under either system of insurance, any substantial increase in values during the policy term should be considered as to its insurance implications.

# CHAPTER 14

# A Model Insurance Policy for Libraries

On February 2, 1962, the Executive Board of the American Library Association gave its formal approval to a model insurance form which had been specifically designed for the insurance of the physical property — other than buildings — of the nation's libraries. The model form was developed by the Gage-Babcock organization and, with minor modifications in certain cases, has been accepted by a number of insurance carriers who are offering this insurance to libraries.

The reader who contemplates this insurance for his library should be aware of certain problems connected with the introduction of new policy forms. In practice, when innovations in insurance provisions are suggested, either by representatives of the industry or by others, a number of companies will be approached to offer the new policy forms to interested purchasers. Frequently, in the initial stages of developing markets for the new forms, the only companies willing or able to venture into new types of coverage and broader combinations of coverage are the "unadmitted companies" (see Glossary), which are not licensed by the insurance department of a particular state. In this situation, neither the company nor the client is regulated by the state insurance department; nor are they given its protection in such matters as premium rates and claim adjustments.

Such is the case with respect to the model policy. Since its inception, the market for the policy has been limited to unadmitted companies, although continuing efforts are being made to expand the market to include admitted companies so that the new form will, in time, be more widely available.

Thus, from the standpoint of the individual library interested in arranging for insurance of this type, it may be that the policy developed for the American Library Association is not available in precisely this form, either because no insurance company — admitted or otherwise — is willing to provide this insurance in a given state, or for other reasons.

In the future, however, as additional markets are developed for this insurance through the efforts of the Library Technology Project and its insurance consultants, such difficulties should be encountered less frequently.

Although in most cases the model policy will be the best solution to the problem of insuring library resources, it is not intended here to imply that this is in any sense a final form, nor necessarily the best form, even regarded in its most general application. Over time it is to be expected that improvements in the present form and in other insurance packages of this type will inevitably be made.

The model policy or an equivalent form is recommended for libraries for which it may be available. However, it is possible that in a particular situation a combination of separate insurance policies may be developed which would provide adequate protection at a lower cost than that for the model policy. For example, in some cases, the Public and Institutional Property form plus a Valuable Papers policy and a Fine Arts policy may provide equivalent protection at a more economical cost and hence may be a more acceptable insurance program. All such alternatives should be investigated in determining the course the individual library should follow.

The Gage-Babcock organization and the advisory committee for the project agreed that it was not practical to include coverage for library buildings in the model policy for two reasons:

First, a great number of library buildings are insured as part of a group of institutional or municipal buildings. Second, library buildings may be insured quite properly and adequately under existing policies. The buildings themselves normally have no special characteristics that call for specialized insurance treatment. On the other hand, the *contents* of libraries do have a special character with respect to insurance; this is the main reason for the development of the model policy.

The policy is presented in the conventional form of an insurance contract. There is usually a covering sheet called a "policy jacket" which carries the key information for the contract: the name and address of the insured library, the face amount of the policy (the total amount of insurance purchased), the premium, and the inclusive dates of insurance coverage. The policy form is printed on separate sheets and inserted into the policy jacket.

The model policy form is presented below with comments, explanatory notes, and illustrations. As will be noted, some of the insurance paragraphs are self-explanatory.

1. *Perils Covered:* This policy in the amount of $_____ insures all risks of loss or physical damage, in accordance with the terms, conditions, and limitations following:

   $_____ on Direct Damage to the insured property owned by the Insured Library or in its care or custody, situated in the United States of America, its territories or possessions and the Dominion of Canada or while temporarily (meaning a period not to exceed sixty [60] days) located elsewhere (see limitation in Paragraph 8), but in no event to exceed a limit of

$_____ in Main Library situated_____

$_____ in Branch Library situated_____

$_____ in Branch Library situated_____

$_____ in _____   _____

$_____ on Extra Expense, as defined in Paragraph 3, necessarily incurred in continuing normal operations as a result of physical damage to personal property covered by this policy, or to a building housing such personal property. Recovery for extra expense incurred in any one month shall be limited to 40 percent of the total amount of insurance provided by this item.

COMMENT:

The scope of protection offered in the model policy is extremely broad. "All risk" means virtually that: the term refers to insurance which provides coverage against all hazards except for a few stated risks which are considered to be uninsurable such as those resulting from war or rebellion, or confiscation by order of a governmental body. All-risk insurance might be contrasted with the type, such as the ordinary fire and extended coverage policy and the usual Public and Institutional Property policy, in which specific hazards are listed in the policy with the understanding that losses from other possible risks would not be covered.

Coverage is, of course, included for the common risks of fire and extended coverage perils, vandalism, theft, water damage of any kind (including flood damage), collapse of the building or stacks, collision of carrying vehicles, explosion of a steam boiler (or other explosion), landslide, earthquake, sand storms and dust storms, damage caused by overheating of the building through faulty operation of heating equipment, and *any other causes not expressly excluded.*

Also note that, except for the so-called iron-curtain countries, there are no geographical limitations. The property is covered wherever it may happen to be: in branch libraries; bookmobiles; on loan; at the repair shop, bindery, appraisers' or processors' offices; in transit to or from the library (including ocean travel) by public or private carriers, by mail or express, and so forth. Many policies now carried by libraries restrict the coverage to the library premises. Under the terms of the model policy, the location of the property, except for the central or main library and branches need not be named, a provision which provides unlimited flexibility.

Except for the library building itself, the insurance provided in the model policy covers all of the property owned by the library and even extends to materials in the temporary custody of the library, e.g., a special collection on loan from another library.

Institutions such as libraries, whose financial support usually comes from tax and endowment funds or contributions, are seldom faced with the prospect of their income being cut off as a result of a fire or other disastrous event. Frequently, however, in a loss situation, there is the problem of paying rent for temporary quarters, the expense of relocating the facilities, or other measures necessary to the continuance of service while repairs are being made. The model policy takes this problem into account and provides for payment to the insured library of all costs which exceed the library's normal operating expenses had the loss not occurred. The extra expense feature increases the scope of the policy so that, depending upon the extent of loss, some or all of the indirect expenses resulting from a loss may be covered. The "extra expense" benefit is further explained in the notes under Paragraph 3.

2. *Property Covered:*

   a.  On the general collections as follows:

| | | |
|---|---|---|
| Adult fiction | @ $ | per volume |
| Adult non-fiction | @ $ | per volume |
| Juvenile materials | @ $ | per volume |
| Reference books | @ $ | per volume |
| Periodicals (bound) | @ $ | per volume |
| Periodicals (not bound) | @ $ | per volume |
| Bound documents | @ $ | per volume |
| Unbound documents | @ $ | per volume |
| Newspapers before 1865 | @ $ | per issue (per volume) |
| Newspapers 1865 to date | @ $ | per issue (per volume) |
| Microcards (includes all forms of microprint) | @ $ | per unit |
| Tape recordings | @ $ | each |
| Sheet music | @ $ | per item |
| Phonograph records | @ $ | per record |
| Pamphlets | @ $ | per item |
| _____ | @ $ | per _____ |
| _____ | @ $ | per _____ |

   b.  On administrative and holdings records:

| | | |
|---|---|---|
| Shelf list | @ $ | per card |
| Adult catalog | @ $ | per card |
| Juvenile catalog | @ $ | per card |
| Registration cards | @ $ | per card |
| Withdrawal records | @ $ | per card |
| Microfilm | @ $ | per reel |
| _____ | @ $ | per _____ |
| _____ | @ $ | per _____ |

   c.  On manuscripts, rare books, and special collection materials:

| | |
|---|---|
| | @ $ |
| | @ $ |
| | @ $ |

@ $
@ $
@ $
@ $

d. On individually described pictures, paintings, sculpture, or other fine arts:

@ $
@ $
@ $
@ $

e. and on similar property of the Insured, not specifically scheduled, but limited to an amount not to exceed 10 percent of the policy amount and then not for more than $250 on any one item;

f. and on furniture, fixtures, tools, equipment, supplies, and similar property owned by the Insured Library or in its care or custody, and improvements and betterments to buildings not owned by the Insured Library, and, subject to a limit of $250, the personal property of any one officer or employee;

g. and on personal property owned by others while in the care or custody of the Insured, but limited to an amount not to exceed 10 percent of the policy amount and then for not more than $250 on any one item provided that, if such property is otherwise insured, this insurance shall operate as excess and in no event as contributing insurance, over and above the amount collectible on such property under such other insurance.

COMMENT:

The policy is written in such a way that the librarian makes his own appraisal of the value of the library's collection. For purposes of insurance, the collection itself and other property to be insured are broken down into categories. (The categories listed in Paragraph 2 are intended to be representative, not necessarily complete.)

Then a valuation per unit for each category is established according to the analysis of costs as suggested in Chapter 8 and Appendix G. An important point to remember here is that books and related materials should be given a value which would include both their replacement cost and the cost of their processing. These valuations are averages. There are wide variations in the real value of individual books within a given classification. A book-by-book appraisal might be made, but in many libraries this would be a monumental task. Moreover, the value of a book changes over time (it might become very much more valuable or almost worthless), and such changes would present difficulties in the adjustment of claims for loss.

In case of loss, the librarian would count the items completely destroyed in each category and multiply these figures by the agreed value per item (as shown in Paragraph 2) and the total of these figures would represent his claim for this type of property.

For items not completely destroyed, the amount of the claim for scheduled property would be the repair costs or the agreed value less salvage value.

The card catalog, shelf list, and other administrative and holdings records are extremely important from the standpoint of insurance because, first of all, they are necessary to determine the extent of damage in a loss situation. In placing a value on such records, the librarian should consider what costs would be entailed in reconstituting them in case of loss. Relevant factors to be taken into account would be the extent of physical exposure to damage present (e.g., have special measures been taken for the protection of the card catalog?), and the degree to which the records had been duplicated and perhaps stored in a separate place.

In Paragraphs 2-c and 2-d, the model policy is similar to insurance providing "Valuable Papers and Fine Arts" protection which previously has been available only in separate policies. Items of more than ordinary value should be listed individually in this category and at the figure for which protection is desired. Appraisal of many such items may be difficult; for this reason, a discussion on the subject of appraising valuable papers is included in this book as Appendix H.

In Paragraph 2-e, the term "similar property" refers to materials of a library nature — books, records, films, etc. — of a class or category not scheduled in Paragraphs 2-a through 2-d and for which average values are not shown. The purpose is to provide coverage for such items acquired after the contract was written.

The authors of the model policy believe that a distinction should be made between library materials as such and other types of property in the library. Thus, the policy provides for full coverage of the physical, movable property owned by the library, which means furniture, fixtures, supplies, etc. In Paragraph 2-g, the term "personal property" is used in its legal sense which means all movable property or removable other than *real* property; the latter term means land and buildings.

A question might arise about the status of stacks and shelving with respect to this clause. Ordinarily, stacks which have been brought into the library building after construction has been completed would be regarded from the insurance standpoint as "trade fixtures." They would, in effect, be *removable* even though perhaps bolted to the floor, and it would be assumed that they would be taken out if the library were to move to another building. Such stacks would be insured under the terms of the model policy. However, if the stacks were an integral part of the structure of the building, as is the case in many libraries — e.g., if the stacks continued upward through several stack levels, or if they served as structural supports for floors — then they must be regarded as part of the building and would be insurable under the building policy at possibly a lower premium rate.

It is often necessary for a library to modify or make improvements in a building which it does not own. Such improvements or modifications create an insurable interest on the part of the tenant library in the continued usefulness of the building. Under the model policy, the library has the option of coverage to the extent that its funds have been spent for such purposes. If, for example, this protection were not provided and a fire forced a library to move to another building, the *use value* created by expenditures for improvements would be lost.

When valuable materials such as special collections are loaned to a library, the recipient is sometimes responsible for their safekeeping. In the past it has been necessary to obtain special insurance coverage for each loan occasion. Paragraph 2-g in the model policy makes this procedure unnecessary. For example, if Library X, which is covered by this insurance, has material on loan from Library Y, such material is automatically covered (subject to certain limitations: see discussion on page 198) under the all-risk protection of Library X's model policy. Of course, Library Y already may have placed insurance on its property and, in case of loss, that insurance would pay for the damages. In cases of this kind, the borrowing library should ascertain whether the loaning library has insurance on the collection while it is in the borrowing library. If so, the borrowing library should not report the value of, or pay premiums on the borrowed collection. Conversely, from the standpoint of the loaning library, the initial insuring clause of the model policy covers listed property regardless of location; the annoyance and expense of buying specific insurance for each loan occasion are eliminated. Establishing in advance a scheduled value for those items intended for loan would be a worthwhile procedure because it would minimize delay in the adjustment of a claim in case of loss.

3. *Definitions:*

    a. The term "personal property" means all physical property other than real property, except as otherwise excluded by the conditions of this form.

    b. The term "sound value" means replacement cost at the time and place of loss, less depreciation, however caused, to the date of loss.

    c. "Extra expense" is defined as the excess of the total cost of conducting operations during the period of restoration over and above the total cost of such operations during the same period had no loss occurred, excluding however

(1) Any loss of profits or earnings;

(2) Any direct or indirect loss or damage to property;

(3) Any expense for physical property unless incurred to reduce extra expense loss, and then not to exceed the amount by which the loss is reduced, with due consideration for the salvage value of such property.

d. With respect to extra expense claims:

(1) The period of recovery shall be limited to only such length of time as would be required with the exercise of due diligence and dispatch to rebuild, repair, or replace that part of the property or housing building which has been damaged or destroyed, commencing with the date of such damage or destruction but not limited by the expiration date of this policy;

(2) This Company shall not be liable for any claim for recovery which may be occasioned by any ordinance or law regulating construction or repair of buildings or structures;

(3) The period of time for which recovery may be claimed is extended for the length of time, not exceeding two consecutive weeks, during which access to the building housing the property covered hereunder is prohibited by order of civil authorities as a direct result of a peril insured against by this policy.

COMMENT:

The most important paragraphs in this section have to do with extra expense. The language is that normally used in extra-expense policies issued specifically for this purpose. The first exclusion (Paragraph 3-c-1) is readily understood: normally, the loss of profits or earnings as a hazard to be guarded against is not a matter of concern to libraries.

The property-loss exclusion in the present section simply establishes that property loss is not insured twice; such losses are covered in the initial insuring clause (Paragraph 1).

The third exclusion under "Definitions" (Paragraph 3-c-3) protects the underwriter's interest against any effort on the part of the insured to profit as a result of the loss event. To clarify this: following a fire, for example, the insured library may incur expenses in excess of the normal operating costs had the fire not occurred. (Such costs are covered in Paragraph 1.) In addition, the library may find it necessary to rent or make purchases of certain physical property during the course of restoration, say, rental of a pickup truck to transport cartons of books, and the policy covers such costs but only to the extent that they are necessary to reduce the extra expense involved; i.e., to prevent further "excess expenses" from developing. The exclusion simply guards against the possibility of expenditures which are not really necessary to the reduction of loss, and which would, in effect, defeat the intent of the policy.

The paragraph which releases the insurance company from special obligations relating to local laws and ordinances governing building construction or repairs has significance because of wide variations in building codes. Such codes ordinarily are not retroactive, but some of them, for the purpose of limiting the period during which substandard buildings may continue to be used, impose a maximum limitation on the amount of repair or alteration to be carried out in lieu of full compliance with the code. Thus the owners of a building damaged by fire, for example, often are not permitted to limit the extent of repair simply to restoration of the conditions existing prior to the fire but rather are required to make major repairs and alterations to conform to the provisions of the code.

In such cases, meeting the requirements of the code might entail considerable extra cost. This creates a situation properly outside the intent of the insurance policy; accordingly, the underwriters have excluded this kind of additional expense.

4. *Exclusions:* This policy does not insure against loss or damage:

    a. By smog; smoke from agricultural smudging or industrial operations; rust; wet or dry rot; mold; inherent vice; latent defect; wear and tear; gradual deterioration; vermin; moths; atmospheric conditions and/or changes in temperature; delay, loss of use, or market; mechanical breakdown; unless there ensues fire, explosion, sprinkler leakage, or smoke from sudden and faulty operation of heating or cooling equipment and then only for the loss or damage from these hazards.

    b. Sustained due to any process, or while actually being worked upon and resulting therefrom, other than damage ensuing from fire or explosion;

    c. Except loss or damage by fire or explosion, caused by or arising out of infidelity or any dishonest act committed, alone or in collusion with others, by any employee of the Insured or by any persons to whom the property may be entrusted (carriers for hire excepted);
Resulting from the Insured voluntarily parting with title or possession of any property if induced to do so by any fraudulent scheme, trick, device, or false pretense;

    d. Caused by electrical injury or electrical disturbance within any article insured hereunder from artificial causes unless there ensues fire, explosion, sprinkler leakage or smoke from sudden and faulty operation of heating or cooling equipment and then only for the loss or damage from these hazards;

    e. Caused by (1) hostile or warlike action in time of peace or war; (2) insurrection, rebellion, revolution, civil war, or usurped power; (3) confiscation by order of any government or public authority;

f. By nuclear reaction or nuclear radiation or radioactive contamination, all whether controlled or uncontrolled, and whether such loss be direct or indirect, proximate or remote, or be in whole or in part caused by, contributed to, or aggravated by the peril (s) insured against in this policy; however, subject to the foregoing and all provisions of this policy, direct loss by fire resulting from nuclear reaction or nuclear radiation or radioactive contamination is insured against by this policy.

g. Of or to accounts, bills, currency, deeds, money, notes, securities, evidence of debt, aircraft, or motor vehicles and trailers licensed for highway use and not customarily used on the premises.

COMMENT:

These are the hazards which the model policy does *not* cover. All other sources of loss are covered. These exclusions are intended to protect the insurance company against three types of losses. The first type might be called "maintenance losses" or "expected" losses. They tend to be characteristic of a material or piece of equipment or location and are usually the consequences of human actions or human neglect. Smog and industrial smoke, for example, are, at least in part, the results of human action. Rot, rust, and mold are consequences of what has been called "inherent vice." These losses occur because of the fundamental nature of the materials involved; no insurance against such damage is possible except perhaps proper care by those in charge.

If, however, the damage is the result, not of inherent vice, but of an included hazard, the policy provides protection. Mold damage which results, for example, from the improper storage of books would be an example of loss from inherent vice. On the other hand, mold damage resulting from the effects of water used to extinguish a fire would be covered under the policy.

The exclusion with respect to damage done to an item while it is being repaired, or, in the case of film, while it is being developed, or in the case of cards, while they are being written or duplicated, is based on the conviction on the part of the insurance company that affording protection against such losses would be, in effect, insuring the quality of work of employees or contractors who should be responsible for their own shortcomings.

The second type of exclusion: dishonesty on the part of employees falls into a field of protection called "bonding," which is actually not true insurance at all. As a result, it is customary to exclude employee-dishonesty and "confidence-game" losses from policies providing *direct* insurance. "Indirect insurance," such as liability insurance, and other forms of protection, e.g., bonding, are discussed in other chapters.

The third major type of exclusion is that against losses which even the insurance company is not big enough to insure, such as damage resulting from war, confiscation, and the effects of nuclear radiation. With respect to the last, however, the policy does provide protection in time of peace against fires resulting from nuclear explosions.

5. *Deductible Provision:* Each loss or damage shall be adjusted separately, and from the amount of each adjusted claim the sum of $_____ shall be deducted.

COMMENT:

The purpose of this provision is to eliminate claims for small losses which occur more or less regularly and which properly should be regarded as operating expenses rather than insurable hazards. The elimination from coverage of losses such as the "mysterious disappearance" of individual books has a marked effect on the amount of premium to be paid. The *amount* of the deductible should be geared to the size of the library operation and an appropriate credit in the premium rate is, of course, allowed for this provision depending on the deductible sum. A large library could afford a higher deductible, a small library a lower one.

In the interests of convenience (from the administrative and accounting standpoint) the writers of the model policy have agreed that specific deductible amounts should be stated, one of which would be selected by the particular library being insured. These amounts are $250, $500, $1,000, $5,000, and $10,000. Higher deductible figures are permitted but should be negotiated at the time of purchase of the insurance.

6. *Reporting of Values:*

    a. The Insured agrees to declare the total agreed value of all scheduled property, the sound value of building improvements paid for by the Insured, and the total replacement cost new of all other property at all locations and in transit, covered at the inception, first, second, and third anniversary dates of this policy.

    b. Full Reporting Clause: As respects all property covered by this policy, liability under this policy shall not in any case exceed that proportion of any loss hereunder which the last value reported prior to the loss bears to the total value existing on the date for which such report was made.

COMMENT:

The philosophy behind this requirement is that the librarian will report his values for premium-payment purposes on exactly the same bases as he will recover his losses. These bases are three: the agreed value for scheduled types of property, the sound value with respect to building improvements (Paragraph 12), and replacement cost new in regard to all other property insured.

Once a year the librarian will report the current value of the property insured. Paragraph 6-b provides that, in the event of failure to report fully, recovery for losses occurring thereafter would be reduced proportionately to the deficiency in the reported values.

The reported value may remain the same or be increased or decreased. An extremely important point should be noted here. It is strongly recommended that, in general, the initial amount of insurance to be purchased be set at a figure approximating 120 to 125 percent of the actual (reported) values to be insured. There are several reasons for this suggestion: First, a larger amount of insurance would take account of upward fluctuations of value which may occur during the policy period; i.e., it is more likely that the value of library property will increase rather than go down.

A second reason: when a serious loss occurs, the insured library may have a borrowed collection in its care, the value of which would not have been reported at the last anniversary date. The basic insuring clause covers such property but the total amount payable (including that for the loss of the borrowed collection) could not exceed the face amount of the policy. Here again, if the amount purchased were greater than the value of the library's own property, there would be ample insurance to cover the loss of the borrowed collection as well.

The objection might be raised that buying an amount of insurance that is 125 percent of the actual value of the property to be insured is, in effect, to be over-insured; i.e., why should the librarian pay the extra premium involved? The answer to this objection is explained in detail in the comment following Paragraph 7.

7. *Premium Adjustment Clause:* The premium hereunder is provisional only, and shall be adjusted on expiration of the policy on the following basis: After deducting the amount of specific insurance, if any (not exceeding, however, the amount of value reported), an average of the total remaining values reported shall be made, and if the premium on such average values at the rate applying exceeds the provisional premium, the Insured shall pay to the Insurer the additional premium for such excess; and if such premium is less than the provisional premium, the Insurer shall refund to the Insured any excess paid.

COMMENT:

This provision gears the eventual premium (the premium as adjusted at the close of the three-year policy period) directly to the actual values exposed as these values fluctuate during the policy term. For one thing, this provision makes it unnecessary to include in the model policy a so-called coinsurance or "contribution" clause, which usually appears in the type of policy carried by libraries at present. A contribution or coinsurance clause is a provision that if, at the time of the loss, there is in force an amount of insurance which is lower than the values existing on the date of loss (or a stipulated percentage of such values), then the loss payment will be reduced proportionately. The absence of such a coinsurance clause in the model policy is one of its most attractive features.

More important (and this point is related to the comment under Paragraph 6), making the premium provisional means that the librarian is paying the premium only on insurance he actually *uses.* This should be explained. First of all, the ultimate premium is based upon the average of the values reported for three successive years. Thus, if the adjusted premium at the end of the period is lower than the initial deposit premium, the insured library is given a refund; if it is higher, the insured library will make up the difference.

Let us take an example: our hypothetical librarian reports an initial property value of $200,000, but he wishes to carry insurance of $250,000 to provide a margin of safety. Let us assume his premium rate is $1.00 per $1,000 of valuation for a three-year policy. His provisional deposit premium is $250. On the report date at the end of the first year, the value of the property has decreased to $150,000 through disposal of a special collection. During the second year, the value is increased to $175,000 through gifts and remains at that level through the third year. The average of his values reported for the three years is $175,000 ($200,000 at inception, plus $150,000 at the end of the first year, plus $175,000 at the end of the second year, plus $175,000 at the end of the third year, divided by four). The adjusted premium for the three-year period, therefore, is $175. He paid a deposit premium of $250 at the beginning of the three-year policy period; he is entitled to a refund of $75. Conversely, if the value of the property had increased over the period, the librarian would, at the time of adjustment, pay the appropriate additional premium.

The insured librarian might *use* part or all of the excess insurance (and thus not be entitled to much, if any, premium refund) if the value of the property is increased during the policy period through an unanticipated bequest, or by purchases, or if the library borrowed a valuable collection or exhibit which itself is uninsured.

Some further comments on reporting values and premium adjustment are pertinent here. The recommendation was made earlier that the librarian purchase insurance in an amount higher than the actual reporting value and the figure of 125 percent was used. It is not the intent of the policy that such excess insurance necessarily be limited to 25 percent, although greater amounts of such excess insurance would probably have to be negotiated between the library and the insurance company. If a librarian, for example, knew in advance that during the forthcoming year his library would be enriched by a large contribution of rare and expensive books, he might request that his initial insurance be written at 150 percent or more of the present reported value.

On the other hand, at any time during the policy period, the librarian is free to increase the amount of insurance carried, and in fact is strongly encouraged to do so. If a substantial but unexpected bequest to the library should be made, the librarian should call his insurance agent to increase the library's insurance, being willing to deposit the additional provisional premium which would be required.

8. *Limitations:*

    a. In regard to loss or damage by water, including flood, this policy is limited to $100,000 or 20 percent of the face amount of this policy, whichever is the smaller. This exclusion, however, shall not apply to water damage resulting from fire, lightning, explosion, vandalism, or the impact of aircraft or vehicles;

    b. In regard to property while temporarily located outside the United States of America, its territories or possessions, and Canada, or while in transit, including property in transit in bookmobiles, coverage is limited to 10 percent of the principal amount of this policy.

    c. Coverage under this policy on individual books or works of art, unless specifically valued under Paragraph 2 of this policy, shall be limited to $250 for each such book or work of art;

    d. In regard to the operation of the Deductible Clause (Paragraph 5 of this policy), it is understood and agreed that in the event of loss or damage from the hazards of theft, mysterious disappearance, and shortages discovered when taking inventory, loss of each item insured in Paragraph 2-a through 2-d will separately be deemed a single loss occurrence. This paragraph shall not, however, apply to loss by burglary.

    e. This policy specifically excludes coverage of any kind on property within the geographical borders of the Union of Soviet Socialist Republics, Czechoslovakia, Poland, Bulgaria, Albania, Rumania, Hungary, and the German Democratic Republic (the eastern sector of Germany plus East Berlin).

COMMENT:

    Insurance experience makes necessary these limitations in the amount of coverage, written in a form which protects against any kind of physical loss or damage, as distinguished from certain *stated* kinds of damage. Paragraphs 8-a and 8-d are limitations on types of losses which are not covered at all in the usual "named perils" type of policy (except for the present policy, insurance against flood per se is simply not available).

The important consideration in Paragraph 8-a is the distinction between two kinds of water damage: that resulting from flood or other "natural" causes, and water damage which is a consequence of those hazards against which this policy is intended to provide protection. To illustrate: water damage to the contents of a library caused by efforts to extinguish a fire would be fully covered; if a fire or explosion, etc., were to cause water pipes in the library to burst, thus causing water damage to the books, the library would be fully protected.

Paragraph 8-b is no significant limitation. The probability is extremely low that, at a given time, more than 10 percent of a library's total property would be in any one foreign location or in any one shipment. Note that, with respect to bookmobiles, the limitation applies only when the property is *in transit* in bookmobiles. If a major fire were to destroy several bookmobiles while they were parked in their regular garage, the contents, as library property insured under this policy, would be fully covered.

The third paragraph is introduced because the underwriters believe that any volume, painting, manuscript, document, or piece of sculpture whose value is over $250 should be individually described in its proper category under Paragraph 2 and covered for the value which the librarian or appraiser may set upon it, primarily to avoid differences of opinion with respect to its value at the time of loss. Therefore the librarian should be encouraged to place values on and list such items in the appropriate class of property under Paragraph 2, which will obviate this limitation with respect to those items.

Moreover, the limitations in Paragraph 8 would apply to a borrowed collection or exhibit unless the items had been individually listed and their respective values indicated. Thus, when a loan collection or other borrowed materials are received in the library, the librarian should immediately ascertain whether the materials are covered by the insurance of the lending institution. If not, the borrower should establish specific values for the items and report the information to his insurance company so that an endorsement to the contract (or "rider") can be written to cover the materials under the provisions of Paragraph 2.

A second point may be made through an example: consider the librarian who has a half-dozen valuable books, not parts of a set, the value of each of which is $300. These six books are completely destroyed in a small fire. If they had not been individually listed under Paragraph 2 with their respective values, they would be subject to the limitation of Paragraph 8-c. Thus, each book could be valued at a maximum of $250 or a total value (for the six) of $1,500. If the deductible amount was, say, $250, the total recovery would be $1,250. However, if the six books had been listed and valued separately, their total value would be $1,800; after applying the deductible, the librarian would be paid $1,550 for this loss.

The main reason for Paragraph 8-d is the belief that librarians expect more-or-less regular losses by theft and mysterious disappearance. These losses are, therefore, in the nature of operating expenses and to cover them by insurance would mean such an increase in premium that the policyholder, in effect, would simply be "trading dollars" with the insurance company. Moreover, if one considers the administrative and clerical expense of processing a large number of such claims — expense which is passed on to the insured library in its premium — the result would probably be an over-all loss to the library.

However, it might be noted that theft, mysterious disappearance, and shortages *are* covered for the amount by which the value of the book exceeds the amount of deductible. Also, this limiting clause does not apply at all to burglary losses; that is, losses caused by someone breaking into ("forcible entry") a locked library or any of its locked areas. Such incidents, which may result in substantial loss, are covered without limitation.

The inclusion of the clause which appears here as Paragraph 8-e has become standard practice because of the difficulties of adjusting claims and negotiating the payment of losses in the countries named.

9. *Agreed Value Clause:* This Company shall not be liable for more than the amounts set opposite the respective articles specifically valued under Paragraphs 2-a, 2-b, 2-c, and 2-d, which amounts are agreed to be the value of said articles for the purpose of this insurance. In the event of loss or damage to any article or articles which are part of a set, this Company shall be liable for the replacement value of the lost or damaged articles and for the reduction in value thereby caused to the other units comprising the set.

10. *Replacement Cost:* The Insurer's liability under Paragraphs 2-e, 2-f, and 2-g of this policy, with the exception of building improvements and betterments, shall be limited to the replacement cost of such property at the time of loss, without deduction for depreciation however caused, and not exceeding the amount which it would cost to repair or replace the property with new material of like kind and quality within a reasonable time after such loss.

COMMENT:

Paragraphs 9 and 10 are closely related. The "Agreed Value Clause" explicitly states that the obligation of the insurance company is to pay the amounts per item set forth in the policy for total loss of those items of property which have been expressly valued by the librarian or the appraiser — that is, items in the general collection, administrative and holdings records, manuscripts, rare books, special collection materials, and individually described pictures, paintings, sculpture, and other pieces of fine art. No arguments; no questions asked.

This clause also makes it clear that when one volume of a set of books (or one unit in another set of articles) is lost or destroyed, thereby reducing the usefulness and value of the rest of the books or articles in the set, the insurance company will pay for the cost of replacing the entire set, less the salvage value of the remaining items in the set. This is a valuable provision of the model policy — one which, so far as we know, is not included in any other insurance contract available for libraries.

The "Replacement Cost" clause (Paragraph 10) states that, with respect to furniture, furnishings, supplies, etc., the insurance company will pay for the actual cost of repairing or replacing such items without deduction for depreciation. This also is an unusually liberal clause and a valuable feature of the model policy.

11. *Other Insurance:* This Company shall not be liable for loss if at the time of loss or damage there is other valid and collectible insurance which would attach if this insurance would not have been effective, except that this insurance will apply only as excess and in no event as contributing insurance and then only after all other such insurance has been exhausted. Notwithstanding the foregoing, this Company shall be liable, on a fully contributory basis, with other policies of the same form as this policy.

COMMENT:

The term "contributory insurance" refers to the situation in which two or more insurance companies split the coverage and share proportionately whatever losses may occur.

The model policy provides what is called "excess insurance"; claims are payable only after any other insurance held by the library has been exhausted. The special situation might arise in which Library X, which is insured under the model policy, is the recipient of a loan collection from Library Y, which is also covered by insurance. In case the borrowed collection were lost, the insurance of Library Y, the owning library, would pay the loss and the provisions covering such losses in the policy held by Library X (the model policy) would become operative only if the loss to that collection exceeded the amount of coverage provided by the owning library. If both libraries are insured under policies of the model policy form, the two insurance companies would share the loss.

12. *Improvements and Betterments:* It is understood and agreed that the interest of the tenant insured under this policy in improvements and betterments to the building shall be construed

as 100 percent of the sound value of the improvements and betterments paid for by the tenant insured.

COMMENT:

"Sound value" is equivalent to *insurable value, i.e.,* that amount which is to be paid in case of loss, and means the replacement cost of the insured property at the date of loss less accrued depreciation to the date of loss.

This clause makes it clear that if the library is the tenant in a building owned by someone else, and if the library has paid for the installation of partitions, special lighting, acoustical wall or ceiling materials, etc., the library can recover the depreciated value of the damaged portion of such property at the time of loss, regardless of the provisions of the lease with respect to ownership of such improvements. The point is that, in some cases, improvements to a building, even though paid for by the tenant, become the property of the owner. Despite this fact, under the model policy, any investment made by the library in improvements is protected.

13. *Policy Not Reduced by Loss:* Any loss hereunder shall not reduce the amount of this policy.

COMMENT:

Many policies provide that the amount of insurance is reduced by the amount of any losses paid. Under those types of insurance, a loss occurring early in a policy period running three, four, or five years would mean a considerable loss of premium to the insured. This cannot happen under the terms of the model policy; the full amount of insurance continues to be payable regardless of any claims that may have been paid.

14. *Payment to Others:* At the option of the Insurer, any loss to property of others may be adjusted with and paid to the owner of such property.

COMMENT:

The model policy, it will be recalled, covers not only the property of the insured library but also the property of others in the care or custody of the library and the property of employees. To avoid the prospect of dealing with a half-dozen or so parties in the adjustment of claims following a loss, the insurance company reserves the right to negotiate directly with the owner of the lost or damaged property.

15. *Debris Removal and Salvage:* This insurance covers expenses incurred in the removal of all debris and the salvaging of property covered hereunder which may be occasioned by loss caused by any of the perils insured against in this policy. However, the total liability under this policy for loss to property, salvaging of property, and removal of debris will not exceed the amount of insurance applying under this policy to the property damaged or destroyed.

COMMENT:

The main point of this clause has to do with the special character of library contents. Whenever a library suffers fire or water damage, it is imperative that cleanup and restoration activity be started immediately. Any delay will decrease the chance of salvage. Under the provisions of Paragraph 15, it is not necessary to wait for an insurance adjuster to make an inspection and authorize restoration. The librarian may act at once knowing that the expenses entailed in cleaning up and restoring the damaged property will be reimbursed.

16. *Waiver Clause:* Any release from liability entered into by the Insured in writing prior to loss hereunder shall not affect this policy or the right of the Insured to recover hereunder.

COMMENT:

Paragraph 25 ("Subrogation," below) requires the insured library, on recovering a loss from the insurance company, to turn over to the insurance company any legal rights of action the library may have against a third party whose negligence may have caused the loss.

The intent of the "Waiver Clause" is such that it logically precedes the "Subrogation Clause"; the former may be clarified through an illustration. If a bookbinder, for example, were to require a release from the library which would relieve the bindery of any liability for loss or damage to the library's books in the temporary custody of the bindery, then the library would have no rights of legal action to turn over to the insurance company in case of loss. The "Waiver Clause" makes it clear that the library is free to sign any such release from liability without endangering its insurance coverage.

17. *Breach of Warranty Clause:* If any condition occurs to void this insurance, said voidance shall apply only to property at the location where the voidance occurs and when such voiding condition is removed, this policy is automatically reinstated.

COMMENT:

It is normally assumed that a contract of insurance is valid when made in good faith. Certain acts of the insured, such as misrepresentation or fraud, are grounds for voiding the contract. The "Breach of Warranty" clause states that if such a voidance occurs, it shall affect the insurance only at the particular location where the action which resulted in voiding occurred. For example, such action occurring in a central library would not cause the insurance covering its branch libraries to be affected.

The intent here is to protect the insurance company against misrepresentation of values or conditions without unduly penalizing insured librarians who inadvertently err in this respect.

18. *Abandonment:* There can be no abandonment to this Company of any property.

COMMENT:

This means that the library must expect to collect only for actual loss and damage. It cannot abandon undamaged property or even the salvage of damaged property and then expect to recover from the insurance company for such abandoned property. Ordinarily, therefore, the insured library must itself dispose of the salvage, unless the insurance company voluntarily agrees to do so on behalf of the library.

19. *Assignment:* Assignment of interest under this policy shall not bind the Company until its consent is endorsed hereon.

COMMENT:

This is another standard provision. The insurance company, while content to do business with the insured library, will not agree, in advance, to continue the policy in favor of any successor owner of the property insured.

20. *Mispresentation and Fraud:* This policy shall be void if the Insured has willfully concealed or misrepresented any material fact or material circumstance concerning this insurance or the subject thereof or in case of any fraud, attempted fraud, or false swearing by the Insured touching any matter relating to this insurance or the subject thereof, whether before or after a loss.

COMMENT:

The intent of this paragraph and of the next three (Paragraphs 21, 22, and 23) is self-explanatory.

21. *Notice of Loss:* The Insured shall as soon as practicable report to this Company or its agent every loss or damage which may become a claim under this policy and shall also file with the Company or its agent within ninety (90) days from date of loss a detailed sworn proof of loss. Failure by the Insured to report the said loss or damage and to file such sworn proof of loss as hereinbefore provided shall invalidate any claim under this policy for such loss.

22. *Examination Under Oath:* The Insured shall submit and so far as is within his or their power shall cause all other persons interested in the property and members of the household and employees to submit to examinations under oath by any persons named by the Company, relative to any and all matters in connection with a claim and subscribe the same; and shall produce for examination all books of account, bills, invoices, and other vouchers or certified copies thereof if originals be lost, at such reasonable time and place as may be designated by the Company or its representatives, and shall permit extracts and copies thereof to be made.

23. *Settlement of Claims:* All adjusted claims shall be paid for or made good to the Insured within sixty (60) days after presentation and acceptance of satisfactory proof of interest and loss at the office of this Company. No loss shall be paid hereunder if the Insured has collected the same from others.

24. *No Benefit to Bailee:* This insurance shall in no wise inure directly or indirectly to the benefit of any carrier or other bailee.

COMMENT:

This is somewhat complicated. The clause is intended to protect the insurance company in a certain kind of situation, namely, a loss occurring while the library property is in transit (in the custody of a "carrier") or in the temporary care of someone else ("bailee") such as a bindery.

Very often the transportation carrier (or other bailee) includes a statement in his bill of lading or service contract to the effect that, in the event of loss, the carrier or bailee will be liable only for the amount of loss in excess of whatever *insurance* may be held by the library on that property.

If such a statement were operative, then the insurance would, in effect, "inure to the benefit of the carrier." Thus, this paragraph in the model policy vitiates the effect of such a bill-of-lading statement; in a loss situation, the policyholder would collect from the insurance company, would subrogate to the insurance company his rights of legal action against the carrier (Paragraph 25), and the company would take legal action against the carrier to recover what is now a loss to the insurance company.

25. *Subrogation:* In the event of any payment under this policy, the Company shall be subrogated to all the Insured's rights of recovery therefor against any person or organization and the Insured shall execute and deliver instruments and papers and do whatever else is necessary to secure such rights. The Insured shall do nothing after loss to prejudice such rights.

COMMENT:

Insofar as this clause is not self-explanatory, it is defined and further explained in the comments under Paragraphs 16 and 24.

26. *Sue and Labor:* In case of loss or damage, it shall be lawful and necessary for the Insured, his or their factors, servants, and assigns, to sue, labor, and travel for, in and about the defense, safeguard, and recovery of the property insured hereunder, or any part thereof without prejudice to this insurance; nor shall the acts of the Insured or this Company, in recovering, saving, and preserving the property insured in case of loss or damage, be considered a waiver or an acceptance of abandonment, to the charge whereof this Company will contribute according to the rate and quantity of the sum herein insured.

COMMENT:

Following a loss, the burden of continuing to care for the damaged and undamaged property still rests on the library. The insured library's employees and agents ("factors") may incur expenses in safeguarding or, in the case of losses in transit, in recovering the insured property. This clause states that the insurance company will pay any reasonable expenses incurred in such activity, but that by doing so (or by the company assisting in these kinds of recovery or protective activities) it is not condoning any abandonment to the insurance company of such property, as was discussed in Paragraph 18.

This clause is derived from the traditional Marine Policy, which is hundreds of years old and is, therefore, couched in antique language (e.g., the expression "it shall be lawful and necessary for the Insured" means "the insurance company has no objection to"), but the meaning and intent are well settled by the courts.

27. *Suit Against Company:* No suit, action, or proceeding for the recovery of any claim under this policy shall be sustainable in any court of law or equity unless the same be commenced within twelve (12) months next after discovery by the Insured of the occurrence which gives rise to the claim. Provided, however, that if by the laws of the state within which this policy is issued, such limitation is invalid, then any such claim shall be void unless such action, suit, or proceeding be commenced within the shortest limit of time permitted by the laws of such state to be fixed herein.

COMMENT:

This paragraph and the last four in the model policy (Paragraphs 28 through 31) are standard insuring conditions and require no special comment.

28. *Appraisal:* If the Insured and the Company fail to agree as to the amount of loss, each shall, on the written demand of either, made within sixty (60) days after receipt of proof of loss by the Company, select a competent and disinterested appraiser, and the appraisal shall be made at a reasonable time and place. The appraiser shall first select a competent and disinterested umpire, and failing for fifteen (15) days to agree upon such umpire, then, on the request of the Insured or the Company, such umpire shall be selected by a judge of a court of record in the state in which such appraisal is pending. The appraisers shall then appraise the loss, stating separately the value at the time of loss and the amount of loss, and failing to agree shall submit their differences to the umpire. An award in writing of any two shall determine the amount of loss. The Insured and the Company shall each pay his or its chosen appraiser and shall bear equally the other expenses of the appraisal and umpire. The Company shall not be held to have waived any of its rights by any act relating to appraisal.

29. *Cancellation:* This policy may be cancelled by the Insured by mailing to the Company written notice stating when thereafter such cancellation shall be effective. This policy may be cancelled by the Company by mailing to the Insured at the address shown in this policy or last known address written notice stating when not less than thirty (30) days thereafter such cancellation shall be effective. The mailing of notice as aforesaid shall be sufficient proof of notice and the effective date of cancellation stated in the notice shall become the end of the policy period. Delivery of such written notice either by the Insured or by the Company shall be equivalent to mailing.

   If the Insured cancels, earned premiums shall be computed in accordance with the customary short rate table and procedure. If the Company cancels, earned premiums shall be computed pro rata. Premium adjustment may be made at the time cancellation is effected and, if not then made, shall be made as soon as practicable after cancellation becomes effective. The Company's check or the check of its representative mailed or delivered as aforesaid shall be a sufficient tender of any refund of premium due to the Insured.

30. *Conformity to Statute:* Terms of this policy which are in conflict with the statutes of the state wherein this policy is issued are hereby amended to conform to such statutes.

31. *Changes:* Notice to any agent or knowledge possessed by any agent or by any other person shall not effect a waiver or a change in any part of this policy or estop the Company from asserting any right under the terms of this policy, nor shall the terms of this policy be waived or changed, except by endorsement issued to form a part of this policy.

# APPENDIX A

# Fire Testing as Applied to Libraries

Wide publicity was given to the fire tests conducted at Norwood, Massachusetts, by the Factory Mutual Insurance Companies and at Ithaca, New York, by Cornell University. The Norwood tests were undertaken upon the recommendation of the New York Public Library to determine the validity of the idea, widely held by librarians, that books do not burn rapidly and that the water used in fighting a fire may be more damaging than the fire itself. In addition, the tests were designed to evaluate the effectiveness of sprinklers in controlling fires in library bookstacks. Conditions in the Norwood tests were intended to duplicate the open-tiered bookstacks installed in the New York Public Library. The test conducted by Cornell University was intended to determine whether sprinklers were required in order to provide adequate protection for Cornell's new John M. Olin Library.

As was pointed out in the Introduction, the two sets of tests produced results which were, to a large extent, mutually opposed. Although the company insuring Cornell's library continues to *recommend* sprinklers as constituting proper protection, it will be recalled that, because of other favorable conditions, the premium penalties for *not* installing sprinklers were later dropped.

The main conclusion to be drawn from the two series of tests is that the fundamental question — should sprinkler systems be installed in the stack areas (or other areas) of libraries? — has not been answered. It cannot be, in fact, because the question itself is too general. The results of the present study demonstrate that a great many factors — more than were present in either test situation — affect the relative safety of libraries from fire. This variety of factors clearly extends to the stacks. On the basis of these two tests, it certainly cannot be claimed that sprinkler systems should be installed in the stack areas of all libraries.

Second, both sets of tests were conducted under conditions ostensibly simulating those in the particular libraries concerned. Therefore, the results of these tests cannot be extrapolated as applicable to libraries in general or even to other libraries with similar conditions.

Four general rules should govern the type of tests under consideration here:

1. The conditions tested must be typical. That is, if the results of tests are to be applied to comparable situations in the real world, the *test* conditions must be typical of the actual conditions to which the results are to be applied.

2. The test agency and personnel must be technically competent, completely objective in their approach and methods, and without any proprietary interest in the application of the results.

3. A full set of data must be taken, supported by adequate instrumentation.

4. The conclusions reached must be confined to the conditions tested.

The tests at Norwood and Ithaca have been described in articles in *Library Journal* and the quarterly journal of the National Fire Protection Association.[1] All of the details need not be repeated here but certain hitherto unpublished facts about the tests are pertinent to this discussion.

Two tests were conducted at Norwood by representatives of the Factory Mutual Insurance Companies. The first was designed to measure the effect of adding a variable (sprinklers) to a set of other variables. The second test was made for control purposes; i.e., it was designed to measure the controlled variables — all of the factors present in the first test except the added variable, sprinklers.

The basic list of variables included: the structure and arrangement of the stacks; the set of combustible materials — mainly books; a source of ignition; air and draft factors — e.g., vertical openings in the stack floors; and the shelving arrangement of the books.

For both tests a four-level set of stacks composed of U-bar shelving was constructed in a large unheated loft building. The arrangement was intended to simulate a portion of the stacks in the New York Public Library. The test stacks consisted of four ranges 12 feet long, on 4½-foot centers, making a 9- by 12-foot test area, 30 feet high. These stacks were unenclosed; they were erected in a corner of the building. The roof level above the stacks was considerably higher than that of the rest of the building.

There were three main types of combustible materials in the test situation. About 14,000 books (discards provided by the Providence, Rhode Island, Public Library) were rather loosely arranged on the shelves in each test. Six-by eight-inch wooden boards were attached to the steel shelves, presumably to serve as backing for the books. The source of ignition was a wooden book truck placed

---

1 George L. Schaefer, "Fire!", *Library Journal* LXXXV (February 1, 1960), 504-5; H. B. Schell, "Cornell Starts a Fire," *Library Journal*, LXXXV (October 1, 1960), 3398-99; *National Fire Protection Association Quarterly* (April, 1960).

close to the shelved books. The book truck carried books on the top shelf and two cardboard cartons containing crumpled paper which was lighted with a match to start each of the test fires.

Abbreviated time tables show the immediate results of the tests:

## TEST 1

| TIME | EVENT |
|---|---|
| 0 min.  0 sec. | Fire lighted with match. |
| 1 min. 10 sec. | Flame appears above book truck. |
| 3 min. 25 sec. | Books begin to burn in first tier. |
| 3 min. 43 sec. | Sprinkler head operates on tier above (19 gpm). |
| 7 min. 53 sec. | Sprinkler head operates on same tier (22 gpm). |
| 8 min.  3 sec. | Fire considered under control. |
| End of test | Time not stated. Extinguishment was gradual and curves extend to 15 minutes. |

## TEST 2

| TIME | EVENT |
|---|---|
| 0 min.  0 sec. | Fire lighted with match. |
| 1 min. 48 sec. | Books begin to burn in first tier. |
| 3 min.  0 sec. | Active burning in first tier. |
| 3 min. 15 sec. | Books begin to burn in second tier. |
| 7 min. 30 sec. | Books begin to burn in third tier. |
| 9 min.  0 sec. | Books begin to burn in fourth tier. |
| 10 min. 23 sec. | Extinguishment started with 1-inch hose line (15 gpm). |
| 10 min. 40 sec. | A 2½-inch hose line (265 gpm) was added to the extinguishment effort. |
| End of test | Not stated. Fire smoldered for hours. |

Results of the tests showed that multi-tier stacks with vertical openings between floors present a fire hazard. Moreover, they showed that sprinklers will extinguish fires in stacks very quickly. However, there are some important aspects of the Norwood tests which bear careful scrutiny. When we apply the first of our four rules, we discover a number of differences between the conditions arranged for these tests and (a) conditions typical of most libraries, and (b) the particular circumstances of the New York Public Library stack area.

A book truck with cartons of combustible trash is an unlikely source of ignition in a library. Wooden backing boards to support books on steel shelves are not characteristic. The loose arrangement of the books on the shelves created wedge-shaped openings which encouraged the fire to develop more rapidly.

More important is the fact that in the Norwood tests, the basic draft conditions were not similar to those in the New York Public Library stacks nor to those in most other libraries. The lack of enclosure and the high roof provided a large volume of freely moving air which contributed directly to the spread of the fire.

Even if these conditions were typical of libraries, there was a more significant defect in the Norwood situation. This was a difference in the controlled variables between the two tests themselves. Conditions for the second test were presumably intended to be identical with those of the first except that the sprinkler system was not used. However, in the unsprinklered test, the original conditions were restored *except that the doors and skylight of the building were opened.* This created a far greater draft for the second fire. Thus, setting aside the effect of sprinklers, the results of the two tests cannot legitimately be brought into comparison.

## The Cornell University fire test

This test was conducted in a concrete-block training building provided by the Ithaca, New York, fire department. The test, engineered by the Ithaca fire department in cooperation with several departments of Cornell University, is regarded by the Gage-Babcock organization as adequately engineered and reliable.

The fire test area was somewhat smaller than that at Norwood. It covered a 9- by 9-foot floor area in a room with a 9-foot ceiling. The stack arrangement was reasonably representative of modern stack construction — sheet-steel, freestanding stacks with the levels completely separated by concrete floors.

For purposes of comparison with the Norwood tests, the same source of ignition was used — a wooden book truck with cartons of trash. To simulate the conditions in the John M. Olin Library stack area, a fire detection system was installed in the ceiling of the test room.

As will be seen, the results of this test contrast sharply with those of both Norwood tests:

| TIME | EVENT |
|---|---|
| 0 min. 0 sec. | Fire lighted with match. |
| 1 min. 0 sec. | Books on book truck burning; covers of books on nearby shelves beginning to catch fire. |
| 1 min. 50 sec. | Alarm sounded by detection system. |
| 2 min. 0 sec. | Flames reaching to fifth shelf. |
| 8 min. 0 sec. | Maximum point of fire. Book truck collapses. Fire begins to die down. |
| 23 min. 0 sec. | Fire department personnel apply stream of water from 1½-inch hose (56 gpm) for about 3 minutes; this followed by application of water fog. Total of 300 gallons of water applied. |

The total number of books used in the test was 2,870. Of these, 112 books on the book truck and 100 on the shelves were burned beyond worthwhile salvage. About 350 others sustained some damage including that by water. Damage to the shelving was minor; structural members supporting the shelving and floor showed no distortion from exposure to heat.

In this test it could be concluded that the solid sheet-steel shelving and the absence of vertical drafts between floor levels had greatly reduced the potential spread of the fire.

Sprinklers probably would have extinguished the fire in a shorter time than was actually taken. However, in this test, the deliberate intent was to allow the fire to get out of control. The fire did not, in fact, get out of control; it was burning quite slowly when it was put out. Moreover, it is possible that portable fire extinguishers might successfully have been used to extinguish the fire shortly after the alarm sounded.

## The Kansas City, Kansas, library fire

Although normally tests are planned with great care and carried out under controlled conditions, it occasionally happens that almost equivalent data can be obtained from actual fires. This is the case with respect to a fire occurring in a Kansas City, Kansas, library in May of 1961. The fire was set deliberately in the library— an act of arson — and because the person responsible was quickly apprehended and made a full confession, it was possible to reconstruct what happened.

The fire occurred in a school library in a single wooden bookcase about 7 feet high and 17 feet wide. The shelves were 8 inches deep and the back was closed by ¼-inch plywood. The library was located in a basement room. One of the entrances was a three-foot passageway behind the bookcase which provided a free draft from all sides. The person who set the fire entered the otherwise unattended school about noon and, proceeding to the library, stuffed papers on top of the books on the third shelf of the right-hand section. These papers and others placed on a table nearby were set on fire. About 45 minutes after the fire had been lighted, a passer-by saw smoke coming from an upstairs window and called the fire department. An open library door and open staircases had prevented the confinement of smoke to the area of the fire's origin. The fire department responded within minutes and put the fire out with a fog nozzle using about 150 gallons of water.

In the forty-five-minute period, the fire (see cut) had destroyed the four shelves of books above it. It had not burned downward at all. The top shelves in the adjacent section were completely burned and the shelf below partially damaged. In the next adjacent section only the top shelf was destroyed with partial damage below. In effect, the upper corner of the bookcase had burned with no further spread of the fire. Over the bookcase, by the time the fire had been extinguished, it had burned through a lath and plaster ceiling, had burned the joists, and was breaking through the floor above. Of the 35 shelves in the bookcase, 25 were untouched by fire, and, because water-fog was used for extinguishing the fire, there was little water damage.

This is a strong indication that books ordinarily burn very slowly in case-type shelving because, as compared with bracket-type shelving, there are fewer openings which might create drafts. It must be recognized, however, that a sprinkler system would probably have extinguished the fire with less fire damage to the books, shelves, and building although with perhaps more water damage to the books.

## Future testing

As matters now stand, the need for further fire testing is still acute. It has been well established that fires can spread rapidly upward in open, multi-tier stacks. This type of stack construction was normal practice for many years and there are a large number of libraries so equipped. The effectiveness of sprinklers has been shown, but this is only one way to approach the protection problem. Another way, and one which is being used, is to close off the openings in the stack at each floor level and enclose stairs and other vertical-draft openings. No tests have yet been run to evaluate this approach.

If the libraries of this country are to solve their protection

Damage resulting from Kansas City, Kansas, school library fire.

problem economically and in a manner acceptable to the librarian, objective tests should be conducted, relating construction features such as materials, horizontal and vertical-draft stops, shelf configurations, ventilation, and other factors affecting fire spread so that the protection afforded can be related to the actual need for it. Certainly there are libraries and areas in libraries where sprinklers may be needed and should be used, but there are also libraries and parts of libraries where other approaches might be used, with the objectives of providing an acceptable degree of protection, decreasing the potentiality of damage, and lowering costs.

What testing should be done? There are many possible variations in the installation of library shelving. To test each alternative style of installation would be a never-ending and expensive process. It should only be really necessary to analyze a few basic points to provide answers to questions not considered in previously conducted tests.

Approximately 75 percent of the shelving being installed today in stack areas is of the metal, double-faced, bracket type. There are three basic types of construction. First there are single tiers, free standing on floors which are a structural part of the building.

The Cornell fire tests have given an indication as to how a fire may progress with this arrangement, and the relatively minor damage which might be expected with early warning given by a heat detection system, but without the benefit of automatic sprinklers which not only give an early warning but also serve to suppress the fire. It is doubtful if it would be worthwhile to conduct further tests which would duplicate those conducted at Cornell.

The second and third arrangements are multi-tier structures which are not necessarily a structural part of the building. In one case, the tiers are separated at each level by a continuous cellular metal floor. In the other, a continuous reinforced concrete floor slab is used. In both cases, the pre-formed steel members supporting the shelves also support the floors and shelving above and, in addition, the weight of books and anticipated live loads which may be imposed on each level. The size and load bearing strength of the vertical supports diminish as the tiers increase in height. (Stairways may, or may not, be enclosed, though enclosures should be provided to prevent upward propagation of heat and smoke.)

Closing the openings in existing open multi-tier stacks at each level would produce a situation comparable to one of the two types of construction described above. However, in doing this, other problems are generated such as added costs for distribution of heat and ventilating air. The paramount question, then, is what will happen in any multi-tier stack if fire occurs, and what can be economically justified in the form of protection.

Vertical steel supports for multi-tier construction are in compression. The results to be expected when one or more fail can be calculated by a structural engineer. Structural steel members in compression are subject to failure when exposed to heat at an elevated temperature for a given time. How much heat, applied for how long, has not been determined for multi-tier stacks in which books, or comparable library materials, are the sole source of fuel. It is quite probable that an undetected extended fire at the lower level might cause the collapse of the entire structure.

It is proposed that one further fire test be conducted. The factors and conditions to be considered are as follows:

1. A building is required of sufficient size to house at least six double ranges divided by a center aisle, three tiers high.

2. The tiers are to be of conventional design with steel supports and reinforced concrete floors. Each level would have superimposed loading to simulate not less than a six-tier structure.

3. There would be no openings through floors, no sprinkler or heat detection systems. (It is already known how each of these contributes to fire spread, extinguishment, or suppression.)

4. Fire would be initiated on the first level and allowed to

progress uninhibited. To make the model more realistic, a quantity of air, calculated in pounds at 70° F. and 50 percent relative humidity (normal conditions for many libraries), would be gradually introduced into the fire area during the combustion period. This would simulate the conditions that would be encountered in a larger stack area containing more air (oxygen) to be consumed by the fire. Burning time and temperatures would be recorded and visual observations made. Protection would be provided for the observers against possible explosion of combustion gases (carbon monoxide, for example).

If such an objective test were to be conducted in a realistic manner, answers to the following questions could be deduced from the results:

1. Do books tightly shelved burn faster or slower than loosely shelved books?

2. Do serials, pamphlets, newspapers, manuscripts, and similar materials burn faster than books? If so, should they be shelved on the upper level?

3. If openings in open, multi-tier structures are closed with suitable fire resistive materials, what effect will this modification have in reducing fire damage?

4. In modern conventional construction, with all levels completely separated, can fires produce sufficient temperatures with the amount of oxygen normally available to cause structural failure and stack collapse? (The same would apply to "3" above.)

5. If it should be proved that collapse is a possibility, would the early response by fire fighting forces through alerting by means of a heat or smoke detection system suffice?

6. With early detection and response, would the lives of the fire fighting personnel be endangered by possible collapse of the stack structure? If so, would the library be liable? What response time can be tolerated?

7. Are sprinkler systems essential to prevent structural collapse and protect the collection and personnel? If so, how should they be designed for copious flows of water, or that amount required to control or extinguish the fire?

As a matter of fact, a second test (or set of tests) might be considered which would be based on information derived from the first. For example, just how much flow from a sprinkler system is required to extinguish a fire under given conditions? This would entail the application of a hydraulically calculated system delivering only that amount of water under controlled conditions required for fire suppression or extinguishment without excessive water damage.

# APPENDIX B

## A Chronology of Library Fires

| YEAR | LIBRARY | REMARKS |
|---|---|---|
| 612 B.C. | Assurbanipal (Ninevah) | Laid waste by the Medes. |
| 430 B.C. | Medical Library, Cnidus, Greece | Time of Hippocrates. |
| 47 B.C. | Alexandrian Library (Brucheum) | Burned during street fighting —Caesar's campaign against Alexandria. |
| A.D. 64 | Roman libraries | Lost when Rome burned. |
| 79 | Octavian Library, Rome | Founded by Augustus, 33 B.C. |
| 192 | Vespasian Library in Temple of Peace, Rome | A large area fire lasting three days; Vespasian Library burned first; Palatine Library lost next day. |
| 192 | Palatine Library, Rome | |
| 272 | Alexandria—Brucheum Library | Burned when Emperor Aurelian destroyed the Greek Quarter. |
| 303 | Various church libraries | Burned to destroy Christian literature. |
| 364 | Library of Trajan, Antioch | Destroyed during civil commotion. |
| 392 | Alexandria—Serapeum Library | Destroyed by edict of Emperor Theodosius. |
| 477 | Theodosian Library— Constantinople | Destroyed in civil commotion during reign of Zeno; contained about 120,000 volumes. |
| 614 | Library of Caesarea | Persian capture of Palestine. |
| 780 | St. Sophia's, Constantinople | |

| YEAR | LIBRARY | REMARKS |
|---|---|---|
| 867 | Canterbury Library, England | Burned by Danes. |
| 870 | Peterborough, England | Large collection of sacred books. |
| 883 | Abbey of Monte Cassino, Italy | Burned by Saracens. |
| 899 | Nonatola, Modena, Italy | Burned by Hungarians; another fire in 1013. |
| 905 | St. Martins of Tours, France | |
| 917 | Verdun Cathedral, Germany | Large part of collection burned; another fire in 1047. |
| 923 | Cambrai, France | Burned again in 1027. |
| 931 | Chalons-sur-Marne, France | Burned again in 963. |
| 937 | St. Gall, Germany | Angry student set fire to library; many books destroyed. |
| 962 | Chartres, France | Burned again in 1019. |
| 989 | Orleans, France | |
| 998 | Buchara, Persia | |
| 1000 | Angers, France | Burned again in 1032. |
| 1002 | Strassburg, France | |
| 1006 | Reicheneau, Germany | Part of library destroyed. |
| 1006 | Paderborn, Germany | |
| 1013 | Hildeshein, Germany | |
| 1018 | Beauvais, France | |
| 1018 | Poitiers, France | |
| 1019 | Rouen, France | |
| 1019 | Corbell, France | |
| 1024 | Commercy, France | Another fire in 1037. |
| 1025 | Samur, France | Twice in 1025; again in 1065. |

| YEAR | LIBRARY | REMARKS |
|------|---------|---------|
| 1026 | Saintes, France | |
| 1027 | Tours, France | |
| 1041 | Brenn, Germany | Also burned by Norse about 1000. |
| 1067 | Canterbury Cathedral, England | |
| 1068 | Cairo Library, Egypt | Pillaged and burned by Turkish soldiers. |
| 1069 | York Minster Library, England | |
| 1084 | Lateran Library, Rome | Destroyed by Norman invasion. |
| 1091 | Croyland Monastery Library, England | About 700 volumes. |
| 1099 | Le Mans, France | |
| 1109 | Tripoli | Burned by Crusaders. |
| 1127 | Salzburg, Germany | Another fire in 1167. |
| 1131 | St. Requier, France | A few manuscripts saved. |
| 1137 | Corbie, France | All Monastery buildings lost. |
| 1137 | York Minster, England | Incident of Scottish border wars. |
| 1160 | St. Jacobs Cloister, Mainz, Germany | |
| 1167 | St. Augustine's Abbey, England | A few books saved. |
| 1172 | Verona, Italy | Many manuscripts destroyed. |
| 1179 | Halberstadt, Germany | |
| 1184 | St. Dunstan, England | Entire Monastery destroyed. |
| 1184 | Glastonbury Abbey, England | |
| 1185 | Gembloux, France | |
| 1258 | Bagdad, Persia | City sacked by Mongol invasion. |

| YEAR | LIBRARY | REMARKS |
|------|---------|---------|
| 1300 | Mont St. Michel, France | Caused by lightning. |
| 1314 | St. Gall, Switzerland | Part of library saved. |
| 1440 | Monastery of Megaspilaeon, Greece | Another fire in 1600. |
| 1451 | Carthusian Library, Cologne, Germany | |
| 1524 | Reinhardsbrunn Library, Germany | Destroyed in Peasants' War; Reinhardsbrunn was just one of many monastic libraries burned during this period. |
| 1536 | Tunis | All Arabic books burned by Emperor Charles V. |
| 1540 | Westminster Abbey Chapter Library | |
| 1541 | Lobbes, Germany | Partly destroyed by fire in 12th Century. |
| 1562 | Fleury-sur-Loire, France | Pillaged by soldiers of Condé. |
| 1622 | Henrico College, Jamestown, Virginia | Burned by Indians. |
| 1649 | Augustinian Library, Mainz | |
| 1666 | London Libraries | Three-day Great Fire of London. |
| | Guild Hall Library | |
| | Royal College of Physicians Library | Founded 1518. |
| | Sion College Library | Founded 1635. |
| | Society of Apothecorios | Founded 1635. |
| | Merchant Taylors School Library | |
| 1674 | Escorial Library, Spain | Started by lightning. 8,000 Arabic books lost. |
| 1685 | Canons of St. Antonio Library, Venice | |
| 1697 | Royal Libraries, Stockholm | Library dated from 1585. |

| YEAR | LIBRARY | REMARKS |
|---|---|---|
| 1728 | Vetus Bibliotheca, University of Copenhagen, Denmark | Library dated from 1482. |
| 1728 | Dominican Library, Stockholm | |
| 1731 | Burgundian Library, Brussels | Founded 1361; state archives destroyed. |
| 1731 | King's and Cottonian Libraries, Westminster, England | Collection of the British Museum. |
| 1747 | Boston Public Library | Founded 1656. |
| 1764 | Harvard Library | Destroyed most of the collection of 5,000 volumes. |
| 1777 | Electorial Library, Bonn, Germany | |
| 1780 | Earl of Mansfield Library, London | Destroyed during Gordon Riots. |
| 1812 | Moscow Library, Russia | Burned in Napoleonic invasion. |
| 1814 | Library of Congress | Burned by British during War of 1812. |
| 1825 | Library of Congress | Heavy damage to collection. |
| 1827 | University and Cathedral Library, Abo, Finland | |
| 1831 | Bristol Library | Riot, civil commotion. |
| 1834 | House of Commons Library | Palace of Westminster also burned in same fire. |
| 1851 | Library of Congress | Unattended fireplaces — about 35,000 volumes lost. |
| 1854 | Indiana University, Bloomington, Indiana | Another fire in 1883. |
| 1865 | State Library, Columbus, South Carolina | |
| 1870 | University of Strassburg | Burned in Franco-Prussian War; library founded in 1621. |

| YEAR | LIBRARY | REMARKS |
|---|---|---|
| 1871 | Chicago libraries | Great Chicago Fire. |
| 1871 | Historical Library of Paris | Burned in Franco-Prussian War. |
| 1872 | Escorial Library, Madrid | Upper Library destroyed. |
| 1873 | Manchester Athenium Library | 19,000-volume library; complete loss. |
| 1879 | Birmingham Free Library | Complete loss, including Shakespeare, Staunton, and Cervantes collections valued at 60,000 pounds. |
| 1879 | Mercantile Library, Philadelphia | |
| 1879 | Irkutoh Geographical Library | |
| 1879 | Notre Dame University, South Bend, Indiana | |
| 1885 | Aberystwith Welch University Library | Total loss. |
| 1886 | Brussels University | |
| 1888 | State Teachers' College, Terre Haute, Indiana | |
| 1888 | Dakota Wesleyan University, Mitchell, North Dakota | Completely destroyed. |
| 1890 | Art Library of Laeken | Total loss. |
| 1890 | University of Toronto Library | Total loss. |
| 1892 | University of Missouri, Columbia, Missouri | Completed destroyed. |
| 1896 | College Library, South Hadley, Massachusetts | |
| 1903 | University of Oklahoma, Norman, Oklahoma | Loss about $36,000. |
| 1904 | National University, Turin | Valuable manuscripts lost. |

| YEAR | LIBRARY | REMARKS |
|------|---------|---------|
| 1906 | San Francisco, California Libraries | Earthquake caused conflagration. |
| 1908 | University of Messina, Italy | Destroyed as result of earthquake. |
| 1910 | Kenyon College Library, Gambier, Ohio | |
| 1911 | State Library, Albany, New York | Major damage. |
| 1914 | Louvain University, Belgium | Incendiary fire: 211,000 volumes lost during German occupation. |
| 1915 | Public Library, St. Paul, Minnesota | |
| 1916 | College Library, Chestertown, Maryland | |
| 1920 | University of Texas Chemistry Department, Austin, Texas | |
| 1921 | Public Library, Middletown, Delaware | |
| 1923 | Public Library, Burlington, Colorado | |
| 1923 | College Library, Spearfish, South Dakota | |
| 1927 | Westminster College, New Wilmington, Pennsylvania | |
| 1927 | Jones Library, Amherst, Massachusetts | |
| 1927 | Public Library, Shawnee, Oklahoma | |
| 1928 | Enoch Pratt Free Library, Baltimore, Maryland | 2,000 books lost. |
| 1929 | Public Library, Marion, South Carolina | |

| YEAR | LIBRARY | REMARKS |
|------|---------|---------|
| 1929 | Fiske Library, Claremont, New Hampshire | |
| 1929 | County Library, Fairfield, California | Located in high school. |
| 1930 | State College Library, Moorhead, Minnesota | |
| 1931 | Public Library, Boston, Massachusetts | Fire in waste paper chute. Loss about $250. |
| 1932 | North Carolina College for Women, Greensboro, North Carolina | |
| 1932 | Newspaper Library, Kansas City, Missouri | Loss about $25,000. |
| 1933 | University Library, Nashville, Tennessee | |
| 1934 | Branch Library, Pittsburgh, Pennsylvania | One death from smoke. |
| 1934 | Washington and Lee University, Lexington, Virginia | Loss about $85,000. |
| 1934 | Municipal Library, Seminole, Oklahoma | Gas explosion; three killed; $35,000 loss. |
| 1936 | Public Library, Bandon, Oregon | |
| 1936 | Public Library, Chelsea, Massachusetts | Painters' supplies; spontaneous combustion. Loss about $5,800. |
| 1937 | County Library, Nashville, Tennessee | Loss about $10,000. |
| 1937 | Branch Library, Tahoe City, California | |
| 1937 | Public Library, Charlotte, North Carolina | |
| 1939 | Olivet Nazarene College, Kankakee, Illinois | Loss about $20,000. |

| YEAR | LIBRARY | REMARKS |
|---|---|---|
| 1939 | Toledo Public Library | Insurance adjustment problems encountered with this fire. |
| 1939-1945 | European libraries in World War II | Heavy loss and destruction of millions of volumes. Sixty county libraries destroyed in England; loss over one million volumes. Guildhall Library, London, destroyed. Greys Inn Library destroyed. Deutsche Bucherei lost 400,-000 volumes, 1943; German Government libraries lost 1,110,000 volumes. |
| 1941 | University Library, Spokane, Washington | |
| 1941 | Public Library, Logansport, Indiana | |
| 1941 | Hampden Sydney College, Hampden-Sydney, Virginia | Periodical collection destroyed. |
| 1941 | Tucson Public Library, Tucson, Arizona | Roof and lobby damaged; loss about $22,000. |
| 1942 | Forbes Library, Northampton, Massachusetts | |
| 1942 | County Library, Elko, Montana | |
| 1942 | St. Francis College, Loretto, Pennsylvania | Completely destroyed; another fire in 1958. |
| 1942 | Regional Library, Yanceyville, North Carolina | |
| 1943 | Willimantic State College Library, Willimantic, Connecticut | |
| 1943 | National Library, Lima, Peru | |

| YEAR | LIBRARY | REMARKS |
|---|---|---|
| 1944 | County Library, Lenoir, North Carolina | |
| 1947 | Public Library, Pascagoula, Mississippi | Complete destruction. |
| 1948 | Public Library, Wyoming, Ohio | Loss about $73,000. |
| 1948 | Public Library, Staunton, Virginia | |
| 1948 | College of Southern Utah, Cedar City, Utah | Loss about $150,000. |
| 1948 | Public Library, Tomah, Wisconsin | |
| 1948 | Public Library, Smyrna, Delaware | |
| 1949 | Law Library, Port Huron, Michigan | |
| 1949 | Music Library, Philadelphia, Pennsylvania | Plumber's blowtorch. |
| 1949 | County Library, Conway, South Carolina | School fire. |
| 1950 | Walsh Memorial Library, Ouray, Colorado | |
| 1950 | Village Library, North Walpole, Massachusetts | Completely destroyed. |
| 1950 | Ferris Institute, Big Rapids, Michigan | |
| 1950 | Colorado School for Blind, Colorado Springs, Colorado | Fire of electrical origin. |
| 1950 | Bureau of Government Library, University of Michigan, Ann Arbor, Michigan | Incendiary origin; loss about $637,000. |
| 1950 | Public Library, Brooklyn, New York | Incendiary origin; loss about $15,000. |

| YEAR | LIBRARY | REMARKS |
|---|---|---|
| 1951 | State Museum Library, Columbus, Ohio | Loss about $100,000. |
| 1951 | Harper Library, University of Chicago, Chicago, Illinois | |
| 1951 | Public Library, New York, New York | Loss about $250. |
| 1951 | State Library, Lansing, Michigan | Water damage from fire of incendiary origin in office building. |
| 1952 | Public Library, Monroe, Oregon | Total loss. |
| 1952 | Public Library, Gaylord, Michigan | |
| 1952 | Snow Library, Orleans, Massachusetts | Electrical origin; loss about $75,999. |
| 1952 | Central Library, San Diego, California | Visual Education Center; loss about $200,000. |
| 1952 | County Library, Newton, South Carolina | |
| 1952 | University Library, Oklahoma City, Oklahoma | |
| 1952 | Branch Library, Loomis, California | |
| 1952 | Library of Parliament, Ottawa, Ontario, Canada | Fire of electrical origin; heavy water damage. |
| 1953 | Town Library, Boxboro, Massachusetts | Overheated chimney; loss about $13,000; frame building built in 1775. |
| 1953 | Humboldt County Library, Eureka, California | $90,000 loss; complete destruction. |
| 1953 | Public Library, Monroe, Oregon | |
| 1953 | Beloit College Library, Beloit, Wisconsin | |

| YEAR | LIBRARY | REMARKS |
|------|---------|---------|
| 1954 | University Library, Nashville, Tennessee | 7,990 volumes lost due to misuse of water. |
| 1955 | Public Library, Montclair, New Jersey | Explosion. |
| 1955 | Loyola College, Baltimore, Maryland | |
| 1955 | Public Library, Peacham, Vermont | |
| 1955 | Public Library, Benton, Illinois | |
| 1955 | Dakota Wesleyan University, Mitchell, South Dakota | Completely destroyed; loss about $250,000 (see fire of 1886). |
| 1955 | Buck Library, Portland, Connecticut | |
| 1956 | County Library, Conway, South Carolina | Community depository. |
| 1956 | Dunklin County Library, Kennet, Missouri | |
| 1956 | Public Library, Malden, Massachusetts | |
| 1956 | Public Library, Edwardsville, Illinois | Improper use of fireplaces; damage about $65,000. |
| 1956 | Hospital Library, Moncton, New Brunswick, Canada | Caused by smoking; damage $35,000. |
| 1956 | Public Library, Murphysboro, Illinois | |
| 1956 | Public Library Branch, Hartford, Connecticut | |
| 1957 | Branch Library, Evergreen, Louisiana | Lost when school burned. |
| 1957 | Association Library, Butler, New Jersey | |
| 1957 | Rogers Free Library, Bristol, Rhode Island | Heavy damage; loss about $73,000. |

| YEAR | LIBRARY | REMARKS |
|------|---------|---------|
| 1957 | Doheny Library, University of Southern California | |
| 1957 | Branch Library, Big Bend, California | |
| 1957 | Branch Library, Cleveland, Ohio | Loss about $200,000. |
| 1957 | Public Library, Colville, Washington | Loss about $10,000. |
| 1958 | Louisiana State University Library, Baton Rouge, Louisiana | Careless smoking; minor damage. |
| 1958 | State Library, Baton Rouge, Louisiana | Faulty design of lights; minor damage. |
| 1958 | Umatilla Women's Club Library, Umatilla, Florida | |
| 1958 | St. Francis College, Loretto, Pennsylvania | Completely destroyed (see fire of 1942). |
| 1958 | School Library, Maplewood, New Jersey | |
| 1958 | Public Library, Galesburg, Illinois | Electrical origin; loss about $650,000; complete destruction. |
| 1958 | Bar Association Library, Detroit, Michigan | Smoke from fire in same building. |
| 1958 | Private Library, Atlantic City, New Jersey | Located in mercantile building. |
| 1959 | Department of Health Library, Oak Park, Illinois | |
| 1959 | Public Library, Austin, Minnesota | |
| 1959 | High School Library, Wilburton, Oklahoma | |
| 1959 | Lewis College, Lockport, Illinois | Electrical origin; loss about $200,000. |

| YEAR | LIBRARY | REMARKS |
| --- | --- | --- |
| 1959 | Public Library, Waterville, Maine | Electrical origin; loss about $40,000. |
| 1959 | Columbia University, New York, New York | Loss about $17,500. |
| 1959 | Public Library, Bayonne, New Jersey | Incendiary origin; loss about $800,000. |
| 1959 | Village Library, Lanark, Ontario, Canada | Spread of lumberyard fire; destroyed library. |
| 1959 | Public Library, Arcanum, Ohio | |
| 1959 | Cape Breton Regional Library, Sydney, Nova Scotia, Canada | Started during building repairs; 19,000 volumes lost. |
| 1960 | Public Library, Butte, Montana | Loss about $175,000. |
| 1960 | Public Library, Reading, Pennsylvania | |
| 1960 | Public Library, Mt. Jewett, Pennsylvania | |
| 1960 | Branch Library, Ackerman, Mississippi | |
| 1960 | County Library, Conway, South Carolina | Community depository. |
| 1960 | Branch Library, Standfield, Oregon | |
| 1960 | Blackburn College, Carlinville, Illinois | Water and smoke damage. |
| 1960 | Municipal Library, Hull, Quebec, Canada | Fire from adjoining building: $35,000 damage. |
| 1960 | Public Library, Wellfleet, Massachusetts | |
| 1960 | USWES Research Library, Vicksburg, Mississippi | Complete destruction. |
| 1960 | Hackensack, New Jersey | |
| 1960 | Wheaton College, Norton, Massachusetts | Sparks from welder's torch; loss about $20,000. |

| YEAR | LIBRARY | REMARKS |
|------|---------|---------|
| 1960 | Bucknell University, Lewisburg, Pennsylvania | Loss reported at $160,000. |
| 1961 | Branch Library, Austin, Texas | Electrical origin. |
| 1961 | School Library, Concord, New Hampshire | |
| 1961 | High School Library, Tomball, Texas | |
| 1961 | Public Library, Babylon, New York | |
| 1961 | University Library, Ann Arbor, Michigan | |
| 1961 | Public Library, Remington, Indiana | Loss in excess of $40,000; total loss to collection; electrical origin. |
| 1961 | Research Library, Washington, D. C. | Fire in air conditioner; smoke damage to books. |
| 1961 | School Library, Kansas City, Kansas | Incendiary origin; loss about $8,000. |
| 1961 | University of Hawaii, Honolulu | Private collection; marine research materials. |
| 1962 | Grambling College Library, Grambling, Louisiana | Fire started during severe thunderstorm. Almost 50,000 books destroyed. |
| 1962 | University of Florida Law Library | Damage about $100,000. |
| 1962 | Far Rockaway Branch, Public Library, Queens Borough, New York | Suspicious origin; loss of 10,000 books. |
| 1962 | Library of Institute of Experimental Medicine and Surgery, University of Montreal | $250,000 loss; valuable cross-index system destroyed. |

# APPENDIX C

## Earthquake Probabilities

Earthquake experience in the United States is studied and re-ported upon by the Coast and Geodetic Survey of the Department of Commerce. The results are presented in an annual publication, *United States Earthquakes,* usually printed about a year or so after the close of the period covered. The seismic map shown here is reproduced from the current volume and shows major earthquakes through 1958.

The seismic map indicates four levels of earthquake intensity, refers to the degree of shock, area affected, and damage caused.

Small dots ............................Intensity VII to VIII
Large dots ............................Intensity VIII to IX
Small circled dots ....................Intensity IX to X
Large circled dots ....................Intensity X to XII

Numerals refer to repeated quake experiences.

Intensities used by Coast and Geodetic Survey refer to the Modified Mercalli Scale of 1931. In abridged form, the upper part of the scale is shown below.

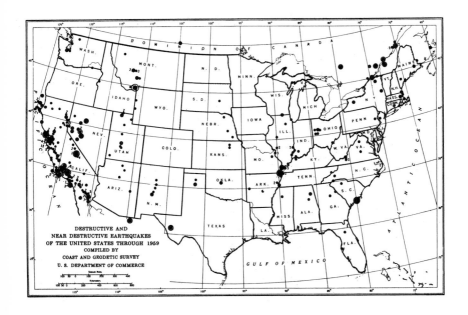

231

    VI. Felt by all, many frightened and run outdoors. Some heavy furniture moved; a few instances of fallen plaster or damaged chimneys. Damage slight. (VI to VII Rossi-Forel Scale.)

    VII. Everybody runs outdoors. Damage negligible in buildings of good design and construction; slight to moderate in well-built ordinary structures; considerable in poorly built or badly designed structures; some chimneys broken. Noticed by persons driving motorcars. (VIII Rossi-Forel Scale.)

    VIII. Damage slight in specially designed structures; considerable in ordinary substantial buildings, with partial collapse; great in poorly built structures. Fall of chimneys, factory stacks, columns, monuments, walls. Heavy furniture overturned. Sand and mud ejected in small amounts. Changes in well water. Persons driving motorcars disturbed. (VIII+ to IX-Rossi-Forel Scale.)

    IX. Damage considerable in specially designed structures; well-designed frame structures thrown out of plumb; great in substantial buildings, with partial collapse. Buildings shifted off foundations. Ground cracked conspicuously. Underground pipes broken. (IX+ Rossi-Forel Scale.)

    X. Some well-built wooden structures destroyed; most masonry and frame structures destroyed with foundations; ground badly cracked. Rails bent. Landslides considerable from riverbanks and steep slopes. Shifted sand and mud. Water splashed (slopped) over tanks. (X-Rossi-Forel Scale.)

    XI. Few, if any (masonry), structures remain standing. Bridges destroyed. Broad fissures in ground. Underground pipelines completely out of service. Earth slumps and land slips in soft ground. Rails bent greatly.

    XII. Damage total. Waves seen on ground surfaces. Lines of sight and level distorted. Objects thrown upward into air.

An intensity of VII (small dot) would indicate a shock affecting an area of over 25,000 square miles. The largest circled dots would involve areas over 1,000,000 square miles.

Full details for any given year are published in *United States Earthquakes* for that year. These are available from 1928 to the current year.

A history of the more important shocks appears in Serial 609 *Earthquake History of the United States*. Part I covers the continental United States and Alaska, exclusive of California and western Nevada. Part II covers California and western Nevada.

The effect of earthquake probability is recognized in varying degrees in the nationally recognized building codes. The most complete documentation is probably that of the Uniform Building Code, which includes a seismic map and sets up three area classifications in accordance with earthquake risk.

# APPENDIX D

## Fire and Insurance Protection
## of Library Resources — Questionnaire

The objective of this questionnaire is to produce a reasonably accurate picture of the factors affecting fire and insurance coverage in libraries and of loss experience in those libraries where fire and other losses have occurred.

It is divided into six categories:

    A. The Library Building
    B. Internal Features
    C. Library Operations
    D. Physical Protective Measures
    E. Financial Protective Measures
    F. Loss Experience

Statistical and engineering analysis of the data submitted by many librarians, supplemented by further study of specific problem areas, will lead to the development of appropriate corrective measures in a realistic manner. The results of this project should benefit all librarians.

Answers in Categories A, B, C, and D should be given only for your principal library building. Similar information on other buildings or system branches may be appended. Answers given in Categories E and F should apply to all of your resources. Additional copies of the questionnaire are available on request.

Two copies are enclosed so that one may be used as a work sheet and retained for your file, if desired. A stamped return envelope is also enclosed. It is requested that the form be completed by writing in or checking as appropriate, and that it be returned promptly to:

### GAGE-BABCOCK & ASSOCIATES, INC.

### A. THE LIBRARY BUILDING

1. Year constructed_____

2. Ground floor area_____

3. Total floor area_____

4. Stories above grade_____

5. Stories below grade_____

6. Total cubical content of building_____

7. Is building owned by the Library operating organization?
   Yes ☐   No ☐

8. Is the Library the sole occupant of the building? Yes ☐   No ☐

9. If not, what is the nature of the other occupancy?_____

_____

10. The Library occupies_____% of the area, and_____% of the volume of the building.

11. How do the local building officials class the construction?
    (a) Fire resistive, noncombustible ☐, (b) ordinary combustible (masonry outer walls, wood interiors) ☐, (c) wood frame combustible ☐.

12. Floor finish is (a) Cement ☐, (b) Stone ☐, (c) Terrazzo ☐, (d) Wood ☐, (e) Tile ☐, (f) Carpeting ☐.

13. Major wall finishes are (a) Glass ☐, (b) Plaster ☐, (c) Wood Paneling ☐, (d) Fiberboard ☐, (e) Plastic ☐, (f) with Combustible Drapes ☐, (g) Noncombustible Drapes ☐, (h) Flameproofed Drapes ☐.

14. Ceiling finishes are (a) Plaster (stone or concrete) ☐, (b) Metal ☐, (c) Wood ☐, (d) Combustible Acoustical Tile ☐, (e) Noncombustible Tile ☐.

15. Does the building have an attic space? Yes ☐   No ☐

16. If Yes, is it used for storage purposes? Yes ☐   No ☐

17. Are at least two exits provided from each major occupied area?
    Yes ☐   No ☐

18. Are the exits marked or lighted? Yes ☐   No ☐

19. Does the building contain a central heating system?
    Yes ☐   No ☐

20. Is the building heated by (a) Space Heaters ☐, (b) Hot Air ☐, (c) Steam Radiation ☐, (d) Electric Heaters ☐.

21. Heating system fuel is (a) Coal ☐, (b) Wood ☐, (c) Fuel Oil ☐, (d) Gas ☐, (e) Electricity ☐.

22. Is the Library air conditioned?  Yes ☐   No ☐

23. Can the system be readily shut down to prevent recirculation and spread of smoke in an emergency?  Yes ☐   No ☐

## B.  INTERNAL FEATURES

24.  What is a rough percentage of your book storage capacity in
(a) Open Shelf Areas_____ (b) Free Standing Stacks_____
(c)  Conventional  Self-Supporting  Multi-Tier  Stacks_____
Number of levels_____ (d)  Single-Tier Stacks attached to
floor and ceilings_____

25.  Are you equipped with book elevators?   Yes ☐   No ☐

26.  Are they enclosed to impede propagation of smoke, heat and
fire?   Yes ☐   No ☐

27.  Are you equipped with passenger/freight elevators?
Yes ☐   No ☐

28.  Are they enclosed to impede propagation of smoke, heat, and
fire?   Yes ☐   No ☐

29.  If there are a number of stack levels are they provided with
fire or smoke barriers so that fire and smoke would be confined
to the area of origin?   Yes ☐   No ☐

30.  Are there meeting or assembly rooms associated with the
Library?   Yes ☐   No ☐
If so, what is the approximate capacity of the largest room?
_____persons.

31.  Are these rooms located or segregated so as not to expose the
collection in case of fire emergency?   Yes ☐   No ☐

32.  Does the Library design include rooms with ceilings well over
10 ft.?   Yes ☐   No ☐

33.  Are mezzanine stack floors used in connection with such rooms?
Yes ☐   No ☐

## C.  LIBRARY OPERATIONS

34.  How many hours/week is the Library open?_____

35.  How many hours/week is the Library closed and completely
unattended?_____

36.  Is any routine watchman service used?   Yes ☐   No ☐

37.  Is any building security check made at closing time?
Yes ☐   No ☐

38.  Where is smoking permitted? (a) Not permitted ☐, (b) Reading Rooms ☐, (c) Public Areas ☐, (d) Stack Areas ☐, (e)
Staff Offices, Rooms and Lounges ☐, (f) Carrels ☐, (g) Vaults

☐, (h) Work Areas ☐, (i) Building Utility Areas ☐, (j) Designated Smoking Areas ☐.

39. Do you have a vault? Yes ☐ No ☐ 39a Is the vault air conditioned? Yes ☐ No ☐ 39b If so, what temperature _____and humidity_____are maintained? 39c What materials are kept in the vault?_____

_____

_____

40. Are any stairway enclosures between floors kept closed at all times, or are the doors apt to be blocked open at times? (a) No Enclosures ☐, (b) Always Closed ☐, (c) Occasionally Open ☐, (d) Always Open ☐.

41. What is the approximate number of volumes in your collection?

Fiction _____

Archives _____

Phonograph Records_____

Special groups including rare books and art objects_____

Bound and Unbound Serials_____

Reference and Technical Books_____

Magnetic Tapes_____

Motion Picture Films_____

Microfilm Material_____

Bound and Unbound Reports_____

42. Are the patrons allowed access to stack areas? (a) Full Access ☐, (b) Limited Access ☐, (c) No Access ☐.

43. Are bookmobiles used in the Library operation? Yes ☐ No ☐

44. Does the Library participate in an area or centralized catalog system? Yes ☐ No ☐

44a. If your card catalog were to be lost in a fire could you reconstitute it from one of the above? (a) Yes ☐ (b) No ☐ (c) Partially ☐ (d) Any other method? ☐

## D. PHYSICAL PROTECTIVE MEASURES

45. What is the status of the local fire department? (a) None ☐, (b) Volunteer ☐, (c) Paid ☐.

46. Is there a Library building fire alarm system? Yes ☐ No ☐

47. What means are used to alert the fire department? (a) City Box ☐, (b) Street Fire Phone ☐, (c) Private Phone Call ☐.

48. Is a fire alarm box located at, in, or close to the Library? Yes ☐ No ☐

49. Does the fire department regularly inspect the Library? Yes ☐ No ☐

50. Does your insurance company or other agency inspect the Library? Yes ☐ No ☐

51. Have you acquainted the fire department with the potential water damage which could result from the ill-considered use of hose lines in a fire emergency? Yes ☐ No ☐

52. Do the fire and/or police departments have emergency access to the Library? Yes ☐ No ☐

53. Are any fire detection systems installed in the Library building? Yes ☐ No ☐

53a. If answer is yes, what type? (a) Heat Sensing ☐, (b) Smoke Sensing ☐.

53b. Where are fire alarms transmitted? (a) Fire Department ☐, (b) Local in Building ☐.

54. Are any theft or burglar alarms installed? Yes ☐ No ☐

54a. Where are alarms transmitted? To (a) Police Department ☐, (b) Local in Building ☐.

55. If security type locks are installed on doors intended only for emergency egress, are they equipped with electrical alarms? Yes ☐ No ☐

55a. Where are alarms transmitted? To (a) Police Department ☐, (b) Local in Building ☐.

56. What types of hand fire extinguishers are provided? (a) Soda-Acid ☐, (b) Pressurized Water ☐, (c) Carbon Dioxide ☐, (d) Vaporizing Liquid ☐, (e) Foam ☐, (f) Dry Chemical ☐.

56a. Are they of such size that female personnel could not conveniently use them? Yes ☐ No ☐

57. Are fire hose stations provided in the Building? Yes ☐ No ☐

57a. Hose size: (a) 2½ in. ☐, (b) 1½ in. ☐, (c) smaller ☐.

58. Are any areas equipped with installed fire extinguishing systems? Yes ☐ No ☐

58a. What type: (a) Automatic Sprinklers ☐, (b) Carbon Dioxide ☐, (c) Dry Chemical ☐.

58b. How extensive is the coverage?  Complete ☐, Partial ☐.

58c. If partial, what do you have protected?_____

_____

_____

_____

## E.  FINANCIAL PROTECTIVE MEASURES

59.  Is your Library covered by any insurance measures?
Yes ☐   No ☐

59a. Please indicate the amounts of any coverage:

    (a)  Building                         $_____

    (b)  Contents  (inclusive)       $_____

    (c)  Furniture and Fixtures    $_____

    (d)  Card Catalog               $_____

    (e)  Valuable papers and Manuscripts $_____

    (f)  Rare books and Fine Art objects  $_____

    (g)  Shelf list                    $_____

    (h)  Other items                $_____

59b. Coverage is against  (a)  Fire ☐,  (b)  Flood ☐,  (c)  Water
Damage ☐,  (d)  Vandalism ☐,  (e)  Mutilation ☐,  (f)  Windstorm ☐,  (g)  Theft ☐,  (h)  Explosion ☐,  (i)  Earthquake ☐.

60.  Are there any laws or local ordinances which regulate or restrict the placement of insurance on your resources?_____
If so, please comment_____

_____

61.  Is the extent of insurance coverage determined by the Librarian
or other Management groups? Librarian ☐, Other Groups ☐.

62.  Is the purchase of insurance a responsibility of the Librarian
or others?  Librarian ☐, Others ☐.

63.  Would the cost of insurance be charged against the Library
budget?  Yes ☐   No ☐

64.  Do you insure collections or loans for which you are responsible while they are in your possession?  Yes ☐   No ☐

65. Do you insure resources which are off your premises and not in branches or bookmobiles? Yes ☐ No ☐

66. If you have been insured and experienced a loss, did you encounter any difficulties in establishing the amount involved and securing a satisfactory adjustment? (a) Yes ☐ (b) No ☐ (c) Have not experienced losses ☐

67. If yes, why? _____
    _____

68. How did you establish the necessary proof of loss?_____
    _____

69. Was the recovered money made available to you for replacement of resources? Yes ☐ No ☐

70. In case of fire, would your shelf list establish proof of incurred losses? Yes ☐ No ☐

71. If not, what other records would be needed?_____
    _____

72. Is your shelf list protected by a fire resistant safe? Yes ☐ No ☐

73. Do you maintain microfilm records of your (a) Shelf list? ☐ (b) Card catalog? ☐ or (c) Other vital documents? ☐ or (d) Do not use microfilm for this purpose. ☐

74. If yes, are the microfilms protected against damage or loss? Yes ☐ No ☐

75. If yes, how do you maintain the film record current?_____
    _____

76. If you were not insured and experienced a loss, how did you finance replacement of resources?_____
    _____

## F. LOSS EXPERIENCE

There are currently insufficient data on the frequency, causes and costs of loss occurrences in libraries. A complete listing of all such known occurrences is requested. Minor occurrences should be included even though there may have been no appreciable damage and no loss claimed. They sometimes become serious, and have a bearing on the total exposure to losses.

77. In your Library system, what loss experience have you had from 19_____ to date with

    (a) Fire?                  Number_____ Est. $ loss_____

(b) Water, flood,
    leaky pipes?        Number_____ Est. $ loss_____

(c) Mold or mildew?    Number_____ Est. $ loss_____

(d) Windstorm?         Number_____ Est. $ loss_____

(e) Vandalism or
    mutilation?        Number_____ Est. $ loss_____

(f) Vermin?            Number_____ Est. $ loss_____

(g) Theft?             Number_____ Est. $ loss_____

(h) Explosion?         Number_____ Est. $ loss_____

(i) Earthquake?        Number_____ Est. $ loss_____

Narrative accounts or details for above items would be appreciated. If more space is needed, separate sheets should be attached _____

78. Do you know of loss experience in other libraries which may not be reached by this questionnaire and which should be further investigated as part of this research study? If so, please advise name of library, location and approximate date of loss occurrence so that it may be followed up.

# APPENDIX E

## Library Fire Loss Summary
## From 1911 through 1961

| | COLLEGE AND UNIVERSITY LIBRARIES | | | |
|---|---|---|---|---|
| | Libraries Reporting Fires | Number of Fires Reported | Number Giving Loss Value | Dollar Loss |
| Alabama | | | | |
| Arizona | | | | |
| Arkansas | | | | |
| California | | | | |
| Colorado | 1 | 1 | 1 | $ 353,000 |
| Connecticut | 2 | 3 | | |
| Delaware | 1 | 1 | 1 | 3,000 |
| Washington, D. C. | | | | |
| Florida | | | | |
| Georgia | | | | |
| Idaho | | | | |
| Illinois | 5 | 5 | 4 | 429,000 |
| Indiana | | | | |
| Iowa | 1 | 1 | 1 | 250 |
| Kansas | 1 | 1 | 1 | 298,000 |
| Kentucky | | | | |
| Louisiana | 1 | 1 | 1 | 250 |
| Maine | 1 | 2 | 1 | 400 |
| Maryland | 2 | 2 | 2 | 5,500 |
| Massachusetts | 4 | 4 | 3 | 52,384 |
| Michigan | 2 | 2 | 1 | 84,248 |
| Minnesota | 2 | 5 | 5 | 75,450 |
| Mississippi | | | | |
| Missouri | | | | |
| Montana | | | | |
| Nebraska | 2 | 3 | 1 | 600 |
| Nevada | | | | |
| New Hampshire | 1 | 1 | 1 | 25 |
| New Jersey | | | | |
| New Mexico | | | | |
| New York | 5 | 6 | 5 | 30,250 |
| North Carolina | 1 | 1 | 1 | 20,000 |
| North Dakota | | | | |
| Ohio | 4 | 4 | 2 | 1,550 |
| Oklahoma | 3 | 3 | 1 | 36,000 |
| Oregon | | | | |
| Pennsylvania | 3 | 6 | 4 | 700,100 |
| Rhode Island | 2 | 2 | 1 | 85 |
| South Carolina | | | | |
| South Dakota | 4 | 4 | 3 | 315,025 |
| Tennessee | 1 | 1 | 1 | 15,000 |
| Texas | 2 | 2 | 1 | 20,000 |
| Utah | 1 | 1 | 1 | 150,000 |
| Vermont | | | | |
| Virginia | 3 | 3 | 2 | 111,777 |
| Washington | 1 | 1 | | |
| West Virginia | | | | |
| Wisconsin | 1 | 1 | | |
| Wyoming | | | | |
| Canada | | | | |
| Totals | 57 | 67 | 45 | $2,701,894 |

| | PUBLIC LIBRARIES | | | | SPECIAL LIBRARIES | | |
|---|---|---|---|---|---|---|---|
| Libraries Reporting Fires | Number of Fires Reported | Number Giving Loss Value | Dollar Loss | Libraries Reporting Fires | Number of Fires Reported | Number Giving Loss Value | Dollar Loss |
| 1 | 1 | 1 | $ 28,581 | | | | |
| 16 | 27 | 27 | 208,785 | | | | |
| 1 | 1 | | | | | | |
| 2 | 2 | | | | | | |
| | | | | 1 | 1 | | |
| 2 | 7 | 4 | 2,000 | | | | |
| 9 | 10 | 7 | 717,200 | 1 | 1 | | |
| 4 | 4 | 1 | 10 | | | | |
| 3 | 3 | 2 | 177 | | | | |
| 2 | 2 | 2 | 40,174 | | | | |
| 1 | 1 | | | | | | |
| 7 | 7 | 7 | 111,464 | | | | |
| 7 | 7 | 5 | 9,090 | 2 | 2 | 1 | $ 3,670 |
| 4 | 4 | 2 | 150 | | | | |
| 3 | 3 | 1 | 975 | | | | |
| 5 | 7 | 6 | 40,563 | | | | |
| 1 | 1 | 1 | 175,000 | | | | |
| 1 | 1 | | | | | | |
| 3 | 3 | | | | | | |
| 5 | 5 | 4 | 506,800 | | | | |
| 1 | 1 | 1 | 50 | | | | |
| 9 | 11 | 8 | 56,041 | | | | |
| 5 | 5 | 2 | 17,500 | | | | |
| 1 | 1 | | | | | | |
| 8 | 12 | 8 | 78,456 | 1 | 1 | 1 | 100,000 |
| 2 | 3 | 3 | 160,000 | | | | |
| 2 | 2 | 1 | 42,000 | | | | |
| 1 | 1 | 3 | | 2 | 2 | | |
| 1 | 1 | 1 | 73,000 | | | | |
| 2 | 4 | 3 | 500 | | | | |
| 2 | 2 | 2 | 18,000 | | | | |
| 2 | 2 | 2 | 585 | | | | |
| 1 | 1 | 1 | 1,333 | | | | |
| 2 | 2 | | | | | | |
| 2 | 2 | 1 | 5,300 | | | | |
| 1 | 1 | 1 | 10,000 | | | | |
| 2 | 3 | 2 | 708 | | | | |
| 4 | 4 | 4 | 359,985 | 1 | 1 | 1 | 35,000 |
| 125 | 154 | 113 | $2,664,427 | 8 | 8 | 3 | $138,670 |

| | GOVERNMENT LIBRARIES | | | |
|---|---|---|---|---|
| | Libraries Reporting Fires | Number of Fires Reported | Number Giving Loss Value | Dollar Loss |
| Alabama | | | | |
| Arizona | | | | |
| Arkansas | 1 | 1 | | |
| California | | | | |
| Colorado | | | | |
| Connecticut | | | | |
| Delaware | | | | |
| Washington, D. C. | 2 | 2 | | |
| Florida | | | | |
| Georgia | | | | |
| Idaho | | | | |
| Illinois | | | | |
| Indiana | | | | |
| Iowa | | | | |
| Kansas | | | | |
| Kentucky | 1 | 1 | 1 | $ 1,30 |
| Louisiana | 1 | 1 | | |
| Maine | | | | |
| Maryland | | | | |
| Massachusetts | | | | |
| Michigan | | | | |
| Minnesota | | | | |
| Mississippi | 1 | 1 | 1 | 500,00 |
| Missouri | | | | |
| Montana | | | | |
| Nebraska | | | | |
| Nevada | | | | |
| New Hampshire | | | | |
| New Jersey | | | | |
| New Mexico | | | | |
| New York | 1 | 1 | 1 | 5,000,00 |
| North Carolina | | | | |
| North Dakota | | | | |
| Ohio | | | | |
| Oklahoma | | | | |
| Oregon | 1 | 3 | 3 | 2 |
| Pennsylvania | 1 | 2 | | |
| Rhode Island | | | | |
| South Carolina | | | | |
| South Dakota | | | | |
| Tennessee | | | | |
| Texas | | | | |
| Utah | | | | |
| Vermont | | | | |
| Virginia | | | | |
| Washington | | | | |
| West Virginia | | | | |
| Wisconsin | | | | |
| Wyoming | | | | |
| Canada | 1 | 1 | 1 | 175,00 |
| Totals | 10 | 13 | 7 | $5,676,32 |

| FIRE LOSSES OUTSIDE LIBRARIES | | | | ARSON FIRE LOSSES | | | |
|---|---|---|---|---|---|---|---|
| Libraries Reporting Fires | Number of Fires Reported | Number Giving Loss Value | Dollar Loss | Libraries Reporting Fires | Number of Fires Reported | Number Giving Loss Value | Dollar Loss |
| 3 | 2 | 2 | $ 219 | | | | |
| 5 | 23 | 21 | 3,541 | | | | |
| 1 | 1 | | | | | | |
| | | | | 1 | 1 | 1 | $ 8,000 |
| 1 | 6 | 6 | 1,300 | | | | |
| 1 | 1 | 1 | 100 | | | | |
| 1 | 10 | 10 | 111 | | | | |
| | | | | 1 | 1 | 1 | 2,850,000 |
| 1 | 1 | 1 | 3,000 | | | | |
| 1 | 52 | 52 | 111 | 1 | 1 | 1 | 200 |
| 1 | 2 | 2 | 1,000 | 2 | 2 | 2 | 800,125 |
| | | | | 1 | 1 | 1 | 15,000 |
| 1 | 2 | | | 1 | 1 | 1 | 250,000 |
| 3 | 5 | 5 | 586 | | | | |
| | | | | 2 | 2 | 2 | 28,404 |
| 1 | 1 | | | | | | |
| 1 | 1 | | | | | | |
| | | | | 1 | 1 | 1 | 300 |
| 21 | 107 | 100 | $9,968 | 10 | 10 | 10 | $3,952,029 |

| | TOTAL FIRE LOSSES | | | |
|---|---|---|---|---|
| | Libraries Reporting Fires | Number of Fires Reported | Fires for which Loss Given | Dollar Loss |
| Alabama | | | | |
| Arizona | 1 | 1 | 1 | $ 28,581 |
| Arkansas | 4 | 3 | 2 | 219 |
| California | 21 | 50 | 48 | 212,326 |
| Colorado | 2 | 2 | 1 | 353,000 |
| Connecticut | 2 | 3 | | |
| Delaware | 3 | 3 | 1 | 3,000 |
| Washington, D. C. | 2 | 2 | | |
| Florida | 1 | 1 | | |
| Georgia | 2 | 7 | 4 | 2,000 |
| Idaho | | | | |
| Illinois | 16 | 17 | 11 | 1,146,200 |
| Indiana | 4 | 4 | 1 | 10 |
| Iowa | 1 | 1 | 1 | 250 |
| Kansas | 2 | 2 | 2 | 306,000 |
| Kentucky | 2 | 7 | 7 | 2,600 |
| Louisiana | 5 | 5 | 3 | 427 |
| Maine | 3 | 4 | 3 | 40,574 |
| Maryland | 4 | 4 | 3 | 5,600 |
| Massachusetts | 12 | 21 | 20 | 163,959 |
| Michigan | 12 | 12 | 8 | 2,947,008 |
| Minnesota | 7 | 10 | 8 | 78,600 |
| Mississippi | 4 | 4 | 2 | 500,975 |
| Missouri | 7 | 60 | 59 | 40,874 |
| Montana | 1 | 1 | 1 | 175,000 |
| Nebraska | 2 | 3 | 1 | 600 |
| Nevada | 1 | 1 | | |
| New Hampshire | 4 | 4 | 1 | 25 |
| New Jersey | 8 | 9 | 8 | 1,307,925 |
| New Mexico | 1 | 1 | 1 | 50 |
| New York | 16 | 19 | 15 | 5,101,291 |
| North Carolina | 6 | 6 | 3 | 37,500 |
| North Dakota | 1 | 1 | | |
| Ohio | 15 | 20 | 12 | 430,006 |
| Oklahoma | 5 | 6 | 4 | 196,000 |
| Oregon | 6 | 10 | 9 | 42,612 |
| Pennsylvania | 9 | 13 | 9 | 728,504 |
| Rhode Island | 3 | 3 | 2 | 73,085 |
| South Carolina | 3 | 5 | 3 | 500 |
| South Dakota | 4 | 4 | 3 | 315,025 |
| Tennessee | 4 | 4 | 3 | 33,000 |
| Texas | 4 | 4 | 3 | 20,585 |
| Utah | 2 | 2 | 2 | 151,333 |
| Vermont | 2 | 2 | | |
| Virginia | 5 | 5 | 3 | 117,077 |
| Washington | 2 | 2 | 1 | 10,000 |
| West Virginia | | | | |
| Wisconsin | 4 | 5 | 3 | 1,008 |
| Wyoming | | | | |
| Canada | 6 | 6 | 6 | 569,985 |
| Totals | 231 | 359 | 278 | $15,143,314 |

| uestionnaires Sent | Questionnaires Received | Percent Returned |
| --- | --- | --- |
| 23 | 12 | 52 |
| 11 | 8 | 72 |
| 17 | 6 | 35 |
| 171 | 83 | 49 |
| 27 | 15 | 55 |
| 37 | 17 | 45 |
| 7 | 3 | 42 |
| 29 | 11 | 37 |
| 20 | 12 | 60 |
| 34 | 18 | 52 |
| 6 | 5 | 83 |
| 113 | 62 | 55 |
| 66 | 39 | 59 |
| 33 | 21 | 63 |
| 30 | 19 | 63 |
| 29 | 10 | 34 |
| 37 | 21 | 56 |
| 13 | 7 | 53 |
| 34 | 18 | 52 |
| 75 | 44 | 59 |
| 82 | 44 | 53 |
| 43 | 24 | 55 |
| 22 | 13 | 59 |
| 60 | 33 | 61 |
| 10 | 7 | 70 |
| 18 | 14 | 77 |
| 4 | 3 | 75 |
| 9 | 5 | 55 |
| 70 | 38 | 54 |
| 12 | 4 | 33 |
| 187 | 92 | 49 |
| 55 | 26 | 47 |
| 7 | 6 | 85 |
| 112 | 69 | 62 |
| 23 | 7 | 30 |
| 25 | 15 | 60 |
| 125 | 63 | 51 |
| 14 | 9 | 64 |
| 26 | 11 | 42 |
| 12 | 8 | 66 |
| 38 | 17 | 44 |
| 79 | 33 | 42 |
| 12 | 7 | 58 |
| 11 | 4 | 36 |
| 38 | 19 | 50 |
| 36 | 19 | 52 |
| 20 | 10 | 50 |
| 47 | 26 | 55 |
| 6 | 3 | 50 |
| 18 | 10 | 55 |
| 2,032 | 1,070 | 53 |

# APPENDIX F

## The Salvage and Restoration of Damaged Materials

### Preparing a plan of attack

The librarian faced with the problem of rehabilitating a quantity of burned and water-soaked materials should make a careful inspection of the area as soon as possible after the fire has been extinguished to determine the extent of the damage and to plan for the orderly salvage and evacuation of the material if these should be necessary. This tour of inspection should certainly be made before any debris is cleared away or any reconstruction of a permanent nature is undertaken.

The librarian will generally find that in a moderate fire the records on top, if they are loose papers on open shelves, will have suffered the greatest fire and water damage but that they have in turn protected the sheets below them. Papers stored in folders or small boxes are frequently found in good condition although the containers may have been burned in some degree. If a considerable quantity of water has been used to extinguish the fire, some of the records on lower shelves or resting on the floor may be completely water-soaked.

After the damage has been appraised, definite plans for handling the material should be made that will result in the greatest amount of salvage in the least possible time and with the least amount of skilled labor. In almost every case of fire and water damage, it is assumed that maximum salvage of all materials is desired, and, if that is true, the plan should be based upon the physical nature and requirements of the various types of materials affected rather than upon their relative values. Bound volumes, because of their complex nature, are subject to the greatest potential damage and should be cared for immediately after the dry, charred papers have been set aside under cover for safekeeping. Wet papers, both burned and unburned, should be handled next, and last of all the dry ones may be sorted and repaired where necessary.

Arrangements should be made as soon as possible for well protected, vacant, ground-floor space, preferably store-type rather than warehouse, for temporary storage of records to be salvaged. Warehouse space is more likely to be unheated and poorly lighted. The area should be large enough to provide working space for salvage operations, with sufficient light to identify the records. Such space should be well heated.

## Need for immediate and rapid action

All types of library materials are not the same in their susceptibility to permanent damage. In some cases, the normal need for immediate action is aggravated by the nature of the materials.

Paper records that have been subjected to water damage, either damp or soggy wet, may deteriorate rapidly because of materials used in the fabrication of the paper itself. Records produced on various types of photographic and heat-sensitive paper are particularly susceptible of rapid fading to a point of illegibility. Within about twenty-four hours, wet pages will begin to adhere to each other but can still be separated without further damage. Legibility at this point will depend on the type of paper and kind of ink or writing materials used in the creation of the records. Within a period of about forty-eight hours, when records in folders within file cabinets begin to dry, individual sheets of paper wrinkle and actually adhere to each other, and the longer the records remain in the folders and cabinets, the more difficult becomes the restoration process. Separation of individual documents becomes more difficult and legibility is progressively impaired.

If water-soaked records housed in folders and file cabinets are allowed to dry intact for about five days, mold from bacteria action begins to form; if they remain in that state for a longer period of time, they become hard and form a mass. Restoration at this point is most difficult if not impossible.

The problem is serious if the records are collection items. It is even more so if the papers concerned are documents vital to library operations, such as the catalog, shelf lists, or other property records.

## First aid

Salvage operations that will aid considerably in the eventual rehabilitation of the materials probably may be carried out advantageously in the following order:

1. Any loose papers scattered on the floor should be picked up, carefully smoothed out where crumpled, and placed individually between white blotters to dry. The identification of the series, or of the individual papers where desirable, may be written directly on the blotters.

2. Any very badly charred, loose papers on shelves should be carefully covered with blotters to prevent loss of fragments but left in place for the time being.

3. All water-soaked volumes should be taken from the shelves

to a dry room where they should be stood on end with their covers spread to permit rapid drying. A glass-topped table is ideal for this unless the material is actually dripping, in which case blotters should be used to remove as much water as possible. The drying of the volumes will be hastened if a fan is used to circulate the air around them. If the water-soaked volumes are removed soon after the damage, the bindings and pages will not stick together, molding will be prevented or at least minimized, and it is unlikely that the dye in the binding materials will stain the paper.

4. Maps should be blotted to remove excess moisture and then spread out singly on a flat surface to dry by exposure to the air. It is not advisable to place this type of record material directly between blotters because the paste in mounting maps may seep through the backing and cause the maps to stick to the blotters.

5. The damp papers that have not been scorched should be carefully separated from one another and ironed immediately or placed individually between blotters to dry. Damp papers embrittled from the heat or burned to any degree should not be ironed but must be dried by interleaving them with blotters.

All this work should be carried out within twenty-four hours after the fire or before the moisture has evaporated to any extent to minimize the amount of subsequent treatment of the material that will be necessary.

Speed is a prime requisite in treating a water-soaked collection. Ideally, sheets of water-soaked materials should be separated immediately and dried, care being taken to maintain their proper sequence. Charred records should be handled as little as possible before actual rehabilitation to avoid crumbling. Documents charred to the point of illegibility can often be read by exposure to invisible ultraviolet light in total darkness.

A potential fire hazard from spontaneous ignition is often present from opening file cabinet drawers which were subjected to intense heat. Spontaneous ignition has occurred as long as three days after a cabinet had been removed from the scene of the fire. Drawers should be opened, exercising proper precautions, as soon as possible after a fire. A suitable hand fire extinguisher should be available as this is done.

## Salvage techniques

After the initial first-aid phase has been completed by mopping up all possible water, with the judicious use of blotting paper in quantity, the librarian will face the task of careful drying. Wet or damp records should not be dried by sunlight or by direct application of heat such as laying the papers on top of radiators or furnace registers. There are several recommended methods of drying records. The selection will depend upon the particular conditions, funds available, and what can be improvised.

## Fast drying

Use a large blueprint or photographic dryer, with a metal cylinder about 42 inches long and 10 inches in diameter, electrically heated with a thermostat control. Five legal-size or letter-size papers can be dried simultaneously on a dryer of this size. Care should be taken not to allow the cylinder to become too hot. Excessive heat will scorch paper. It is better to re-run documents through the dryer several times, until they are completely dry. Most commercial blueprinting or photographing firms have such dryers.

## Slow drying

Use a photocopy dryer with a metal cylinder about 27 inches wide and 28 inches in diameter, electrically heated and with a thermostat control. This is similar to the blueprint dryer, except that it dries much less rapidly. However, it is more suitable for large documents. Such a dryer is also available at most blueprinting or photographic reproduction firms.

## Room or space drying

Spread records on the floor or on tables in a warm or hot room with an air-circulating fan running at low speed. It will be necessary to turn the documents periodically. If the material being dried is bound in volumes or large documents, interleaf the documents with blotting paper, periodically changing it as it becomes wet or damp. This will be the technique necessary for most libraries, where the collection is made up principally of bound volumes.

## Clothesline drying

This method is very good for drying large individual documents such as blueprints, land plats, or sectional maps. Hang the documents on a clothesline strung in a warm or hot room. A boiler room is ideal. Periodically, about every two hours, reverse the documents on the clothesline. Wet documents can be dried by this process in approximately 30 to 48 hours.

## Large volume drying

In most rural communities there may be one or more seed drying mills, where all types of grain are dried and polished. Such facilities can be adapted to drying records in large volumes.

Seed mills usually have rows of bins; the bins are approximately 12 feet long, 8 feet wide, and 10 feet high. Each bin is enclosed on four sides and at the top with a base of screen mesh wire. The bins can be heated to about 100°F., and air can be circulated throughout at about 25 miles per hour. Place the wet records and folders upside down in cardboard boxes, and then place the boxes in the bins. Before assembling the boxes, however, holes approximately two inches in diameter should be cut in the bottom, two sides, and both ends of each box with the top left open. This permits air to circulate through each box of records. Examine the records in a few boxes approximately six hours after they have been placed in the bins. It will require approximately eight to fourteen hours to thoroughly dry records by this process.

## Other techniques

The drying methods listed have some advantages in that they are simple and the necessary materials are ordinarily available. They are not the only possible approaches and, following the Library of Parliament fire in Ottawa in 1952, a number of other techniques were investigated.

Considered as an engineering problem, drying requires only a means of supplying the latent heat necessary for the evaporation of water and a way of removing the water vapor which results. Experiments were carried out on low-temperature, infra-red, vacuum, freeze, silica-gel, oven, kiln, and radio-microwave drying. Most of these proved to be too slow and relatively inefficient for use with water-soaked books. Kiln drying gave good results, but was difficult to control and many books dried out of shape. Microwave drying was excellent for single books although metallic stampings introduced complications through local overheating.

If either kiln or microwave drying techniques could be further refined, they might be highly useful. In general, however, fan drying is usually the best solution, and preferable with inexperienced personnel. This was the basic approach used after the Ohio Historical Museum fire at Columbus in 1951. The process was carried out by operating the heating system to keep the building at 80 to 90°F. while holding the building at below 60 per cent relative humidity with dehumidifiers temporarily installed for this purpose.

## Paper stock variables

Paper is essentially a mat of cellulose fibers formed in sheets from a water suspension. When simple papers which have been wetted can be given prompt salvage treatment, excellent results are often possible. When paper has been sized with glue, starch, or clay to improve surface finish and printability, it is apt to be ruined by contact with water. The sized surfaces tend to adhere to each other so closely that separation is almost impossible without ruining the page.

## Salvaging singed or scorched records

Brittleness and fading are the usual results of records being subjected to intense heat. Careful handling, slow drying, and immediate duplication of the damaged documents are recommended for such damage. If the damaged records are originals and must be maintained in their original form, lamination or similar treatment to prevent further damage is advisable. However, before such processes are undertaken, expert advice should be obtained.

## Salvage techniques for various types of materials

The salvage of library materials is not confined to drying alone. Removal of the water is only the preliminary step to completing the repairs, and here the techniques required depend upon the size of the sheets and what binding or backing may be involved.

## Further repair of maps

When the maps are fairly dry, they should be placed between waxed paper and then in turn between white blotters and pieces of corrugated paper. This arrangement may be built up to include a number of maps and then weighted until drying is complete. A large piece of masonite or other wallboard is excellent for providing the even pressure over the large surface required for map flattening. If necessary, additional weight may be supplied by placing heavy objects on top of the board. The maps should be allowed to remain for several days under this pressure to provide ample time for complete drying and also to prevent the later curling or buckling of the material.

Bits of charred paper or other foreign materials may be removed from the surface afterwards by gentle scraping or lifting with a thin knife. In some instances, superficial dampening of the surface may be required to aid in the removal of the dirt, but this means should not be employed unless the former method has failed. After the maps have dried thoroughly, the edges should be carefully examined to determine whether the water has loosened them from their cloth backing. Any parts that are not securely attached to the mount should be repasted. If the pasting needed is extensive, the maps should be replaced under the weight to dry again.

If a map on tracing cloth has become thoroughly wet, it may apparently have lost a substantial amount of its sizing and will be limp and somewhat out of shape. While still fairly damp, the map should be carefully suspended from a taut cord or a rust-proof wire so that it may hang freely in the air with the warp (or lengthwise grain) of the material hanging vertically. The sheet should be carefully attached to the cord across the entire width so that all parts will hang down smoothly without sagging. The cloth should hang undisturbed in this way until almost dry at which point it may be safely handled. It may then be taken down and pressed lightly with a warm iron on a firm ironing surface. A tracing treated carefuly as described should show little or no distortion or other ill effects of its having been wet.

## Further repair of volumes

After the bindings of the volumes have become moderately dry by exposure to the air, as previously suggested, simple jackets of heavy waxed paper should be made for them. Thus the books may be laid flat with the covers closed without risk of the binding cloth sticking to or staining the pages or the surface on which the books rest. The next step consists of examining the pages of the wet volumes, separating them from one another by inserting a thin spatula if necessary, and interleaving the sheets with thin white blotters or other absorbent paper. The volumes, stacked with heavy blotter padding between them, should then be placed in a book press under light pressure to flatten the sheets and to eliminate warping of the boards during the drying. Care must be exercised that the pressure is exerted only on the boards and that the hinges and backs of the books extend beyond the press. After twenty-four hours, the volumes should be removed from the press and examined. The pages may not be perfectly dry but, under ordinary circumstances, they should have no tendency to cling together when the damp blotters are removed. However, if the paper is extremely heavy and has been thoroughly soaked, it may be desirable to replace these blotters with dry ones and repeat the treatment.

When the blotting papers are finally removed, the books, still in their waxed paper jackets, should be stacked in piles with their title strips alternating from left to right. It is recommended that the volumes be separated from each other in these piles by placing corrugated paper between them. A weight of about five to ten pounds should be placed on the top of each pile and this whole arrangement should be left undisturbed in dry air for at least a week or until the covers have dried thoroughly.

If the volumes have been too badly damaged to respond to this simple treatment it may be necessary to uncase them, flatten the boards and dry the pages separately, and then replace the casing. Under ordinary conditions, however, if the treatment of the wet volumes is undertaken promptly, there should be little need of resorting to this method, which is not only time-consuming but also requires the services of an experienced bookbinder. In any case, volumes that have been partially burned and have shrunk or warped somewhat around the edges will certainly require expert care. The old boards must be entirely discarded and new ones large enough to protect the pages adequately must be provided. During the rebinding process, the pages should be carefully examined and repaired if necessary. Probably nothing need be done where charring has been superficial and has been confined to the edges, unless the paper has been subjected to such intense heat that it has become noticeably discolored or embrittled. In such cases, the pages must be painstakingly separated and individually laminated or otherwise strengthened before they are rebound. Badly charred pages must, of course, be strengthened before rebinding.

## Further repair of loose papers

After the maps and volumes have been satisfactorily disposed of, attention may be directed to the repair of the loose papers. Those that had been water-soaked, whether burned or not, would have been separated while wet and placed between blotters as a first-aid measure. It would now be advisable systematically to examine and sort out the other papers, separating those that have been burned to a greater or lesser degree and needing repair from those remaining in good condition. Unless the papers in folders are very weak and badly charred, they may be most conveniently handled by transferring them with their identification from the old, damp, or charred folders to new ones. The papers that had lain free on the open shelves will probably be more seriously injured than the others and these should be interleaved with blotters to protect them as much as possible from loss and deterioration until their repair may be undertaken.

After the whole collection has been carefully examined and sorted, the material will probably be divided into several well-defined groups: (1) the water-soaked and burned sheets between blotters; (2) badly burned sheets between blotters; (3) the free papers in good condition requiring no treatment; (4) papers which have been placed in new folders and which are brittle and should be repaired; (5) papers in new folders requiring no treatment; and (6) papers in the original folders.

Of these categories, those sheets placed between blotters should be given first attention. Those merely water-soaked may be dried by ironing or by pressure and will need no other treatment. The burned papers should be carefully laminated by means of heat and pressure with transparent thermoplastic sheeting, or if this technique is not available, the documents may be covered with a sheeting supplied with an adhesive for direct hand application. Either method will provide sufficient additional strength for the safe handling of charred papers.

## Large scale rehabilitation of fire- and water-damaged materials

In the foregoing discussion, it has been assumed that the bulk of damaged material has been relatively small but valuable and that the resources of equipment and labor for its rehabilitation have been rather limited. If the damage is extensive, however, and labor, equipment, and materials are plentiful, certain modifications may be suggested. Large quantities of wet papers may be quickly and effectively handled by ironing with a mangle. Large quantities of charred papers can be handled most economically by laminating with heat and pressure. If such equipment is not available close to the scene of the catastrophe, the documents may be safely shipped to a commercial laminating firm by interleaving them individually with blotters somewhat larger than the documents and tying the bundles securely with string. There appears to be no really satisfactory rapid method of treating wet volumes on a large scale, but it is extremely important that all of them be removed from the shelves and separated from one another as quickly as possible before the glue sizing of the book cloth binds them together into a solid mass. If papers or books are allowed to remain in wet masses for any prolonged period, they not only stick together but may mildew and become stained with the inks and dyes used in their manufacture. Some of the water-soluble inks may blur or disappear entirely under such circumstances but, if the material is separated and handled promptly, little real permanent damage may be expected.

## Later salvage

Although it is always desirable, it is not always possible to begin salvage with fire-damaged materials immediately, and the librarian may sometimes be faced with the problem of salvaging what he can from a fire which has occurred a month or two earlier. Here the problem is quite different and the approach must necessarily be modified to some extent. The percentage of salvage may be as great, but the task will be far more time-consuming and expensive than it would have been if immediate first-aid treatment could have been undertaken. More equipment and more careful and highly skilled workmen will be required. The volumes may be found glued together, the boards warped, and the colors streaked and staining the pages. The loose sheets may also be stuck together and badly shrunk or wrinkled. The process of separating these pieces must be carefully carried out, using a very thin, large spatula to lift each sheet. The papers must be moistened by exposure to air of high humidity and then ironed or flattened under pressure. Pages of bound volumes may be handled in the same way with little danger of damage, but the bindings themselves will at times defy satisfactory separation and it is to be expected that a relatively large proportion of the bindings, which otherwise may have been in good condition, must be discarded and replaced with new ones. If the pages have been stained by the dye of the bindings, there is nothing that may be safely done to remove the discoloration because any bleach that would be effective would also dangerously weaken the paper. Mildew stains on paper are also extremely resistant and no attempt should be made to remove them other than to dust the sheets with a soft cloth. Mildew on bindings may be reduced and often eliminated completely by wiping the bindings with a cloth moistened with a non-toxic, non-flammable cleaning solvent. Leather bindings that have been wet or exposed to excessive heat will benefit considerably by a liberal application of a suitable leather dressing, rich in neat's-foot oil. This treatment will help to prevent excessive brittleness and premature decay. Salvageable buckram bindings may give satisfactory service without treatment but their appearance and general texture will be improved if a coating of a clear lacquer, which does not contain cellulose nitrate, shellac, or varnish, is applied. The ethyl cellulose and the vinylite resin-base lacquers have been found suitable for this use. The volume should be air-dry and conditioned to the normal humidity of the storage area before any lacquer is applied.

## Restoration of library materials

To this point, the emphasis has been on water damage and drying out the collection as quickly as possible. The restoration of material damaged by fire and heat is another subject and, in this regard, speed is less essential.

When book materials are exposed to intense heat, there first is a surface scorching. The heat then slowly travels through to the center. The paper turns brown, then is blackened. The process is actually a destructive distillation in which at first all volatile components are driven off, then the cellulose molecule itself is broken down, leaving only a carbon residue. When this occurs there is a progressive increase in brittleness and the paper becomes extremely fragile.

During the early stages of heat damage, lamination is a simple and widely accepted method of restoration. In severe cases, it is necessary to provide a new base material. The procedure described in various references recommends application of a ricinated collodion with a soft brush, then after this has been dried, to separate the strengthened sheet from the one below by careful use of a razor blade. It is probable that almost any plasticized transparent film base material could be substituted, and spray application might have advantages over a brush.

Even when paper has been badly charred, it is usually possible to read the written or printed text because of the difference in chemical composition of paper and inks. This may require viewing under oblique light or by ultraviolet light. Accordingly, once the sheet has been strengthened enough to handle, photographic methods should be employed to produce a usable copy with good legibility.

Parchment and vellum manuscripts act differently. These are of animal origin and, under the influence of heat, the material appears to be transformed into a sort of gelatin which shrinks as moisture is driven off. The destructive distillation progresses with the production of a tarry residue which cements the leaves into a solid mass.

The first step in treating fire-damaged parchment is to restore the moisture content by prolonged exposure to low-temperature steam. This brings about a parting of the leaves, which then may be separated, cleaned with a sponge, and saturated with a warm formalin solution. It then becomes possible to gently stretch the book toward its original dimensions. This is followed by a weak alkaline bath of potassium acetate potassic soap. A number of baths and dryings may be necessary. Art work is then done on the characters using special solutions to restore their original colors.

## Summary

From this discussion, it will be apparent that, although fire and water damage have always ranked high among the enemies of libraries and have caused the complete destruction of enormous quantities of their holdings in the past, such damage should not, in most cases, be considered irreparable. A high percentage of salvage from all but major disasters is generally possible if the problem is approached and handled promptly in a logical and orderly manner based on the physical requirements rather than on the intrinsic value of the books affected. If the materials are carefully prepared in the best manner available, the over-all destruction can often be minimized.

# APPENDIX G

## Evaluation of Library Materials for Insurance Purposes

The Insurance for Libraries Committee of the Library Administration Division, ALA, offers the following information which is intended to bring up to date a report presented by the previous Committee in the *ALA Bulletin* for June, 1959. The present report includes figures quoted from "Index of Book Prices by Category," which appeared in the January 28, 1963, issue of *Publishers' Weekly.* Also included are figures cited in the 1962 *Bowker Annual* and in the October 1, 1962, issue of *Library Journal.* Opinions registered by many librarians in their discussions of the subject with Committee members have also been incorporated here.

When it comes to establishing values for library materials several questions arise: How much insurance should be obtained?; how can we account for depreciation?; and into what categories should library materials be classified?

It is understood that when a library is arranging for insurance for the first time, the first thing that must be done is to conduct an inventory to ascertain the value of the collection. It is wise to establish some form of inventory technique that will determine valuations no less often than every three years to bring them up to date. For the most part, this need not be a complete physical inventory in the normal sense of taking inventory but may adopt many abbreviated forms.

For the purposes of the present report: the *average insurable value* for a book is the average present-day replacement cost new, less an average amount for depreciation. Values for periodicals were calculated on the basis of current subscription cost for each volume plus $4.00 for the average cost of binding. Binding costs will vary from periodical to periodical; therefore, this figure should be checked carefully.

Discounts will vary among libraries by type of book purchased and even by area. For this reason the Committee did not list average discount values. It would be reasonable, however, for many libraries to establish an average discount of 35 percent for trade publications and 15 to 20 percent for technical publications.

The average cost of a book today is about $6.00. The librarian can establish an evaluation in the following manner: the average cost of a book, $6.00, less, for example, 35 percent discount (which establishes the net cost to the library) less the depreciation figure established (in the case of nonfiction, 25 percent). This would determine the average insurable value per book or category of books for which the librarian would obtain insurance.

The librarian administering a general library, with no (or few) specialized departments, could set up three or four categories only and have one special class into which rare and unusual items could be insured at prices to be determined on an individual basis. A library of this type might establish its average insurable values as follows: $2.00 for children's books; $4.00 to $5.00 for general books; and $7.50 to $8.50 for technical books. Again, these figures are merely suggested to illustrate how a library may establish its insurance levels. Special libraries, departmentalized libraries, and especially college and university libraries, will establish their average insurable values considerably higher than these figures and will use more categories.

The cost of binding was not included in these estimates. The consensus of the Committee is that, in most cases, binding will not increase the value of the book over the original cost and should be regarded only as an item which may reduce the depreciation allowance. If binding is a major cost of a particular library's operation, the librarian may effect slight reductions in the depreciation figures to account for these expenditures. Some librarians have calculated binding costs separately. In this case, a reasonable procedure would be to take the average insurable value, plus a depreciated percentage of the binding cost — perhaps two-thirds of the average cost of binding a book ($2.00). However, the Committee does not recommend this procedure. The Committee holds that binding costs should have already been considered when depreciation percentages were assigned.

# EVALUATION FIGURES COMPILED BY INSURANCE FOR LIBRARIES COMMITTEE

## DECEMBER, 1962

| CATEGORY | AVERAGE COST |
|---|---|
| Adult fiction | $ 4.50 |
| Juveniles | 2.75 |

Adult nonfiction

| | |
|---|---|
| Architecture | 13.00 |
| Biography | 6.25 |
| Engineering | 7.50 |
| Fine Arts | 9.50 |
| General | 6.00 |
| Law | 10.00 |
| Medicine | 10.00 |
| Music | 6.50 |
| Psychology | 5.75 |
| Reference (general) | 5.00-30.00 |
| Science | 9.75 |
| Technology | 10.25 |

Periodicals: subscriptions and binding

| | |
|---|---|
| Architecture | 16.00 |
| Fine Arts | 14.00 |
| Chemistry and Physics | 16.00 |
| Geology and Zoology | 11.00 |
| General | 9.00 |
| History and English | 9.00 |
| Law | 10.00 |
| Mathematics | 12.00 |
| Medicine | 16.00 |
| Music | 9.00 |
| Psychology | 12.00 |

Documents

| | |
|---|---|
| Paper bulletins | .31 |
| Paperbound volumes | 1.90 |
| Bound volumes | 4.00 |
| Periodical volumes | 4.00 |

Music[1]

| | |
|---|---|
| Sheet | .60 |
| Maps | 1.00 |

[1] No figures are available for scores because of the diversity of materials.

| CATEGORY | AVERAGE COST |
|---|---|

Microreproductions
    Microfilm (per reel) ....................$ 24.00
    Microprint (per card) ...................   .35
    Microcard (per card) ...................   .20

Audio-visual materials
    Films — silent
    16 mm. black and white (per reel) ........  30.00
    16 mm. color (per reel) ..................  55.00
    Film — sound
    16 mm. black and white (per reel) ........  68.00
    16 mm. color (per reel) .................. 115.00

Filmstrip
    Black and white (per unit) [2] .............  3.00
    Color (per unit) .......................  5.00

Slides
    Black and white (2 x 2) .................   .30
    Color (2 x 2) ..........................   .50

Phonograph records — 78 rpm
    10" disc .............................  1.00
    12" disc .............................  1.25

Phonograph records — 33⅓ rpm
    10" disc .............................  2.10
    12" disc .............................  3.60

Phonograph records — 45 rpm
    7" disc ..............................  1.10
Stereophonic records .......................  3.60
Tapes .....................................  12.50

Many libraries are insured on a coinsurance-clause basis; others are covered by a repair-and-replace clause. The model library insurance policy developed by the Library Technology Project (see Chapter 14) has adopted the repair-and-replace clause feature. This means that a policyholder will be fully reimbursed on the basis of the value established.

The following depreciation figures are suggested either when figures are required by insurance underwriters or when the librarian decides (and usually correctly so) that there is wisdom in not insuring the depreciated portion of the material.

2 Number of frames determines length of unit.

| CATEGORY | PERCENT |
|---|---|
| Adult fiction | 60 |
| Adult non-fiction | 25 |
| Juveniles | 60 |
| Reference books | 20 |
| 16 mm. film (per reel) | 50 |
| 8 mm. film (per reel) | 75[3] |

Records

| | |
|---|---|
| 78 rpm | 33⅓ |
| 33⅓ rpm | 50 |
| 45 rpm | 50 |
| Stereophonic | 50 |
| Slides | 33⅓ |

We are indebted to Mr. Robert E. Kingery, Chief of the Library Preparation Division of the New York Public Library, and Mr. George L. Schaeffer, Business Manager of that library, for providing us with the formula to establish the cost of rehabilitating a destroyed catalog and shelf list.

A. Situation

1. Catalog and shelf list completely destroyed.
   *Formula:* The number of different titles not destroyed (including those out on circulation) multiplied by the cost of cataloging a single title (including the cost of card reproduction).

Notes:

(a) The number of titles not destroyed in a "total loss" will vary from library to library. However, this number can be estimated by adding the average number of books out on circulation to the number of titles housed in other locations (branches, etc.).

(b) The cost of cataloging a title varies among libraries and depends on the type of library (public, college, research, etc.), size of library, and procedures. Each library would have to calculate its own cost of cataloging a single title.

2. Catalog and shelf list damaged, but all information on cards remains intact.
   *Formula:* The number of different titles not destroyed (including those out on circulation) multiplied by the average cost of pulling a set of catalog cards, *plus* the product of multiplying the average number of cards per title by the average cost of reproducing a single card.

---

3 Due to type of projector.

Notes:

(a) Although the cost of pulling a set of catalog cards will vary between libraries, it can readily be calculated by each library. The average number of cards per title cataloged will also vary from library to library.

(b) The cost of reproducing a single card will depend on the method (photography, Xerography, etc.) used.

B. Demonstration. The New York Public Library

1. Use of formula developed for Situation 1 (see above).
1,000,000 titles not destroyed multiplied by the cost ($3.50) of cataloging a single title results in a total cost of $3,500,000.

2. Use of formula developed for Situation 2 (see above).
1,000,000 titles not destroyed multiplied by the average cost ($1.00) of pulling a set of catalog cards *plus* the product of multiplying the average number (8) of cards per title by the average cost ($.05) of reproducing a single card by Xerography results in a total cost of $1,400,000.

It should be remembered:

a. Since we are actually dealing with variables, there is no way that a firm figure applicable to *all* libraries can be established.

b. The above formulae should be used only by those libraries that have not taken the precaution of microfilming their catalogs and shelf lists.

c. In addition to having microfilms of its catalog and shelf list, some libraries store extra copies of their catalog cards in a vault outside the library.

d. Smaller libraries with less complicated cataloging problems and fewer cards per set will probably have a smaller unit cataloging cost. There are some public libraries and library systems that calculate their processing costs (ordering, cataloging, and physical preparation) as being about $1.25 to $1.50 per title, the greater part of which cost can be assigned to cataloging. Some college libraries have indicated $6.50 per title as not unrealistic, although many probably have a smaller unit cost. The Committee will be engaged in a continuous study of the entire subject.

# APPENDIX H

## The Evaluation and Insurance of Great Rarities

By Roland Baughman,
Head of Special Collections
Columbia University Libraries

By their nature, certain library materials — unusually valuable printed works, book manuscripts (both old and modern), association items, archives, and the like — are, for the most part, irreplaceable, and the recovery of their dollar value through insurance may be small recompense for their loss. For this reason many librarians take the position that insurance serves them no valid purpose, that its cost would for them be excessively high, and that the money might be more wisely and soundly used to increase the degree of the physical security of the materials. This view is held principally in research institutions with extremely rich holdings concentrated in one or a few well-defined subject areas, and where exceptionally high standards of protection are already being maintained. To such a library, the loss of its collection would mean the loss of its whole raison d'etre; it exists only for its specialized usefulness to a specialized clientele, present and future, and the replacement of its collections with dollars would reduce its functional value to nought. A library famed for its holdings in Elizabethan drama, for example, could never replace its collections, no matter what sums were recovered: the replacement materials simply do not exist in available form. Moreover, even if they should exist, it would take years, perhaps generations, to assemble them, and the present insurance values (the recovered dollars) would represent only the merest fraction of the probable cost of doing so. For such libraries the only true insurance lies in the provision of maximum physical protection.

On the other hand, the great majority of libraries do not fall into this specialized class. Not only are they less uniquely based; they may also be for various reasons — functional as well as budgetary — unable to apply perfect measures to the extent such might exist for the physical security of irreplaceable materials. Although the libraries may possess substantial holdings of rarities and although these rarities may give pre-eminence in certain limited fields, such holdings usually constitute, quantitatively, only a small part of the total resources. This is true especially among the larger public and university libraries, which are emerging more and more prominently as recipients, both by gift and by purchase, of unique research materials. For such institutions, the budgetary commitment for insurance can usually be assumed without delay, while the highly desirable and ultimately necessary means of providing optimum conditions of surveillance and housing may require long-range planning. Moreover, to put the matter cold-bloodedly, in regard to the fundamental purposes of such an institution, the inability to replace individual rarities — and even collections — is less inimical; the substitution of dollars for materials, though tragic in its consequences to certain phases of scholarship, would affect only a fraction of the library's basic coverage, and would, to a degree, be offset by expending the recovered funds to acquire other, comparably useful resources, though perhaps in a quite different field.

For such libraries, even though every possible protective measure is taken, adequate insurance of special rarities on a Fine Arts (or equivalent) policy — which is in insurance terminology a "valued" form of contract — would seem to be sound economy, and the only remaining questions revolve around the term "adequate." What *is* "adequate"? How is adequacy established? How is the financial worth of a given rarity at any specific time decided? (The selection of an arbitrary amount is unsafe; if the amount is too low, the insurance is not "adequate"; if it is too high, a useless expense has been contracted.)

The librarian's responsibility, therefore, is to provide an accurate and detailed census of the items to be placed on special insurance, listing the unusual points of each piece, and including the best possible estimate of each item's current value.

If the librarian is an authority in such matters, or if he can refer to recent records showing actual sale prices, he is in a position to set the values himself. For printed works of exceptional value (Caxton imprints, Shakespeare quartos, and the like), published auction records will be useful, provided the records are sufficiently up to date; for works of lesser price, dealers' catalogues will be more reliable guides. In the cases of unique items that have been in his library for some time, however, the librarian may be in some difficulty. His best procedure would be to employ an outside appraiser who is familiar with the current market for similar items. The best general source for such help is the membership list of the Antiquarian Booksellers' Association of America, Inc., which indicates the geographical location and the specialties of more than 250 firms throughout the United States — most of which include appraisal work among the activities. (The librarian, of course, may have access to a competent appraiser who is not a member of the ABAA; that organization is mentioned here only because of its availability and its established record of dependability.)

Once the list of rarities is made, the attached values should be agreed to by the insurer. This should be done formally, so that in the case of loss no item on the list will be subject to question.

There is a further requirement for "adequate" insurance; namely, keeping abreast of changing levels in the rare-book market, and revising the appraisal values of the insured items to accord with the changes. Difficult as this may sound, its requirements are principally the interest and responsibility of the librarian. If the list of insured rarities is small, the work of revision is small. If it is large, the work may be simplified by categorizing the items — for example, one grouping devoted to early illuminated manuscripts, another for medieval and renaissance text manuscripts, a third for authors' manuscripts of the printing era, and so on. For *printed* works, grouping by general kind would be useful (Elizabethan drama; Restoration drama; travel books through the 16th century; early science; 17th century American imprints; western Americana; the "Lake poets"; fine printing; American literature, etc.).

The object in formulating such groups is to bring like materials together, thus enabling competent outside authorities in particular fields to survey the various parts of the list. Such authorities should be able to establish coefficients of rise or fall in market values reflecting collector activity in their specific fields. The coefficients can then be used to change the evaluations of the insurance list. Although this procedure may seem cumbersome and inexact at first glance, it may be the only valid means of estimating the shift in value of items for which no current sales records exist.

Reappraisal should be undertaken no less frequently than every five years, a period which should enable major shifts in the activities of collectors to become established. In actual experience, of course, such shifts occur much more rapidly, and should be taken into account as soon as they are known. The entrance of a single important collector — institutional or individual — into a specific field may alter the going rates for items in that field drastically, speedily, and permanently. The recent proliferation in institutional projects to gather and publish the papers of important American historical figures — Jefferson, Franklin, Hamilton, Jay, etc. — has caused such papers to drift out of private hands into those of permanent repositories, with a consequent dramatic increase in the going price of the few such letters still available for the market.

Finally, a word must be said about the value level at which Fine Arts insurance should begin. Many libraries have established fixed and arbitrary levels (for example, $500), and in far too many cases the level, once decided, remains in force despite general agreement that the buying power of the dollar is only a fraction of what it was in the past. Such a policy means, under present conditions, that an unrealistically high ratio of items must be insured, items which earlier would not have been considered. This becomes a great burden to libraries that have large numbers of marginal rarities — books which, without regard to their intrinsic merits, can fluctuate in dollar value back and forth across the Fine Arts insurance beginning level.

Obviously, the dilemma requires careful thought. It would seem that two very fundamental considerations should be brought to bear. The first is that the *true importance of a unique document cannot be stated in terms of dollars, because the document cannot be replaced,* but even so, if it deserved to be insured for $500 in the mid-thirties, it deserves (all other things being equal) to be insured for at least $1,000 today. Secondly, if the Fine Arts insurance level was $500 in the mid-thirties, it should certainly be as high as $1,000 today to take into account the same type of material. What this means is simply that, if the library in question, no matter whether it is large or small, is an insuring library, its policy should be so written that the level of its general coverage and the actual evaluations that are placed against individual items (in the absence of other data) can be factored to reflect the changing value of the dollar. By the same token, the librarian must see to it that the base level for his Fine Arts insurance is made to conform with the general conditions. In this way the effect of fluctuation in the value of rarities below the revised level can be taken into account where it properly belongs — namely, in the general coverage.

# APPENDIX I

## Liability For Copyright Infringement

Many libraries offer photocopying services. Such services are a great convenience to the library's patrons and, in ordinary practice, almost never detract from the commercial value of the material photocopied. Nevertheless, the Copyright Act is written in terms that prohibit all copying of a copyrighted work. There is, therefore, at least a theoretical risk that the library, or its employees, may be sued for copyright infringement in copying a work. How great is this risk and what can be done to minimize it?

From time to time copyright owners have sought to enforce their copyrights against nominal infringements. Recognizing that the categorical language of the copyright law covers such infringements, and further recognizing that copyright relief in such cases is undesirable, the courts have developed the doctrine of "fair use," which excuses such nominal infringements under certain conditions. The most frequently quoted definition of fair use states:

> "Fair use may be defined as a privilege in others than the owner of the copyright, to use the copyrighted material in a reasonable manner without his consent; notwithstanding the monopoly granted to the owner by the copyright." (Ball, *The Law of Copyright and Literary Property.*)

Unfortunately, neither this nor any other definition of such judicial doctrine can possibly tell with certainty whether a particular act of photocopying will come within the limits of fair use.

In theory, therefore, the only sure way to avoid risk is by obtaining permission from the copyright owner prior to making a photocopy. This is true, incidentally, whether the copy is made for internal use of the library or is made as a service to a patron for a fee.

This problem led to efforts of librarians and other groups to provide guides for action on this matter and to obtain, at least in a limited sense, the consent of the copyright owners. While no general legal consent has been obtained from copyright owners, these efforts have delineated reasonable practice and have withstood the test of more than a quarter of a century's experience.

The first of these efforts was the so-called "Gentlemen's Agreement" of 1935, negotiated between the Joint Committee on Reproduction of Materials for Research of the American Council of Learned Societies and the Social Science Research Council on the one hand, and the National Association of Book Publishers on the other.[1] This Agreement emphasizes the legal prohibition against copying any part of a copyrighted work by any means, without the written permission of the copyright owner. Nevertheless, the agreement extends an "exemption from liability" to libraries making a single photographic reproduction (or reduction) of a part of a book or a periodical volume for a scholar who states in writing his desire for such a copy in lieu of loan or manual transcription, solely for purposes of research. Moreover, such exemption applies only if the scholar is given written notice of his liability for misuse of the copyright and if the library makes no profit by the transaction.

The "Gentlemen's Agreement" was the basis for the American Library Association's "Materials Reproduction Code" of 1940.[2] These two statements provided the principal basis for library photocopying of copyrighted materials from 1935 on.

Beginning in 1957 the matter was restudied by the Joint Libraries Committee on Fair Use in Photocopying, representing the American Association of Law Libraries, American Library Association, Association of Research Libraries, and Special Libraries Association, which employed as legal counsel the New York firm of Webster, Sheffield, Fleischmann, Hitchcock and Chrystie. In 1961 the Committee announced the doctrine that the granting of a reader's request for a single copy of published materials in its collection is a direct and natural extension of traditional library service. In addition, it reported its conclusion, resulting from studies of the actual conditions of library photocopy in a number of institutions, that this does not inflict measurable damage on copyright proprietors. The Committee consequently recommended that it be library policy to fill an order for a single copy of any published work or part thereof[3] and this recommendation has been approved by all the participating organizations.[4] In order to avoid damage to copyright owners it is obvious that the recommendation must be applied with discretion by individual libraries, as was urged by the Executive Secretary of the American Library Association in announcing the adoption of the policy.[5]

There has been no known case, either under 27 years of the "Gentlemen's Agreement" or the much shorter period since the Joint Committee recommendation was made, in which a library or

[1] *Journal of Documentary Reproduction*, II (March, 1939), 29-36.

[2] *ALA Bulletin*, XXXV (February, 1941), 64.

[3] *Special Libraries*, LII (May-June, 1961), 251-55; *ALA Bulletin*, LV (June, 1961), 571-73; *Bulletin of the Copyright Society of the U.S.A.*, IX (October, 1961), 79-84.

[4] *Law Library Journal*, LV (February, 1962), 14.

[5] *ALA Bulletin*, LV (Sepember, 1961), 680-81.

its employee has been sued for infringement as the result of supplying a single copy of a copyrighted work.

Although the risk of liability will continue to exist, it may be
regarded as small, if proper precautions are observed. It is not
likely that any standard form for insurance protection against such
liability would be approved. Nevertheless, one major university
library was able to secure such protection by an endorsement of
a Comprehensive General Liability Policy as follows:

# INFRINGEMENT OF COPYRIGHT LIABILITY
# COVERAGE ENDORSEMENT

It is agreed that such insurance as is afforded by the policy
applies to injury to or destruction of property caused by an infringement of copyright by the named insured, subject to the following provisions:

(1) Insuring Agreement II of the policy does not apply to any
suit seeking injunctive relief unless substantial damages for
injury to or destruction of property are alleged in connection
therewith, but the company may elect to defend any injunctive suit.

(2) The insurance under this endorsement does not apply:
   (a) to liability assumed by the insured under any contract
   or agreement;
   (b) To the expense of recovering or destroying any property
   which is the subject of the infringement, or to property
   rendered unusable or required to be destroyed because of
   such infringement;
   (c) To infringements of copyright committed by or in connection with a radio or television broadcast;
   (d) to injury to or destruction of the property of any person
   who is an employee of the named insured at the time of the
   publication of the infringing matter. The exclusions of the
   policy do not apply to this endorsement.

(3) The limit of liability stated below as applicable to "each infringement" is the total limit of the company's liability hereunder for all damages on account of injury to or destruction of
property of one person arising out of the publication of any one
document; and the limit of liability stated below:

An "aggregate" is, subject to the above provision respecting
"each infringement," the total limit of the company's liability hereunder for all damages. The limits stated in the declarations of the

policy do not apply to the insurance under this endorsement.

Regardless of whether insurance protection is obtained, however, there are practical considerations that can be applied to minimize the copyright risk. These considerations include:

1. A policy of making only a single copy at a time (as distinguished from accepting an order for, say a dozen copies of some one page in a book).

2. A policy of making such copy only of a limited portion of any single book (as distinguished from accepting an order to reproduce a complete book).

3. A policy of conducting the copying service on a non-profit basis, so that the library cannot be accused of competing with the copyright owner in terms of profiting from the work.

4. A policy of accepting only written orders on a form containing some indication that the order is for use in research in lieu of borrowing a copy of the book from the library.

It is not suggested that all of these precautions be rigorously observed at all times, or that they will provide assurance of complete protection against legal action, if they are observed. But to the extent that they can be followed without interference with normal library operations, their application is desirable.

A few libraries have found it convenient to leave photocopying services to commercial concerns. The act of copying, the decision as to what to copy and what not to copy, and all financial arrangements are then the responsibility of the organizations making the copy. This alternative, in almost every situation, makes the library immune to possible copyright liability.

Some libraries also follow the practice of requiring a statement from persons ordering copies that, in effect, absolves the library of all liability and undertakes to "save the library harmless" from all litigation arising out of such copying. Such statements will not prevent the library being a party to legal action, should it occur. Further, they are of little value if the person ordering copies does not have the financial resources to support any legal action which may develop as a result of such copying. These reasons — together with the limited nature of the legal risk in any event — make this a practice of dubious value. In special instances, especially in dealing with responsible business entities, a "save harmless" statement may be justified.

As this is written, the entire problem of photocopying by libraries is under examination as a part of a general revision of the U. S. Copyright Law. The Register of Copyrights has recommended a somewhat more liberal policy in those sections pertaining to photocopying, but to what extent these recommendations will be incorporated in the final statute is not known.

# GLOSSARY

## A

**abandonment.** The owner of damaged property may seek to "abandon" his property to the company for the purpose of claiming a total loss. This is not permitted under the terms of the Fire Insurance policy. (See *salvage.*)

**accession list.** A record maintained of pertinent data covering each item added to a library collection in the order received.

**accident control or prevention.** (See *loss prevention service.*)

**accident insurance.** Pays benefits for injury or death caused by accident. Coverage is divided into separate optional categories as: (1) indemnity for loss of time, (2) medical and hospital costs, (3) indemnity for loss of limbs or sight, (4) indemnity for death. The policy defines the accidents covered and coverage may be limited to a certain type of accident.

**accommodation line.** An insurance company at times will accept (from an agent or broker whose entire account is satisfactory), business which would ordinarily be rejected on a strict underwriting basis. Such business is known as an "accommodation line."

**acquisition cost.** The cost to the company of securing business: commissions to agents and brokers, and in some companies field supervision costs.

**act of God.** An accident or event that is the result of natural causes, without any human intervention or agency, that could not have been prevented by reasonable foresight or care, e.g., floods, lightning, earthquake, storms.

**actual cash value.** The present-day value of property measured in cash, arrived at by taking the replacement cost and deducting for depreciation brought about by physical wear and tear, and obsolescence.

**actuarial data.** Statistics which can be used as a basis for determination of insurance rates.

**adjuster.** An individual representing the insurance company in discussions leading to agreement about the amount of a loss and the company's liability. Adjusters may be salaried employees of adjusting organizations operated by insurance companies, individuals operating independently and engaged by the companies to adjust a particular loss, and special agents or staff adjusters employed by the company. (In the casualty business the term "claim representative" is commonly used.) None of the foregoing should be confused with "public adjusters" who represent claimants only.

**adjustment.** The process of determining the cause and amount of a loss, the amount of indemnity that the insured may recover after all proper allowances and deductions have been made, and the proportion that each company (if more than one) is required to pay under its contract.

**admitted company.** A company is termed "admitted" within a given state when licensed to do business in that state.

**after charge.** (See *unsafe*.)

**agent, general.** The general agent is the company representative in a given territory, entrusted with the task of supervising the company's business within that territory. He may appoint local agents whom he services. The general agent is an independent contractor compensated on a commission basis.

**agent, local.** An insurance agent, frequently referred to as a "local agent" or "producer," is an independent contractor. He represents insurance companies in a sales and service capacity and is paid on a commission basis. He is licensed by the state in which he operates. His powers are limited by the terms of his agency contract and by the state laws.

**agent, policy-writing.** A local agent who is authorized to write and sign insurance contracts for his company. Although there are a number of technical divisions of producers, as a general rule, in all forms of stock company insurance except life, an agent has such authority and responsibility, while a broker has not. (Agents are often also brokers.)

**agent, recording.** (fire term) A recording agent is a local agent who issues company policies and has the power to commit his company within the scope of his authority as delegated in the agency agreement held by him. (Another name in the fire business for policywriting agent.)

**agent, special or agent, state.** The special agent or state agent is an employee of the company. He serves as the personal contact between the company and its agents in a given territory.

**all-risk insurance.** Insurance protecting the insured from loss arising from any cause other than those causes specifically excluded by name. This contrasts with the named-peril policy, which names the peril or perils insured against.

**American agency system.** The system of selling insurance through agents compensated on a commission basis. This is in contrast to the system of selling insurance through salaried company representatives who write insurance for one company only. (See *direct writer.*)

**American Society for Testing Materials (ASTM).** An association of engineers, scientists, and skilled technicians organized to promote knowledge of the materials of engineering and the standardization of specifications and testing methods. Address: 1916 Race Street, Philadelphia 3, Pennsylvania.

**amount subject.** The value which may reasonably be expected to be lost in one fire or other casualty. It depends on the protection and construction of the risk, and the distribution of concentration of values. Estimating the amount subject is a major responsibility of inspectors and underwriters.

**analytic system.** A copyrighted schedule for analysis of properties in order to determine a basis for setting an insurance rate.

**Antiquarian Booksellers Association of America.** An association of dealers in rare and out-of-print books. Address: 3 West 46th Street, New York 36, New York.

**application.** A questionnaire which must be filled in, when required, by the person seeking insurance. It gives the company full information about the proposed subject of insurance and the person to be insured, for the purpose of determining whether the company will issue the policy and if so, to have it prepared properly.

**appraisal.** A survey of property made for determining its insurable value or the amount of loss sustained.

**archives.** An organized body of records covering transactions of a person or persons, preserved for record purposes.

**arson.** The willful and malicious burning of property, sometimes with the intent of defrauding insurance companies.

**assessment.** The requirement of a mutual insurance company or a reciprocal exchange that an insured pay an additional amount to meet losses greater than those anticipated.

**assigned risk.** A risk which underwriters do not care to insure but which, because of state law or otherwise, must be insured. The insurance is therefore handled through a pool of insurers and assigned to companies in turn.

**assignment.** The transfer of the legal right or interest in a policy to another party, generally in connection with the sale of property.

**Associated Factory Mutual Insurance Companies (FM).** A group of eight mutual fire insurance companies maintaining a common Engineering Department and Laboratories at Norwood, Massachusetts.

**Association of Casualty and Surety Companies.** A service organization of more than 100 capital stock insurance companies writing casualty and surety lines, designed to provide a forum for discussion of general problems of common interest to member companies and to provide public service through such varied fields as accident prevention, claims, legislation, public relations, and research.

**assumed liability.** (See *contractual liability*.)

**assured.** Synonymous with *insured*.

**audit.** An examination of the insured's books and records to determine actual exposures for premium computation purposes. Audits are most commonly made in Workmen's Compensation, Manufacturers' and Contractors' Liability, Product Liability and Reporting Form lines and on Automobile Fleet, Gross Receipts and Garage Payroll policies, where the premium is based on such items as the insured's payroll, gross receipts, values on hand, owned automobiles or units handled or sold.

**audit bureau.** (See *stamping office*.)

**automatic cover.** Provided in many forms of insurance usually for a specified period and limited amount, to cover increasing values, newly acquired and changing interests.

**automatic reinstatement.** (See *reinstatement*.)

**average distribution clause.** (See *pro rata distribution*.)

**average rate.** In fire insurance, average rates are published by a rating bureau covering more than one item of insurance (i.e., several buildings or buildings and contents) under one blanket rate. Affidavits of values must be furnished as a basis for weighting the individual rates.

**average weekly benefit.** (Usually called weekly compensation in Workmen's Compensation insurance.) The amount payable per week for disability or death as prescribed by law. This is usually a percentage of the average weekly wage, subject to a minimum and maximum amount.

**average weekly wage.** The average rate of remuneration per week, computed as prescribed by law. The several Workmen's Compensation laws and Disability Benefit laws vary widely in the methods of computation prescribed.

# B

**bailee.** A person who has been entrusted with the legal possession of personal property belonging to another.

**beneficiary.** The person or persons named in a policy by the insured to receive the death benefit of the policy. This word is also freely used in connection with fiduciary bonds where the deceased in his will names recipients of his estate.

**bid bond.** A guarantee that the contractor will enter into a contract, if it is awarded to him, and furnish such contract bond (sometimes called performance bond) as is required by the terms thereof.

**binder.** A preliminary agreement to provide immediate insurance until a policy can be written, either by an agent or company. It should contain a definite time limit, should be in writing and clearly designate the company in which the risk is bound, the amount and the perils insured against, as well as the type of insurance.

**blanket policy.** An insurance policy which covers several different items of property under a single amount of insurance.

**bodily injury liability insurance.** Protection against loss arising out of the liability imposed upon the insured by law for damages because of bodily injury, sickness, or disease sustained by any person or persons (other than employees).

**border line risk.** (See *accommodation line*.)

**branch office.** A company office for the purpose of supervising business within a certain territory. It is operated under a manager, is usually headquarters for a number of special agents, claim men, engineers, and auditors, and provides service to agents within its territory.

**broker.** The broker, as contrasted with the agent, is the agent of the insured and not of the company although he receives his income in commissions paid by the company. He is licensed by the state to transact insurance and he acts as the representative of the insured in placing insurance for him with the insurance companies.

**budget plan.** With certain provisions, large fire insurance policies may be divided into smaller policies, to expire and be renewed on consecutive years, the policies being written at pro rata of the 3- or 5-year rates, so the premium is spread over several years.

**building code.** A law or ordinance which sets up minimum standards for the construction of buildings in the interests of public health, welfare, and safety.

**bureau, rating.** An organization that classifies and promulgates rates and in some cases compiles data and measures hazards of individual risks in terms of rates in a given territory.

**burglary.** Breaking and entering into premises of another, with felonious intent, and with visible signs of forced entry.

## C

**cancellation.** The termination of an insurance policy or bond before its expiration by either the insured or the company. The notice necessary before such cancellation becomes effective is almost invariably stated in the contract.

**capital stock insurance company.** A company having, in addition to surplus and reserve funds, a capital fund paid in by stockholders.

**capital sum.** The amount specified in an accident policy for payment in the event of the loss of limb or sight of the insured.

**carbon dioxide ($CO_2$).** A gaseous fire extinguishing agent which acts by diluting the oxygen content of the air below the point needed to support combustion.

**carrier.** The insurance company that assumes the risk and issues a policy.

**cash value.** (See *actual cash value*.)

**casualty insurance.** A division of insurance the scope of which has been determined by tradition and company charter restrictions. The general area embraces such coverages as public liability insurance, workmen's compensation, automobile liability, plate glass, burglary and theft, accident insurance, boiler coverage, and aviation. Some casualty companies also write fidelity and surety bonds and are designated as casualty and surety companies.

**civil commotion.** Periods of violence exclusive of war when control is lost or not exercised by authorities charged with maintaining law and order.

**claim.** As used in reference to insurance, a claim may be a demand by an individual or corporation to recover under a policy of insurance for loss which may come within that policy or may be a demand by an individual against an insured for damages covered by a policy held by him. In the latter case such claims are referred to the insurance company for handling on behalf of the insured in accordance with the contract terms.

**class A fire.** A fire which involves the burning of wood, cloth, paper, and similar combustible materials.

**class B fire.** A fire which involves flammable liquids.

**class C fire.** Any fire in which the risk of electrical shock in firefighting is an important consideration.

**clause.** A section of a policy contract, or of riders attached to it, dealing with a particular subject in the contract, as the "insuring clause," or the "coinsurance (average) clause."

**coinsurance.** See discussion of coinsurance in Chapter 8.

**coinsurer.** One who shares the loss sustained under an insurance policy or policies. Usually applied to an owner of property who fails to carry enough insurance to comply with the coinsurance provision and who therefore suffers part of the loss himself. (See *co-surety*.)

**combination policy.** An insurance policy or, more often, two policies printed on one joined sheet, which provides coverage against several hazards under the one document. Sometimes affiliated fire and casualty companies offer insurance under such a policy.

**combustibility.** The tendency of a substance to ignite and support combustion. In fire rating, occupancies are analyzed on the basis of their tendency to ignite as one factor; and their tendency to burn vigorously and create a hot fire as a second factor.

**commercial report.** (See *credit report*.)

**commissioner of insurance.** The state official charged with the enforcement of the laws pertaining to insurance in the respective states. Sometimes called the superintendent or director.

**common carrier.** A person whose occupation is to provide transportation for persons or chattels to anyone who chooses to employ and remunerate him.

**common law defenses.** Pleas which would defeat an injured workman's suit against his employer (and which are still effective in the absence of Workmen's Compensation or Employers' Liability legislation). They are:

1. Contributory negligence on employee's part.
2. Injury being caused by fellow servant.
3. Assumption of risk by the employee in the course of his work.

**common law liability.** Liability arising out of the application of common law, as opposed to statutory law or liability arising out of contract. A major branch of the common law is negligence with which liability insurance is largely concerned.

**compensation award.** An order by the state industrial commission to pay compensation, sometimes in installments, for a number of periods, either definite or indefinite, as the character of the injury requires.

**completed operations.** A form of liability insurance which covers accidents arising out of operations which have been completed or abandoned, provided the accident occurs away from premises owned, rented, or controlled by the insured.

**composite rate.** A single rate for a policy covering several different exposures to loss which are ordinarily rated independently and in a different manner. The purpose of this composite rate is to enable the company readily to adjust the premium to fluctuations in business during the policy term. A premium base is selected which will adequately reflect the insurance company's over-all exposure to loss (such as payroll, receipts, sales, etc.). The composite rate is the one which when multiplied by this base will produce the same premium as would have been produced by rating each exposure separately. While this exact relationship does not hold true during the entire policy term, it will be close enough for all practical purposes.

**comprehensive policy.** A term applied to policies giving broad protection. Perhaps the most important ones applying to libraries are the comprehensive general liability and the comprehensive automobile liability policies. These have important automatic coverage features for new exposures which arise during the policy term and are within the scope of the policy coverage.

**compulsory insurance.** Any form of insurance which is required by law. In Massachusetts and New York, for example, automobile liability insurance is compulsory for all owners of automobiles.

**concurrent insurance.** Two or more insurance policies which provide the same coverage for the same property and for the same interests are concurrent. (See *non-concurrency*.)

**consequential loss.** Standard fire and some other policies cover only against "direct" loss resulting from the peril insured against. Indirect losses, as a consequence of physical damage to the property covered, are not infrequent. Such losses are described as "consequential losses."

Examples:
> (1) Damage to goods in cold storage through failure of refrigeration caused by fire directly damaging the refrigerating apparatus but not the goods — such damage to goods being indirectly caused by the fire, or in consequence thereof.
> (2) Reduction in value of parts of suits because of damage to other parts.

Both of these can be covered, as well as many others, by a special endorsement.

**construction, fire resistive.** Construction usually of reinforced concrete or of steel and masonry with the steel structural members encased in concrete or other fire resistive material.

**construction, mill.** Sometimes called "slow burning." A building with thick brick walls, floor of 3- or 4-inch planks, on 8-inch to 12-inch wood posts and girders; no concealed spaces behind interior finish. Desirable construction, used especially in factories and warehouses.

**construction, noncombustible.** Steel or steel and masonry structures with exposed structural members.

**construction, ordinary.** A building in which the supporting walls are brick and the floors are wood joists; the interior finish usually conceals space in which fire can spread; there is little protection of stair shafts. Compare with *construction, mill.*

**construction, wood frame.** Construction in which all structural members are wood.

**constructive total loss.** A loss which is legally total although the property is not entirely destroyed. Examples: (1) a ship is wrecked and the cost of salvaging exceeds the value; (2) an automobile is damaged to the extent that the cost of repairs exceeds the value.

**contingent liability.** Refers to contingent liability from operation of building laws. (See discussion under contingent coverages in Chapter 8.

**contract bond.** A guarantee of the faithful performance of a construction contract and the payment of all labor and material bills incident thereto. In those situations where two bonds are required, one to cover performance and the other to cover payment of labor and material, the former is known as a performance bond, the latter as a payment bond.

**contract carrier.** A private carrier as opposed to a common carrier. One who agrees by contract with a particular person to carry his chattels for hire.

**contractual liability.** Liability assumed under any contract or agreement. Such liability is generally excluded from liability policies, but in most cases may be covered for an additional premium.

**co-surety.** One of a group of sureties directly participating in a bond. The obligation is joint and several, but common practice provides a stated limit of liability for each surety.

**countersignature.** Signature of licensed agent or representative on a policy necessary to validate the contract.

**countersignature law.** Statute regulating the countersigning of insurance policies in a particular state.

**coverage.** In insurance practice, the word "coverage" is used synonymously with the word "insurance" or "protection."

**credit report.** A confidential report made by an independent individual or organization who has investigated the financial standing, reputation and record of an applicant for insurance. (See *moral hazard.*)

**credits.** Reductions in the basic rate for elimination or confinement of hazards which may have existed.

**criticism.** (See *stamping office.*)

# D

**daily report.** An abbreviated copy of pertinent policy information, identical copies of which are usually prepared so that the insurance company's home office, branch office, interested agents and brokers may each have one. A daily report of an expired policy is, after review, often used as an application for the renewal policy.

**DDD policy.** A package policy providing blanket fidelity, forgery, and broad-form burglary coverage by specific insuring agreements.

**death benefit.** (See *principal sum.*)

**debris removal.** A clause often added to a policy covering fire and allied lines under which the company assumes liability for the removal of debris resulting from damage to the property covered by the insured peril.

**declaration.** A statement by the applicant for insurance usually relative to underwriting information. Sometimes, as in most casualty policies, this becomes a part of the policy.

**deductible clause.** A clause specifying an amount to be deducted from any loss or makes the company liable only for the excess of a stated amount. This is used largely on risks where many small losses are to be expected such as scratches and dents to automobile bodies (collision insurance).

**deposit premium.** The premium deposit required by the company on those forms of insurance subject to periodical premium adjustment. Also called "provisional premium." (See *audit.*)

**depreciation.** Decrease in the value of property over a period of time due to wear and tear and obsolescence.

**depreciation insurance.** (See *replacement cost insurance.*)

**design criteria.** The conditions which must be satisfied if a design is to be satisfactory and meet stated objectives.

**direct writer.** An insurance company which sells its policies through salaried employees or agents who represent it exclusively, rather than through independent local agents or insurance brokers. Usually, the advantage is lower cost; the disadvantage is that the insured does not have the service of an agent or broker in helping him buy the insurance best fitted to his needs, and to assist him when he has a loss.

**disability benefit law.** A statute which imposes upon an employer the legal liability to provide non-occupational weekly benefits to employees who sustain accidents or sickness outside of employment. Such a law is "Article 9 of the Workmen's Compensation Law of New York State," which is commonly referred to as "D.B.L."

**disability insurance.** That branch of insurance which pays weekly or monthly benefits for loss of time and medical reimbursement benefits for disability caused by sickness or accident. These are accidents not covered by Workmen's Compensation.

**discovery period.** Under certain bonds and policies, provision is made to give the insured a period of time after the cancellation or expiration of a contract in which to discover that he has sustained a loss that occurred during the time that the contract was in force and would have been recoverable had the contract continued in force. This period varies from six months to three years where the company can fix the period of time to be allowed. It may also be governed by statute and in certain bonds the period is indefinite because of such statutory requirement.

**dismemberment.** (See *capital sum.*)

**distribution clause.** (See *pro rata distribution clause.*)

**divisible contract clause.** A clause which provides that a violation of the conditions of the policy at one insured location will not void the policy at all locations.

**dry chemical.** A fire extinguishing agent comprised principally of finely pulverized sodium bicarbonate. The term may now also apply to silicone treated mono-ammonium phosphate.

**dry-pipe sprinkler system.** A system in which pipes are kept filled with air under pressure to prevent freezing in cold weather. Opening of any heads permits the air to escape and water to flow to these heads. (See also: *pre-action sprinkler system.*)

**dry-pipe valve.** A special valve used in connection with dry-pipe sprinkler systems.

### E

**effective date.** The date on which an insurance policy or bond goes into effect, and from which protection is furnished.

**electrical supervision.** A design feature in fire detection and alarm circuits which provides a continuous test of circuit readiness for use in order to insure a high degree of reliability.

**encumbrance.** Any outside interest in or right to property founded on legal grounds, such as a mortgage or lien for work and materials. It diminishes the interest of the person owning the property.

**endorsements.** Special circumstances frequently require that a policy be altered. Such alterations are effected by attaching an endorsement to the policy.

**engineer, fire protection.** A professionally qualified person who specializes in fire hazard evaluation, together with the design and specification of corrective measures to the extent justified by economic and life safety considerations.

**engineer, safety.** An engineer who has specialized in the detection of all conditions which might lead to injury or loss of life. He would be able to inspect a property and submit a list of corrections that should be made in order to promote reasonable safety.

**engineering service.** (See *loss prevention service*.)

**evacuation planning.** Setting up a procedure for orderly removal of all personnel, both normal and casual occupants, who may be endangered by an emergency situation or impede measures taken to meet it.

**excess insurance.** An insurance policy which contributes to a loss only after an initial amount of loss has been exceeded. This insurance is said to be "excess of the primary amount," and the primary amount may be insured in whole or in part, or may be carried by the insured at his own risk.

**exclusion.** A provision of an insurance policy or bond referring to hazards or property with respect to which no insurance is afforded.

**expense constant.** Flat amount added to the premium of a risk below the experience rating size (generally below $500 premium). Designed to offset the fact that the expense loading on the smaller risk does not yield enough money to cover the minimum cost of issuing and servicing a policy. This term is found in a Workmen's Compensation policy.

**expense ratio.** The percentage of the premium used to pay all the costs of acquiring, writing and servicing business.

**experience.** The loss record of an insured or of a class of coverage.

**experience rating.** Large risks may qualify for experience rating under liability and Workmen's Compensation policies. Several plans are available whereby the individual experience of the risk will have more or less effect in modifying the premiums produced by manual rates.

**expiration.** The date upon which a policy will cease to cover, unless previously canceled.

**exposure.** This term refers chiefly to the state of being open or subject to loss from some hazard or contingency such as "windstorm exposure," or "liability exposure." It also means proximity to adjoining property, with the resulting danger that a fire therein may spread to the property in question. It is also used as a measure of the rating units or the premium basis of a risk; e.g., an exposure of 15 vehicles or a payroll exposure of $400,000.

**extended coverage endorsement.** An endorsement extending the fire policy, usually to cover loss with certain exceptions caused by windstorm, hail, explosion (except of steam boilers), riot, civil commotion, aircraft, vehicles, and smoke.

**extra expense.** Extra funds needed to continue a business uninterruptedly, after damage. Applied to dwellings, it is called "additional living expense." Coverage is available through extra expense insurance and additional living expense insurance.

**extrapolation.** The process of making predictions outside the range of available data on the basis of apparent trends.

# F

**fault of management.** (See *unsafe*.)

**fidelity bond.** A bond which will reimburse an employer for loss up to the amount of the bond sustained by an employer named in the bond (the insured) by reason of any dishonest act of an employee covered by the bond. Blanket fidelity bonds embrace groups of employees.

**fiduciary.** A person who occupies a position of special trust and confidence (for example, in handling or supervising the affairs or funds of another).

**financial responsibility law.** A statute requiring motorists to furnish evidence of ability to pay damages, either before or after an accident.

**fine arts policy.** An inland marine policy designed to insure statuary, paintings, and similar objects of art, which may include rare books and manuscripts.

**fire.** The term "fire" is not defined by the policies but court decisions have been quite specific. There must be a rapid oxidation or combustion accompanied by a flame or glow. The courts have also stated that the fire must be hostile for there to be coverage under a fire policy. A friendly fire is one confined to the receptacle intended for it while a hostile fire has gone outside of those bounds. The term in the fire policy "direct loss by fire" also requires that the hostile fire be the proximate cause of the loss. Therefore, damage caused by heat from a hostile fire would be covered but if caused by a friendly fire it would not. Damage caused by water used to extinguish a hostile fire would be covered as fire damage.

**fire area.** A space enclosed by fire barriers or separations within which a fire would be confined.

**fire brigade.** A private organization charged with acting against a fire emergency *until arrival of the fire department.*

**fire control.** An endeavor to restrict the spread of or extent of fire either by detection devices, restriction of hazards, or limiting devices such as fire walls, fire doors, etc.

**fireproof.** The term "fireproof" is a misnomer. Fire occurring in an adjoining building or in the combustible contents of a building may cause damage to any structure. Therefore, no building can accurately be termed "fireproof." The term "fire resistive" is a better description of modern incombustible construction. (See *construction, fire resistive.*)

**fireproofing.** Applying a flame retardant finish or treatment to combustible materials and to steel structural members in a building to prevent failure and collapse when exposed to heat.

**fire resistance rating.** The extent to which a structure or portion thereof can withstand continued exposure to fire without collapse, while offering a barrier to fire spread. It is usually expressed in hours or fractions of an hour.

**fire separation.** A general term referring to anything which prevents the spread of fire from one area to another. It usually refers to a standard fire wall in a building which divides the building into two or more separate fire divisions which are separately rated. It may, however, refer to such things as a clear space in a lumber yard.

**fixed fire protection.** Systems for the detection and/or extinguishment of fires which are permanently installed as part of a building.

**flame spread rating.** The rate at which a flame will propagate over the surface of a given material when tested under specified conditions. It is expressed in terms of an arbitrary scale based on cement-asbestos at 0 and good quality red oak at 100.

**flammable liquid.** A liquid having a flash point lower than 200° F. based on standard conditions known as a closed cup test.

**flash point.** The lowest temperature of a substance at which it gives off vapor with sufficient rapidity to form, with the surrounding air, a mixture which is capable of burning when ignited.

**flat cancellation.** When liability has not existed thereunder, policies may be cancelled back to the effective date free of any charge to the insured. Such terminations are known as "flat cancellations."

**flat rate.** This term is used in several ways: (1) the rate used when no coinsurance clause is attached to the policy, or the rate from which the credits for coinsurance are deducted. In some states this is called the gross rate. (2) sometimes used for judgment rates. (See *judgment rates.*)

**floater policy.** A policy under the terms of which protection follows movable property, covering it wherever it may be; for example, a policy on tourist's baggage.

**foam.** An extinguishing agent consisting of a fluid mass of bubbles which may form a smothering blanket over a fire. The bubbles may be produced by either chemical or mechanical action.

**forgery.** Falsely making or materially altering, with intent to defraud, any instrument which if genuine would create a legal claim.

**form.** A descriptive form attached to a policy setting forth the nature of the property covered, the location, and other pertinent data. It may grant certain privileges or impose certain obligations on the insured.

**free standing stack.** Library stacks whose principal support is the building floor upon which they are erected.

**friendly fire.** (See *fire.*)

## G

**gross rate.** (See *flat rate.*)

**group insurance.** Broadly, any insurance plan by which a number of employees (and their dependents) are insured under a single policy, issued to their employer, with individual certificates given to each insured employee. The most commonly written lines are life, accidental death and dismemberment, weekly disability benefits, hospital, surgical and medical expense, and poliomyelitis expense.

## H

**health insurance.** Various plans of coverages providing indemnity for loss of time and medical expenses due to sickness.

**heat actuated device (HAD).** A device used to operate fire detection systems, alarm systems, or extinguishing systems.

**hired car.** A land motor vehicle, trailer, or semi-trailer used under contract in behalf of or loaned to the named insured provided such automobile is not owned by or registered in the name of (a) the named insured, or (b) any executive officer thereof, or (c) an employee or agent of the named insured who is granted an operating allowance of any sort for the use of such automobile.

**home office.** The place where an insurance company maintains its chief executives and general supervisory departments.

**hospitalization insurance.** Various plans of coverage providing indemnity for hospital, nurse, surgical and miscellaneous medical expenses due to bodily injuries or illness.

**hostile fire.** (See *fire.*)

**housekeeping.** The general care, cleanliness and maintenance of an insured property. Good housekeeping is a primary consideration from the underwriters' and inspectors' points of view because poor housekeeping is a major cause of fires and accidents.

## I

**improvements and betterments.** Additions or changes made by a lessee at his own cost which enhances the value of a building he is occupying. These become part of the realty and require special insurance consideration.

**incendiary.** (See *arson.*)

**incurred losses.** Losses occurring within a fixed period whether adjusted and paid or not.

**indemnify.** To compensate for actual loss sustained. Many insurance policies and all bonds promise to "indemnify" the insureds. Under such a contract there can be no recovery until the insured has actually suffered a loss. Many liability contracts have replaced "indemnify" with clause "to pay on behalf of the insured."

**indirect damage.** Loss resulting from a peril, but not caused directly and immediately thereby. Indirect damage may be covered by insurance, as for example, business interruption, leasehold interest, profits and commissions, rent or rental value, and consequential coverage.

**inherent explosion.** Explosion caused by some condition existing and natural to the insured premises, as a dust explosion in a grain mill.

**inherent vice.** A defect or cause of loss arising out of the nature of the goods in question.

**in kind.** To replace like for like, such as horses for horses, or apples for apples.

**inland marine insurance.** Various types of insurance developed originally by marine underwriters to cover goods while in transit by other than ocean vessels. It now includes any goods in transit, except trans-ocean, and numerous floaters, as personal effects, personal property, jewelry, furs, etc., the essential condition being that the insured property be movable. Bridges, tunnels, and similar instrumentalities of transportation are also considered inland marine.

**inspection bureau or rating bureau.** A legally recognized group organized and supported by capital stock fire insurance companies for the purposes of determining rates of individual risks on the basis of hazards involved.

**insurable interest.** In order for a claim for loss of property under an insurance policy to be valid, the insured must have an interest in the property based on legal right which will suffer a diminution, the pecuniary value of which may be measured, in the event the property is damaged or destroyed.

**insurable risk.** (See *insurance.*)

**insurable value.** (See *actual cash value,* and *replacement cost insurance.*)

**insurance.** A contract whereby, for an agreed premium, one party undertakes to compensate the other for a loss on a specified subject by specified perils. In the abstract it is a device by which the uncertain risks of loss to which many people are subject are transferred to a single insurance carrier. Through the operation of the law of large numbers, the uncertainty is to a great extent removed and a small constant premium paid by the many will provide funds to pay the losses of the few who sustain them.

**insurance company.** An organization chartered under state or provincial laws to act as an insurer. In the United States, insurance companies are usually classified as fire and marine, life, casualty, and surety companies and may write only those kinds of insurance which are specifically authorized in their charters. Many company charters have now been broadened to include several of these types.

**insurance policy.** Broadly, the entire written contract of insurance. More narrowly, the basic written or printed document, as distinguished from the forms and endorsements added thereto.

**insured.** (Also called *assured.*) The person(s), partnership, association, trust, or corporation whose insurable interest is protected by the policy. Usually called "obligee" in connection with surety bonds and referred to as the "employer" in some fidelity bonds.

**insurer.** (See *insurance.*)

**insuring clause.** The part of an insurance policy or bond which recites the agreement of the insurer to protect the insured against some form of loss or damage. This is the heart of the contract of insurance.

**internal revenue bonds.** Bonds required by the U. S. Government which guarantee payment of federal taxes and compliance with government regulations.

# J

**judgment rates.** Rates established by the judgment of the underwriter without the application of a formal set of rules or schedule.

# K

**kidnaping coverage.** Insurance against the hazard of a person being seized outside the insured premises and forced to return and open the premises or a safe therein, or to give information which will enable the criminals to do so.

# L

**label.** (See *Underwriters' Laboratories.*)

**larceny.** Generally, the unlawful taking of the personal property of another without his consent and with intent to deprive him of the ownership or use thereof. This offense is defined by statute in practically all states and provinces and these statutory definitions differ somewhat.

**legal liability.** (See *liability.*)

**lessee.** The person to whom a lease is granted, commonly called the tenant.

**lessor.** The person granting a lease, also known as the landlord.

**liability.** Broadly, any legally enforceable obligation. The term is most commonly used in a pecuniary sense.

**liability insurance.** An insurance contract by which the insurance company agrees to pay on behalf of the insured any sums he may become obligated to pay which arise out of his legal liability as defined and restricted in the contract. It also provides for legal defense against groundless claims.

**license and permit bonds.** Bonds required by various municipalities or public authorities to indemnify them against loss in the event of violation of regulations or ordinances under which the permit is required.

**limit of liability.** The maximum amount which an insurance company agrees to pay in case of loss.

**line.** Colloquial term with several meanings. It may be used in connection with a particular type of insurance. ("Agent Jones writes the fire line on the Ajax building.") It may also be used to describe all the various types of insurance written for a property owner. ("The Ajax Company line is handled by the Jones agency.") The term is sometimes used to describe the amount of insurance on a given property. ("The Jones agency has a $10,000 line on the Ajax Company garage.") In casualty insurance "line" may also refer to specific categories such as automobile liability, general liability, burglary, and Workmen's Compensation coverages.

**line sheet.** A guide prepared by an insurance company for its underwriters, setting forth the amount of liability it is willing to assume on the various classes of risks.

**live stock insurance.** Insurance against the death of an animal from named perils.

**Lloyds of London.** An association of individuals acting as insurance carriers. There are hundreds of members but they do business by forming themselves into small groups called syndicates. Ordinarily, each syndicate has a professional underwriter who has power to accept risks on behalf of the members of the syndicate and bind each member for his predetermined share. Each member so bound is liable for his share of losses incurred and his personal fortune guarantees the payment. Due to careful screening of underwriters and high standards of requirements, a default on an obligation is practically unknown.

**loading.** An amount added to the basic rate or premium to cover the expense to the insurance company in securing and maintaining the business. This term is also used in connection with inland marine insurance, as the amount added to the fire rate to cover additional perils.

**local agent.** (See *agent*.)

**loss.** Any loss of or damage to insured property which results in a claim under an insurance policy. Under a liability policy, it is the amount of damages paid to a third party. In either case the adjustment expenses are regarded as a part of the loss on company records.

**loss constant.** Flat amount added to the premium of a risk below the experience rating size (generally $500 premium); designed to offset worse-than-average loss experience of the smaller risk. This term is found in Workmen's Compensation insurance.

**loss prevention service.** Engineering and inspection work done by insurance companies or independent organizations for the purpose of changing or removing conditions which would be likely to cause loss.

**lost policy release.** A statement signed by the insured releasing the insurance company from all liability under a lost or mislaid contract of insurance.

**loss ratio.** The percentage of losses to premiums.

# M

**malpractice.** Alleged professional misconduct or lack of ordinary skill in the performance of a professional act. A practitioner is liable for damage or injuries caused by malpractice. Such liability, for some professions, can be covered by insurance.

**manual.** A book published by an insurance or bonding company, a conference or a rating association or bureau, giving rates, classifications, and underwriting rules for some phase of insurance or bonds in a particular territory.

**manual rates.** Usually the cost of a unit of insurance or bond protection of the various kinds of insurance and bonds as published in the pertinent manuals, but the term may also refer to rates developed by the application of a recognized rating plan.

**marine insurance.** That form of coverage which is primarily concerned with the protection of goods in transit and the means of transportation. This term is applied in common usage to risks involving ocean transit. (See *inland marine*.)

**medical expense insurance.** Coverage available in various forms against expenses incurred for medical treatment and care as a result of bodily injury or illness. Examples: major medical expense insurance, surgical expense insurance, hospitalization insurance.

**medical payments insurance.** An optional insuring agreement available under various liability policies which pays for medical and funeral expenses as a result of accident to third parties. This covers regardless of the legal liability of the insured. Under broadened conditions of the extended medical payments clause available on privately owned passenger automobiles, this even extends to accidents (as defined in the policy) sustained by the insured and members of his family.

**microfilming.** A system of copying records, documents, etc., onto photographic film. Microfilm is usually a roll of 8, 16, or 35 mm. film.

**minimum premium.** The smallest premium which an insurance company may charge under the rules for writing a particular policy or bond for a designated period. It is intended to cover the expense incurred in writing the policy or bond, for which premiums on a strict pro rata basis are often insufficient.

**monopolistic state fund.** A state or provincial Workmen's Compensation insurance plan which prohibits the writing of this coverage by private carriers.

**moral hazard.** The possibility of loss being caused or aggravated by dishonesty or carelessness of the insured, his agents or employees. It arises from the character and circumstances of the insured, apart from the nature of the interest or property covered, or its location. The latter is called the physical hazard.

**mortgage (or mortgagee) clause.** A provision attached to a fire or other direct damage insurance policy covering mortgaged property, reciting that the loss shall be payable to the mortgagee as his interest may appear and that his right of recovery shall not be defeated by any act or neglect of the insured and giving the mortgagee other rights and privileges.

**multiple line.** Insurance which combines more than one of the coverages of fire, inland marine, and casualty in a single policy. These have been kept separate by law until the advent of multiple-line legislation.

**multiple-line underwriting laws.** Statutes granting underwriting powers which enable one company to write both fire and casualty insurance.

**multi-tier stack.** A library bookstack arrangement of several levels in which the upper levels are supported by those below as a structural entity, independent of the surrounding building.

**mutual insurance company.** A company in which capital stockholders do not share in profits. Economies in operation or savings from favorable experience are returned to policyholders in the form of dividends. There may be provisions for assessments if losses impair their financial security. Large mutual companies may accumulate enough guarantee capital to limit the assessment liability of policy holders or eliminate it entirely.

## N

**named insured.** Any person, firm or corporation, or any member thereof, specifically designated by name as insured (s) in a policy as distinguished from others who, though unnamed, are protected under some circumstances. A common application of this latter principle is in liability policies wherein by a definition of "insured" protection is extended to interests (not designated by name) according to their status or in particular situations or circumstances.

**named perils.** Named-peril (or hazard) policies specify what hazards are insured against, contrary to so-called all-risk policies.

**National Association of Insurance Agents.** The country-wide organization of stock fire and casualty insurance company agents, which has for its primary purpose the protection and advancement of the American agency system.

**National Board of Fire Underwriters.** The clearinghouse of stock fire insurance companies, which is concerned with promoting the interests of its members and of stock fire insurance as a whole, cultivating public good will, and the study of underwriting, administrative, loss adjustment, fire prevention, and fire protection problems. It takes no part in rate-making other than to supply information to rate-making bodies based on inspection and grading of towns and cities of over 25,000 population, and on the classification and tabulation of loss experience by territories and by classes of risks.

**National Bureau of Casualty Underwriters.** An organization of stock casualty companies which collects and analyzes experience; establishes underwriting rules, classification of risks, manual rates and minimum premiums; establishes and administers rating systems and plans to measure correctly the hazards of individual risks which are not measured correctly by classification experience alone; and performs certain other functions on behalf of its member companies.

**National Fire Protection Association.** An organization including manufacturers, merchants, fire-fighters, scientists, and insurance men, both stock and mutual, the purpose of which is indicated by its name.

**Nationwide Marine Definition.** A statement of the types of insurance that may properly be written under marine or inland marine policies. This statement, on recommendation by the National Association of Insurance commissioners, has been adopted in most states, with exceptions in some. There is a committee on interpretation (of this definition) composed of representatives of fire, casualty, and marine, and inland marine departments of the industry.

**negligence.** Failure to use that degree of care which an ordinary person of reasonable prudence would use under the given circumstances. Negligence may be constituted by acts of either omission, commission, or both.

**non-board company.** An insurance company that does not subscribe to the rates and rules of the rating bureaus.

**non-concurrency.** The situation which exists where a number of insurance policies, intended to cover the same property, for the same interests, and against the same hazards, are not identical, as to the extent of coverage. Non-concurrencies which cause the most trouble involve policies insuring partly different subjects, or using different coinsurance percentages.

**nozzle.** The device which terminates a hose line and controls the quantity and character of the flow of water or other extinguishing agent.

## O

**obligee.** Broadly, any one in whose favor an obligation runs. This term is used most frequently in surety bonds where it refers to the person, firm, or corporation protected by the bond. The obligee under a bond is similar to the insured under an insurance policy.

**obligor.** Commonly called principal; one bound by an obligation. Under a bond, strictly speaking, both the principal and the surety are obligors.

**occupancy.** In insurance, this term refers to the type and character of the use of property in question. It plays a very important part in computing rates and in determining the acceptance or rejection of risks.

**other insurance clause.** A provision found in practically every insurance policy stating what is to be done in case any other contract of protection embraces the same property and hazard.

**over-insurance.** The situation which exists where a risk is insured for more than its fair or reasonable value. Such a state of affairs is undesirable for all parties concerned.

## P

**package policies.** Combination policies wherein several coverages are included in one contract. Examples: storekeepers' burglary and robbery policy, residence all-in-one policy, home-owner's policy, comprehensive dwelling policy, 5-point automobile policy, and DDD policy.

**participating insurance.** Insurance or reinsurance which contributes proportionately with other insurance on the same risk. Compare with *excess insurance.*

**payroll audit.** An examination of the insured's payroll records by a representative of the insurer to determine the premium due on a policy written on a payroll basis. (See *audit.*)

**peril.** This term refers to the causes of possible loss, for instance: fire, windstorm, explosion, and the like.

**permanent partial disability benefits.** Periodic indemnities for a disability which impairs earning capacity but which does not involve total inability to work.

**permanent total disability benefits.** Periodic indemnities, generally weekly, for a disability of a kind that renders any employment impossible. Such compensation may be limited by a maximum time or a maximum amount, but if unlimited may run for life.

**personal hazard.** (See *moral hazard.*)

**personal property.** Property which is not attached to the land and the title of which would not be conveyed by a deed to the real property. There are certain types of property which are on the borderline and may be real property under certain sets of fact and personal property under others. Trade fixtures, for example, may be attached to the building and yet be removable by the tenant at the expiration of his lease. There is quite a body of case law ruling on the conditions under which such property is real or personal.

**physical hazard.** The physical characteristics of an insured property such as combustibility, susceptibility to the starting of fires, and damageability, which may be measured or statistically evaluated. This is as opposed to "moral hazard," which cannot be measured.

**pilferage.** Petty theft, especially theft of articles in less than package lots. This constitutes one of the greatest causes of small marine insurance losses and is usually excluded.

**policy.** A written contract of insurance.

**policyholder.** One who possesses an insurance contract. In most cases this term is used as synonymous with "insured."

**pre-action sprinkler system.** A system in which the pipes are normally empty. Activation of a supplemental heat detection system, usually more sensitive than the sprinkler heads, permits water to flow into the pipes and out any heads which may be subsequently opened.

**premium.** In insurance and bonding, the consideration to be paid for a policy or bond. This term has a variety of meanings in other business practice.

**pressurized water extinguisher.** An extinguisher filled with water and a compressed gas, usually air, at about 150 psi. Upon opening of the valve, the air pressure expels the water.

**principal.** In suretyship the party whose actions, honesty or responsibility are to be guaranteed. In a fidelity bond, for example, the bonded employee is the principal. (See *obligor.*)

**principal sum.** The amount specified under an accident policy as death benefit.

**producer.** Term commonly applied to an agent, solicitor, broker, or other person who sells insurance, producing business for the company.

**product liability.** Liability imposed for damages caused by accident and arising out of the handling or use or the existence of any condition in goods or products manufactured, sold, handled, or distributed by the insured or others trading under his name, if the accident occurs after possession has been relinquished to others and away from premises owned, rented, or controlled by the insured.

**professional liability.** (See *malpractice.*)

**proof of loss.** A formal statement made by the insured to the insurance company regarding a loss. The purpose of the proof of loss is to place before the company sufficient information concerning the loss to enable it to determine its liability under the policy or bond.

**property damage liability insurance.** Protection against liability for damage to the property of another not in the care, custody, and control of the insured, as distinguished from liability for bodily injury (public liability). In the majority of cases, property damage insurance is written in connection with the bodily injury protection, the premiums and limits of insurance being distinct. (See also *liability insurance.*)

**proprietary alarm system.** An alarm system owned and operated by the owner of the property involved, generally located at a constantly supervised point on the premises.

**pro rata cancellation.** The termination of an insurance contract or bond, the premium charge being adjusted in proportion to the exact time the protection has been in force. Compare with *short rate.*

**pro rata distribution.** This provision, also known as the pro rata distribution clause, is used in the writing of certain blanket policies. Its purpose is to divide the amount of insurance carried under a single item in the policy form among the several subjects of insurance, in that proportion which the value of each subject of insurance bears to the total value of all property covered under that single item in the policy form. Example: $10,000 insurance covering two buildings under one item. Value of Building A, $10,000, value of building B, $5,000. Insurance would be divided 10/15 x $10,000 = $6,667 on Building A and 5/15 x $10,000 = $3,333 on Building B. These amounts are the maximums the insured can collect for each building.

**protected.** In fire insurance, a risk located in an area protected by a fire department. In burglary insurance, a risk equipped with a burglar alarm.

**protection.** (1) A term used interchangeably with the word "coverage" to denote the insurance provided under the terms of a policy. (2) A term used to indicate the existence of fire-fighting facilities in an area known as a "protected" area.

**provisional premium.** (See *deposit premium.*)

**proximate cause.** The dominating cause of loss or damage; an unbroken chain of cause and effect between the occurrence of an insured peril and damage to property or persons; e.g., fire is the proximate cause of damage done by water used in extinguishing it.

**psi or psig.** Pressure in pounds per square inch.

**public liability insurance.** A general term applied to forms of "third party liability insurance," both as respects bodily injury and property damage. The term is still sometimes used to indicate forms of bodily injury liability insurance as distinguished from property damage insurance, but the better practice in the interest of clarity is to designate by their respective titles these different forms.

**pure premium.** The pure premium is the premium required to pay losses only. The actual premium is made up of the pure premium with loadings to cover commissions, taxes, and other expenses with a margin of profit for the insurance company.

# R

**railroad sidetrack agreement.** A contract entered into between a railroad and an industry, under the terms of which the railroad agrees to build and maintain a switch track on the industry's premises to facilitate shipments, and the industry agrees to release the carrier from liability to a certain extent.

**rate.** The cost of a unit of insurance. In fire insurance, the rate is the cost per $100 of insurance. In liability insurance, a suitable rate base is selected to measure the exposure to loss (i.e., payroll, sales, admissions). The rate, then, is the amount which must be charged per unit of the rate base in order to produce adequate premiums to cover losses and expenses.

**rating bureau.** A rating organization. (See *inspection bureau.*)

**reciprocal exchange (reciprocal insurance company).** Reciprocals, sometimes called "reciprocal exchanges" or "reciprocal insurance companies," are controlled by an attorney-in-fact. Each member or subscriber signs a power of attorney which gives the attorney-in-fact power to obligate them severally within the limits of the power. In essence, each subscriber insures all of the other subscribers.

**reinstatement.** The payment of a claim under many forms of insurance reduces the principal amount of the policy by the amount of the claim. Provision is usually made for a method of reinstating the policy to its original amount. This may be done automatically either with or without premium consideration or at the request of the insured.

**renewal.** The reinstatement in form, force, and effect of something that is about to expire. With an insurance policy it is made either by the issuance of a new policy or renewal receipt or certificate under the same conditions, to take effect upon the expiration of the old policy.

**replacement cost insurance.** Insurance providing that the insured will be paid the cost of replacing the damaged property without deduction for depreciation. The usual replacement cost form provides that the property must actually be replaced before the insured may collect a claim under it. It is available only for buildings, with some few exceptions.

**representation.** Oral or written statement, made by the insured to the insurer, of certain facts or conditions tending to induce the insurer to assume the risk. (See *warranty.*)

**reserve.** A name common to certain funds that are earmarked for specific purposes. Insurance examples are: reserves for unearned premiums and reserves for losses in process of adjustment.

**retroactive restoration.** A provision in a policy or bond whereby — after payment of a loss — the original amount of coverage is automatically restored to take care of prior undiscovered losses as well as future losses.

**retrospective rating.** A plan or method which permits adjustment of the final premium for risk on the basis of its own loss experience subject to maximum and minimum limits. (See *experience rating.*)

**return premium.** The amount due the insured if a policy is canceled, reduced in amount or reduced in rate. (See *short rate.*)

**riders.** Another name for clauses or endorsements; but more especially, printed forms of special provisions that are not contained in the policy contract. In bonding, and always in the personal accident department, such clauses are called riders instead of endorsements. (See *endorsement.*)

**risk.** (1) Any chance of loss. (2) The insured or the property to which the insurance policy relates.

**robbery.** The felonious taking, either by violence or threat of violence, of the personal property of another. Contrast larceny, where the theft is accomplished by stealth and the degree of turpitude is measured by the value of personal property. Robbery is commonly known as "hold-up."

## S

**salvage.** The value of property after it has been partially damaged by fire or other perils. Also used as a verb meaning to save endangered property and to enhance the value of damaged property. (See *Underwriters Salvage Corporation.*) In marine insurance it means the cost of saving property exposed to a peril. Salvage, in suretyship, is that which is recovered from the principal or an indemnitor to offset in whole or in part the loss and expense paid by a surety in satisfying its obligation under a bond.

**schedule of insurance.** The list of individual items covered under one policy as the various buildings, animals and other property in farm insurance or the list of the rings, bracelets, etc., insured under a jewelry floater.

**schedule (rating).** A table showing the charges and credits applied by the rating bureau in establishing a "specific" rate. The interested insured is entitled to a copy of the schedule showing the make-up of his rate, so that he may see what conditions call for penalties, and what improvements may be made to reduce his rate.

**shelf list.** A record of the books in a library, arranged in the order in which they stand on the shelves.

**short rate.** The term "short rate" in insurance and bonding is used to describe the charge required for insurance or bonds taken for less than one year, and, in some cases, the earned premium for insurance or bonds canceled by the insured before the end of the policy period or term of bond.

**sickness insurance.** Provides for payment of a substantial part of earned income lost through disability caused by illness and for payment of medical expenses incurred as a result of illness.

**single interest policy.** Insurance protecting the interest of only one of the parties having an insurable interest in certain property, as that protecting a mortgagee but not the mortgagor, or protecting the seller but not the buyer of merchandise.

**sinking fund.** A fund from which losses are paid. Regular income is derived from appropriations in lieu of insurance premiums.

**sliding stacks.** A system of stacks which fold or slide away to permit access to additional stacks immediately behind.

**slow-burning construction.** (See *construction, mill.*)

**smoke damage insurance.** Insurance against damage done by smoke from the "sudden, unusual, and faulty" operation of a heating or cooking unit but only when such unit is connected to a chimney by a smoke pipe and while on the premises described in the policy. Smoke damage from fireplaces and industrial apparatus is excluded. (Damage caused by smoke from a hostile fire (see *fire*) is covered by a fire insurance policy.)

**Society of Fire Protection Engineers (SFPE).** An association of engineers in or practicing fire protection as an engineering science. It was founded in 1950 as a section of the National Fire Protection Association and is to become an independent organization when practicable. Membership is by election after review of qualifications, to grades of Junior Member, Associate Member, and Member, rated in that order. Address: 60 Batterymarch Street, Boston 10, Massachusetts.

**soda-acid extinguisher.** An extinguisher filled with a soda solution in water and an acid in a separate container. When turned over, the acid combines with the soda to produce large quantities of carbon dioxide gas, the pressure of which expels the contents.

**sonic boom.** Shock waves set up in the air and caused by an aircraft when it goes through the sound barrier, i.e., exceeds the speed of sound.

**sound value.** Usually used after a fire to indicate the value of the insured property immediately before the damage. (See also *actual cash value.*)

**specific insurance.** (a) Applying separately to specifically named objects or locations. (b) Inaccurately used in referring to primary insurance which must be exhausted before excess insurance applies.

**specific rate.** A rate applying to an individual property, determined by a schedule. (See *schedule.*)

**sprinkler head.** A nozzle fitted with a deflecting cap so that water is broken up into a spray as it leaves the nozzle. Heads are usually kept closed by a fusible link device which releases whenever a predetermined temperature is exceeded, and this permits water to flow.

**sprinkler system.** A network of carefully placed and sized pipes and sprinkler heads which will cover a given area with a discharge of water when actuated by a fire.

**stamping office.** A stamping office is a central office or bureau to which agents and companies send certain daily reports and endorsements for auditing before transmittal to the insurance company. If incorrect, notice is sent to the writing office and company requesting correction.

**standpipe.** A water line in a building which is especially intended to supply hose streams for fire fighting.

**stock company.** (See *capital stock company.*)

**structural member.** An essential load-bearing beam or column constituting part of a structure.

**structure.** Any self-supporting framework or building.

**subrogation.** The right of an insurance company, after having paid a property insurance loss to its insured, to succeed to all rights of the insured against a third party who might be legally liable for the loss.

**superseded suretyship riders.** When a company writes a bond that takes the place of another that has been canceled as of the effective date of the new bond, a rider should be attached agreeing to pay losses that would be recoverable under the first bond except for the fact that the "discovery period" has expired. Losses caused by dishonest employees frequently are found to have occurred at various times stretching over a period of years which may involve a chain of numerous bonds, each one superseding a prior obligation. If there is any lapse of time between the cancellation of the prior bond and the effective date of the succeeding bond, the chain is broken and no "superseded suretyship rider" is attached.

**Surety Association of America (The).** An Association composed of more than 70 leading capital stock companies which are engaged in fidelity, surety, and forgery bond underwriting. The Association establishes classifications of risks, manual rates, minimum premiums, and rating plans; creates and revises standard forms, provisions, riders, and other forms; collects and analyzes statistical data; makes filings with regulatory authorities in behalf of its members and subscribers; provides a forum for the discussion of problems of common interest to member companies; promotes sound underwriting practices; engages in educational activities; and performs certain other functions for its members.

**suretyship.** Stated in its simplest terms, suretyship embraces all forms of obligations to pay the debt or answer for the default of another.

**survey.** (1) A careful examination of the insurance requirements of an insurance buyer and the report of such examination. (2) An insurance engineer's study of a risk for underwriting and/or accident and occupational disease prevention purposes.

## T

**target risks.** Policyholders or prospects for insurance whose business develops large premiums are considered targets for competing insurance agents and brokers. Also used to describe risks of large value or limits and severe hazards that are difficult to insure, or for companies to reinsure.

**tariff rate.** The insurance rate established by the rating organization having jurisdiction over the class and territory.

**temporary disability benefits.** The term generally used when speaking of the weekly benefits payable to employees for non-occupational accidents and sickness. This term or the abbreviated form "T.D.B." is commonly used when referring specifically to coverage as provided under the New Jersey Temporary Disability Benefits law. (See *disability insurance, disability benefit law,* and *temporary total disability benefits.*)

**temporary total disability benefits.** The weekly benefit payable to an employee as prescribed by a Workmen's Compensation law because he is temporarily unable to perform any duties for his employer due to an accident or sickness sustained within and arising out of his employment.

**term.** A period of time for which a policy or bond is issued.

**term insurance.** Common expression for policies written for more than one year.

**theft.** Theft includes larceny, burglary, and robbery.

**third party insurance.** Generally, this insurance protects the insured against his liability arising out of bodily injury to others or damage to their property.

**trade report.** (See *credit report.*)

## U

**umpire.** The impartial third member of a team of arbiters or appraisers whose duty it is to settle differences of opinion and achieve agreement.

**unadmitted company (insurance).** A company which has not registered with the insurance commissioner of a given state. Unadmitted companies generally operate in such areas through correspondence.

**under-insurance.** A condition in which not enough insurance is carried to cover the insurable value and, especially, to satisfy a coinsurance clause.

**underwriter.** Any individual officer or employee of an insurance company who has the responsibility of accepting risks and determining in what amounts their insurance should be written.

**Underwriters' Laboratories, Inc.** An institution sponsored by stock fire insurance companies of the United States. Various equipment, material, and devices are submitted by their makers and tested to establish their effectiveness, usually for fire prevention and safety. Inspection is also made at the shops of manufacturers, and labels issued by the Underwriters' Laboratories are affixed to the appliances as evidence of compliance with standards.

**Underwriters Salvage Corporation.** A company, sponsored by stock insurance companies, with the major purpose of processing and reselling merchandise damaged by fire, thus reducing the net loss paid by the insurers.

**unearned premium.** That portion of the original premium that has not yet been "earned" by the company as the policy still has some time to run. A fire or casualty insurance company must carry all unearned premiums as a liability in its financial statement for if the policy should be cancelled, the company would have to pay back a certain part of the original premium.

**union catalog system.** A catalog which includes the holdings of a group of libraries and is used by all in common.

**unoccupied.** Furnished but not lived in. The standard fire insurance policy prohibits vacancy and unoccupancy beyond a specified period. Permission for unlimited vacancy and unoccupancy is usually given in the forms for use in protected territory without charge. In unprotected territory, the permission is given as necessary, and a charge is made.

**unprotected.** (See *protected*.)

**unsafe.** A term used in schedule rating to describe a condition for which a penalty is applied, and which can usually be easily corrected, with the removal of the charge and reduction in rate. Some schedules use the term "fault of management," some "after charge."

# V

**vacant.** Not lived in and void of furnishing. (See *unoccupied*.)

**valuable papers policy.** An inland marine policy designed to protect written, printed, or otherwise inscribed documents or records against all perils.

**value.** (See *actual cash value.*)

**valued policy.** A policy which provides that a special amount shall be paid in event of a total loss of the property. Most fine arts and some other inland marine policies have this provision. In fire insurance any such provisions are illegal in most states. However, in some states there are "valued" policy laws which require that fire insurance on buildings be treated as "valued" policies.

**vaporizing liquid.** An extinguishing agent which is effective by reason of its smothering action and special chemical characteristics. Typical agents are carbon tetrachloride and chlorobromomethane. Not recommended for indoor use for toxicity reasons and prohibited by law in some areas.

## W

**waiver.** Waiver is the giving up or surrender of a right or privilege which is known to exist.

**waiver of restoration premium.** A provision in certain contracts, especially in bonds, wherein the company agrees not to charge any additional premium for reinstating the contract after loss has occurred.

**warranty.** Statement or stipulation in the policy as to the existence of a fact or a condition of the subject of the insurance, which, if untrue, will void the policy. (See *representation.*)

**wet water.** Water to which has been added a low surface tension agent so that it may readily penetrate into porous materials and extinguish deep seated fires. Most detergents may act as wet water agents.

**world-wide coverage.** In some policies a world-wide coverage is provided. For example, jewelry-fur, personal effects, and personal property floaters.

**write.** In insurance terms this means to insure, to underwrite; as, the "XYZ Company writes the line" on so and so. Sometimes it is used to mean to sell insurance, as by an agent.

# USEFUL REFERENCES

## PHYSICAL PROTECTION

AMERICAN INSTITUTE OF STEEL CONSTRUCTION. *Fire-Resistant Construction in Modern Steel-Framed Buildings.* New York: The Institute, n.d.

AMERICAN SOCIETY FOR TESTING MATERIALS. *Standard Methods of Fire Tests of Building Construction and Materials* (ASTM Designation: E 119058). Philadelphia: The Society, 1958.

————. *Standard Method of Test for Surface Burning Characteristics of Building Materials* (ASTM Designation: 84-61). Philadelphia: The Society, 1961.

"THE ARCHITECT — AND FIRE SAFETY," *Journal of the American Institute of Architects,* XXV (May, 1957), 37-42.

"THE ARCHITECT'S RESPONSIBILITY FOR FIRE SAFETY," *Bulletin of the American Institute of Architects,* AIA File No. R9, (March-April, 1956).

BAHME, CHARLES WILLIAM. *Fire Protection for Chemicals.* Boston: National Fire Protection Association, 1956.

BOND, HORATIO, ed. *NFPA Inspection Manual.* 2nd ed. Boston: National Fire Protection Association, 1959.

————. *Research on Fire.* Boston: National Fire Protection Association, 1957.

"BOOKS DESTROYED AND DAMAGED," *National Library of Medicine News,* XII (October, 1957).

BUGBEE, PERCY. "Fire Protection Progress," *Safety Standards,* X (September-October, 1961), 1-6.

BUILDING OFFICIALS CONFERENCE OF AMERICA. *Basic Building Code,* Supplements 1-4. New York: The Conference, 1955-1958.

BUILDING RESEARCH ADVISORY BOARD, COMMITTEE ON FIRE RESEARCH. *School Fires — An Approach to Life Safety.* Washington, D. C.; National Academy of Sciences — National Research Council, 1960.

COE, THEODORE I. "Fire — Friend and Foe of Man," *Bulletin of the American Institute of Architects,* AIA File No. R9, (January-February, 1954).

COMMITTEE OF FIRE RESEARCH, DIVISION OF ENGINEERING AND INDUSTRIAL RESEARCH. *Directory of Fire Research in the United States* (Publication No. 904). Washington, D. C.: National Academy of Sciences — National Research Council, 1961.

DURHAM & BATES, INC. *Stop Fires — Save Lives.* Portland, Ore.: The Corporation, n. d.

EDUCATIONAL FACILITIES LABORATORIES, INC. *Ring the Alarm.* New York: The Laboratories, 1959.

FACTORY MUTUAL ENGINEERING DIVISION. *Fire Tests of Library Bookstacks, Laboratory Reports.* Norwood, Mass.: The Division, 1959.

FEDERAL FIRE COUNCIL. *News Letter,* II (October, 1961).

FINCHUM, R. N. and BOERRIGTER, GLENN C. *School Fires: Prevention, Control, Protection.* Washington, D. C.: U. S. Department of Health, Education, and Welfare, Office of Education, 1962.

"FIRE AFTERMATH: WATERVILLE, MAINE, PUBLIC LIBRARY," *Library Journal,* LXXXIV (June 15, 1959), 2016.

FIRE EQUIPMENT MANUFACTURERS ASSOCIATION. *FEMA Handbook of Safety Codes.* Pittsburgh: The Association, 1959.

"FIRE PROTECTION INVESTIGATION," *ALA Bulletin,* LV (February, 1961), 201.

"FIRE SPRINKLER SYSTEM TO BE INSTALLED AT NEW YORK PUBLIC LIBRARY," *Library Journal,* LXXXV (October, 1961), 3413.

"FIRE TESTS OF LIBRARY BOOK STACKS" (film). New York Public Library and Associated Factory Mutual Fire Insurance Company, 1960.

"FIRES AND FIRE-TRAPS," *Library Journal,* LXXXIII (May 15, 1958), 1508.

"FLOOD DAMAGE," *Connecticut Historical Society Bulletin,* XX (August, 1955).

FYAN, L. D. "The Michigan State Library — An Account of Water Damage and Salvage Operations," *ALA Bulletin,* XXXXV (May, 1951), 164-66.

HAMILTON, ROBERT M. "The Fire at the Library of Parliament," *The American Archivist,* XVI (April, 1953), 141.

HEADQUARTERS, DEPARTMENT OF THE ARMY. *Repairs and Utilities, Automatic and Manual Fire Alarm Systems, Inspection and Prevention Maintenance* (TM 5-695). Washington, D. C.: The Department, May, 1958.

————. *Repairs and Utilities, Automatic Sprinkler and Standpipe Equipment, Inspections, Operations and Preventive Maintenance* (TM 5-696). Washington, D. C.: The Department, August, 1957.

HEMPHILL, B. F. "Lessons of a Fire," *Library Journal,* LXXXVII (March 15, 1962), 1094-95.

HUFF, WILLIAM H. "Serial Services Cost Indexes," *Library Resources & Technical Services*, 158-60 (Spring, 1960).

HUGHES, CHARLES A. *Effect of Element-Wall Thickness on Operation of Continuous Fire-Detector System.* New York: Pittman Publishing Co., 1956.

IIAMS, THOMAS H. *Foxing and the Deterioration of Books.* M.A. thesis, University of Chicago, n.d.

IIAMS, THOMAS H. AND BECKWITH, T. D. "Notes on the Causes and Prevention of Foxing in Books," *Library Quarterly,* V (October, 1935), 407-18.

INTERNATIONAL CONFERENCE OF BUILDING OFFICIALS. *Uniform Building Code.* Los Angeles: The Conference, 1958.

KIMBALL, WARREN YOUNG. *Fire Department Terminology.* Boston: National Fire Protection Association, 1955.

KNIGHT, KENNETH C. "Fire Disrupts the State Library," *Michigan Librarian,* XVII (1951), 7.

KURTH, WILLIAM H. "U. S. Book and Periodical Prices — A Preliminary Report," *Library Journal,* LXXXV (January, 1960), 54-57.

LAYMAN, LLOYD. *Attacking and Extinguishing Interior Fires.* Boston: National Fire Protection Association, 1952.

LOS ANGELES FIRE DEPARTMENT. *Operation School Burning.* Boston: National Fire Protection Association, 1959.

———. *Operation School Burning* (No. 2). Boston: National Fire Protection Association, 1961.

LYNDENBURG, HARRY M., and ARCHER, JOHN. *The Care and Repair of Books.* New York: Bowker, 1931.

MADDOX, JANE. "The Norwood Book Burning," *Wilson Library Bulletin,* XXXIV (1960), 412-14.

"MEMO TO MEMBERS," *ALA Bulletin,* LII (June, 1958), 392.

MINOGUE, ADELAIDE E. "Treatment of Fire and Water Damaged Records," *The American Archivist,* IX (1946), 17-25.

MOULTON, ROBERT S., ed. *NFPA Handbook of Fire Protection.* 11th ed. Boston: National Fire Protection Association, 1954.

NATIONAL ACADEMY OF SCIENCES — NATIONAL RESEARCH COUNCIL. *School Fires: An Approach to Life Safety.* Washington, D. C.: The Council, 1960.

NATIONAL BOARD OF FIRE UNDERWRITERS. *Fire Alarms Standards.* New York: The Board, 1949.

———. *Fire Prevention Code.* New York: The Board, 1960.

————. *Fire Resistance Ratings.* New York: The Board, 1959.

————. *Fire Resistance Ratings of Less Than One Hour.* New York: The Board, 1956.

————. *Fire Safe Schools.* New York: The Board, 1959.

————. *Heat Producing Appliances.* New York: The Board, 1959.

————. *National Building Code.* New York: The Board, 1957.

————. *Special Bulletin No. 294.* New York: The Board, 1956.

NATIONAL COMMISSION ON SAFETY EDUCATION, NATIONAL EDUCATION ASSOCIATION. *Action for Safety.* Washington, D. C.: The Commission, 1961.

————. *Checklist of Safety and Safety Education in Your Schools.* Washington, D. C.: The Commission, 1953.

————. *Fire Safety.* Washington, D. C.: The Commission, 1951.

NATIONAL COMMISSION ON SAFETY EDUCATION AND NATIONAL SCIENCE TEACHERS ASSOCIATION, NATIONAL EDUCATION ASSOCIATION. *Safe Use of Electrical Equipment.* Washington, D. C.: The Commission, 1951.

NATIONAL FIRE PROTECTION ASSOCIATION. *Air Conditioning and Ventilating Systems of Other Than Residence Type* (NFPA No. 90A). Boston: The Association, 1961.

————. *Building Exits Code* (NFPA No. 101). Boston: The Association, 1960.

————. *Fire Control Film List* (300 titles of motion pictures). Boston: The Association, 1963.

————. *Fire Doors and Windows* (NFPA No. 80). Boston: The Association, 1959.

————. "Fires and Fire Losses Classified" (in successive October issues of the Association's *Quarterly Journal*). Boston: The Association, 1957-1961.

————. *Flammable Liquid Code* (NFPA No. 30). Boston: The Association, 1961.

————. *Gas Appliances and Gas Piping* (NFPA No. 54). Boston: The Association, 1959.

————. *Incinerators, Rubbish Handling* (NFPA No. 82, 82a). Boston: The Association, 1960.

————. *National Electrical Code* (NFPA No. 70). Boston: The Association, 1959.

————. *National Fire Codes.* Vols. I-VII. Boston: The Association, 1960-1961.

————. *NFPA Fire Protection Handbook* (formerly Crosby-Fiske-Forster. *NFPA Handbook of Fire Protection*). Boston: The Association, 1962.

————. *NFPA Inspection Manual.* Boston: The Association, 1959.

————. *Occupancy Fire Record: Libraries* (Fire Record Bulletin FR 60-1). Boston: The Association, 1961.

————. *Portable Fire Extinguishers* (NFPA No. 10). Boston: The Association, 1961.

————. *Proprietary Protective Signaling Systems* (NFPA No. 72). Boston: The Association, 1961.

————. *Spray Finishing* (NFPA No. 33). Boston: The Association, 1961.

————. *Standard Types of Building Construction* (NFPA No. 220). Boston: The Association, 1961.

————. *Standards for the Installation of Sprinkler Systems* (NFPA No. 13). Boston: The Association, 1961.

————. *Standpipe and Hose Systems* (NFPA No. 14). Boston: The Association, 1952.

————. *Static Electricity* (NFPA No. 225). Boston: The Association, 1961.

NEW YORK STATE EDUCATION DEPARTMENT. *Fire Prevention Education.* New York: Bureau of Elementary Curriculum, University of the State of New York, 1958.

PAINE, P. M. "What to Save First," *Library Journal,* XXXXVIII (1923), 509-10.

"PLANNING FIRE SAFE SCHOOLS," *School and College Safety,* XXIII (1960), 13-15.

"POTENTIAL HEAT OF MATERIALS IN BUILDING FIRES," *National Bureau of Standards Technical News Bulletin,* XXXXIV (November, 1960), 184-87.

"RESTORING BOOKS AND PAPERS INJURED BY FIRE," *Scientific American, Supplement* LXXXXVI (September, 1918), 165.

ROBERTSON, A. F., GROSS, D., and LOFTUS, J. *A Method for Measuring Surface Flammability of Materials Using a Radiant Energy Source.* Philadelphia: American Society for Testing Materials, 1956.

SCHAEFER, G. L. "Fire!" *Library Journal,* LXXXV (February 1, 1960), 504-05.

SCHELL, H. B. "Cornell Starts a Fire," *"Library Journal,* LXXXV (October 1, 1961), 3398.

SOUTHERN BUILDING CODE CONGRESS. *Southern Standard Building Code*. Birmingham, Alabama: The Congress, 1957-1958.

STILL, JOHN S. "Library Fires and Salvage Methods," *The American Archivist*, XVI (April, 1953), 145.

SUMPTION, MERLE R., and CASTALDI, BASIL. *How Safe Is Your School? — A Checklist of 100 Danger Points*. Urbana, Illinois: University of Illinois, College of Education, 1959.

UNDERWRITERS' LABORATORIES, INC. *Building Materials List*. Chicago: The Laboratories, 1961.

————. *Fire Protection Equipment List*. Chicago: The Laboratories, 1961.

————. *Wood-Fire Hazard Classification* (C 60, Card Data Service No. 6E.527). Chicago: The Laboratories, 1955.

U. S. DEPARTMENT OF HEALTH, EDUCATION, AND WELFARE, OFFICE OF EDUCATION (No. OE-15023). *Library Statistics of Colleges and Universities, 1959-60, Part 1: Institutional Data*. Washington, D. C.: The Office, 1961.

U. S. PRESIDENT'S CONFERENCE ON FIRE PREVENTION. Washington, D. C.: Govt. Print. Off., 1947.

VON NELL, CARL C. Salvaging Book Materials in Libraries Damaged by Fire and Flood from 1936 to 1953 in the United States and Canada. M.S. thesis, Drexel Institute of Technology, 1954.

WALFORD, C. "Destruction of Libraries by Fire Considered Practically and Historically," *Library Journal*, IV (1879), 414-15.

WEISS, H. B. and CARRUTHERS, R. H. *Insect Enemies of Books*. New York: New York Public Library, 1937.

WILLIAMSON, JAMES J. *Fire Extinguishment and Fire Alarm Systems*. New York: Pittman Publishing Company, 1958.

————. *Fire Hazards and Fire Prevention*. New York: Pittman Publishing Company, 1951.

WRIGLEY, WALTER. *Fire Control Principles*. New York: McGraw-Hill, 1959.

"YOUR FIRE SAFETY EDUCATION PROGRAM MAY BE INADEQUATE," *Safety Education*, XXXVI (January, 1957), 6-8.

## INSURANCE

AMERICAN LIBRARY ASSOCIATION. "Report of Committee on Insurance Rates for Libraries," *ALA Bulletin*, IX (1915), 36-38.

————. "Report of Committee on Fire Insurance Rates," *ALA Bulletin*, X (1916), 35-37, 394-98.

————. "Report of Committee on Insurance Rates for Libraries," *ALA Bulletin,* XI (1917), 2-9, 306-12.

AMERICAN LIBRARY ASSOCIATION COMMITTEE ON FIRE INSURANCE. "Annual Report," 1936-1939. *ALA Bulletin,* XXX (May, 1936), 383-86; XXXI (September, 1937), 562-64, XXXII (September, 1938), 638-40; XXXIII (September, 1939), 617-18.

————. "Annual Report," 1941-1942. *ALA Bulletin,* XXXV (October 15, 1941), 619-20; XXXVI (October 15, 1942), 713-14.

————. "Report," *ALA Bulletin,* LIII (June, 1959), 540-01. Also in *American Library and Book Trade Annual.* New York: Bowker, 1960.

AMERICAN LIBRARY ASSOCIATION INSURANCE COMMITTEE. "Don't Get Caught Short," *ALA Bulletin,* XXXXIII (July-August, 1949), 243-44.

AMERICAN MUNICIPAL ASSOCIATION. *Organization and Operation of the Fire Insurance Industry.* Chicago: The Association, 1952.

ANGELL, FRANK JOSEPH. *Insurance: Principles and Practices.* New York: The Ronald Press Company, 1959.

BARNES, R. S. *Fire Insurance for Local and State Governments.* Chicago: Municipal Finance Offices Association, 1945.

BEST'S INSURANCE GUIDE WITH KEY RATINGS. (Annual.) New York: Alfred M. Best Co., Inc.

BOECKH, E. H. *Manual of Appraisals.* 5th ed. Washington, D. C.: E. H. Boeckh & Associates, 1956.

CARNIE, B. L. "Insurance for Canadian Libraries: A Report of the Recent Revision of the Fire Insurance Program of the Windsor Public Library," *Ontario Library Review,* XXXIX (August, 1955), 168-70.

COMI, J. J. and THOMPSON, W. D., JR. "Contents Insurance," *New Hampshire Public Libraries,* XXXVI (1940), 148-49.

DEALE, H. V. "Insurance Re-evaluation," *Library Journal,* LXXX (December 15, 1955), 2814-818.

DICKERSON, O. D. *Health Insurance.* Homewood, Illinois: Richard D. Irwin, Inc., 1959.

DOMINGE, CHARLES C. and LINCOLN, WALTER O. *Building Construction as Applied to Fire Insurance and Inspecting for Fire Underwriting Purposes.* 4th ed. Philadelphia: The Spectator, 1949.

"FIRE INSURANCE FIGURES: SUMMARY OF 76 REPLIES TO A QUESTIONNAIRE," *ALA Bulletin, XXIX* (August, 1935) 505.

HIRON, J. M. "Insurance of Special Libraries," *Aslib Proceedings,* VI (May, 1954), 88-93.

"How Are You Fixed for Fire Insurance?" *ALA Bulletin*, LV (January, 1961), 54-55.

Huebner, S. S. and Black, Kenneth, Jr. *Property Insurance*. 4th ed. New York: Appleton-Century-Crofts, Inc., 1957.

Hyde, William A. *Insurance Simplified*. Cincinnati: The National Underwriter Co., 1959.

Insurance Literature. ed. and pub. by Insurance Division, Special Libraries Association. Boston: New England Mutual Life Insurance Co., 501 Boylston Street.

Insurance Statistics: Property, Casualty, Inland Marine, Surety. New York: Insurance Information Institute.

King, Clifford L. "The Oakland Public Library's Insurance Program," *Library Journal*, LXII (1937), 734-37.

Krettek, Germaine. "What You Should Know About Library Insurance," *Library Journal*, LXXXII (October 1, 1957), 2301-03.

Kulp, C. A. *Casualty Insurance: An Analysis of Hazards, Policies, Insurers and Rates*. 3rd ed. New York: The Ronald Press Company, 1956.

Lincoln, Walter O., Tisdale, George W., and Babcock, John T. W. *Fire Insurance Inspection and Underwriting*. 7th ed. Philadelphia: The Spectator, 1953.

A List of Worthwhile Health Insurance Books. New York: Health Insurance Institute.

Lucas, George G. R. and Wherry, Ralph H. *Insurance: Principles and Coverages*. New York: Holt, Rinehart and Winston, 1954.

Mackall, Luther E. *Surety Underwriting Manual*. New York: Luther E. Mackall, 1958.

Magee, John H. *General Insurance*. 6th ed. (The Irwin Series in Risk and Insurance). Homewood, Illinois: Richard D. Irwin Inc., 1961.

McGill, Dan M., ed. *All Lines Insurance*. (The S. S. Huebner Foundation for Insurance Education — "Lectures"). Homewood, Illinois: Richard D. Irwin, Inc., 1960.

Mehr, Robert I. and Cammack, Emerson. *Principles of Insurance*. 3rd ed. (The Irwin Series in Risk and Insurance). Homewood: Richard D. Irwin, Inc., 1961.

Miller, R. F. "Insurance for Libraries," *Idaho Librarian*, XX (October, 1959).

Mixer, Charles W. "Columbia Insures Its Main Card Catalog," *Library Journal*, LXXXIII (October 1, 1957), 2304-311.

————. "Insurance Evaluation of a University Library's Collection," *College & Research Libraries,* XIII (January, 1952), 18-23.

————. "New Insurance for Library Collections," *Library Journal,* LXXIX (September 15, 1954), 1539-543.

PATTERSON, EDWIN W. *Essentials of Insurance Law: An Outline of Legal Doctrines in Their Relations to Insurance Practices.* 2nd ed. New York: McGraw-Hill, 1957.

REED, PRENTISS B. *Adjustment of Property Losses.* 2nd ed. New York: McGraw-Hill, 1953.

RICH, W. G. "Insuring and Placing Insurable Values on Your Library Collection," *Special Libraries,* XXXIII (February, 1942), 49-52.

RISKS WE FACE: AN INTRODUCTION TO PROPERTY INSURANCE. New and rev. ed. New York: The National Board of Fire Underwriters, 1956.

RODDA, WILLIAM H. *Fire and Property Insurance.* Englewood Cliffs, New Jersey: Prentice-Hall, 1956.

————. *Fire and Property Insurance.* New York: McGraw-Hill, 1959.

ROGERS, R. D., "Appraising a Research Collection," *College & Research Libraries,* XIII (January, 1952), 24-29.

SINGER, DOROTHEA M. *The Insurance of Libraries: A Manual for Librarians.* Chicago: The American Library Association, 1946.

TALESE, G., "14,000 Books Burn in Insurance Test," *Canadian Library Association Feliciter,* V (January, 1960), 8.

WELCH, HELEN M. "Cost Indexes for U. S. Periodicals: A Progress Report," *Library Resources & Technical Services,* IV (Spring, 1960), 150-57.

————. "Proposed Indexes for Procedures for Establishing a Cost of Periodicals Index," *Library Resources & Technical Services,* IV (Summer, 1959), 202-8.

# INDEX